SNOWDONIA ROCKY RAMBLES:
Geology Beneath Your Feet

Bryan Lynas

Published by Sigma Leisure – an imprint of
Sigma Press, 1 South Oak Lane, Wilmslow, Cheshire SK9 6AR, England.

British Library Cataloguing in Publication Data
A CIP record for this book is available from the British Library.

ISBN: 1-85058-469-9

Reprinted 1999

Typesetting and Design by: Sigma Press, Wilmslow, Cheshire.

Cover design: MFP Design & Print

Maps, photographs and illustrations: The author, except where indicated

Printed by: MFP Design & Print

Foreword

by James E. Lovelock

There are few activities more pleasant and fulfilling than a walk in the countryside, or on the shore line, with a good friend or, better still, someone you love. Thanks to the foresight of those who founded the National Parks and the National Trust, we can walk freely almost anywhere on the coastline or on the mountains of these islands. I like to walk through familiar places and breathe in the sweet air and just receive the sights and sounds. As in any ritual, the repetition of such a pleasant experience reconfirms it in the mind as a comforting recollection.

Yet sometimes, this is not enough and I long for adventure. Then we plan a purpose to our walk. It could be the quest to find a rare animal, bird or plant. It also can be the wish to know more about the body of the land as we walk over it. To discover its geology. If this is your need then this book is for you. It is a splendid guide for walks in the mountains of Wales. The walks alone will satisfy but, for those like me, with a wish to get to know the Earth better, it opens the mind's eye to the form and structure of the land.

We are so fortunate to live on these islands. Ours is one of the most rewarding geologies of anywhere on the Planet. From the east coast to the western edge of the island there are rocks going from the most recent to the Precambrian. Wales is a fine choice for geological walks. Not for nothing are periods of the Earth's history named after the tribes of Wales, the Ordovices and the Silures. I doubt if those Welsh tribesmen ever imagined their names would be remembered in text books world-wide for the rocks they lived on. Still less would they have expected that, until recently, the earliest history of the Earth, lost in the mists of time, would be called Precambrian, the time before Wales.

I share Bryan Lynas's feeling for the mountains and for the Earth itself. Now that we as a species threaten the habitats of all else that lives on this amazing Superorganism of a planet, we need to know it better. There is no better way to know the Earth than by walking on it and this book will be your guide. Use it to enjoy a walk or a scramble in Wales and come back enriched in mind as well as body.

James E. Lovelock

James Lovelock, FRS, is best known for his formulation of the Gaia theory, which suggests that the Earth is "a single living entity . . . endowed with faculties and powers far beyond those of its constituent parts". His first book, in 1979, was "Gaia: a new look at Life on Earth". This was followed by "The Ages of Gaia", published in 1988 and as a new edition in 1995. Of equal importance was his invention of the electron capture detector, an extremely sensitive device used to measure the amounts of ozone-destroying CFCs in the atmosphere.

Preface

Double, double toil and trouble;
Fire, burn; and cauldron; bubble.
(Macbeth, The Three Witches, Act IV, Scene 1 by William Shakespeare)

To liken Snowdonia's long and complex history to the witches' cauldron and their enchantments is a good metaphor. Here, Nature herself plays her eternal witches' role, stewing and stirring the bubbling pot of earth, air, fire and water over hundreds of millions of years ... and she hasn't finished yet. Only recently has she completed a particularly vigorous period of fashioning the landscape we know and love, using another tool in her armoury: ice. In a few million more years, she will knock it all down and start again.

Today, we creep about amongst the latest relics of Nature's dalliance and – when we learn to read the message in the rocks and scenery – are awestruck. We are but puny players in Nature's great theatre of Time. Yet our brief fumblings and scratchings around the planet's surface already foul the nest, the thin skin we call the biosphere, upon which all life depends; life which has taken at least four thousand million years to evolve into today's myriads of species of which we are just one. We humans, like grotesque cuckoos, are crushing the other nestlings and fouling the nest even though it's the only one we've got. So it is good to stop the busy rush of our seemingly important lives and walk into these mountains and observe ... and think ... and understand our place. Cars, television, stock markets, power, greed, wealth ... what importance does this have for any of us if by having it and always wanting more, we spoil everything not only for our descendants but for all life everywhere? We have astonishing power to destroy but little to heal.

Nature is neither kind nor cruel. She is indifferent to the struggles and sufferings of life on her planet. As the Gaia Hypothesis (devised by James Lovelock who kindly wrote the Foreword for this book) suggests and the fossil record shows, she extinguishes those creatures which have overstayed their welcome just as surely as nuclear bombs will. The writing is on the wall. Human beings may be next, through their own blinkered greed and folly.

Being amongst mountains offers us all perspectives over such weighty matters if we care to stop and think rather than belting along eroding paths and bagging summits. I have been fortunate enough to learn something about earth science in the widest sense in a career which has taken me to live and work in many parts of the world with many different people. I hope that I succeed in getting over to you my own sense of excitement and wonder about Snowdonia as you ramble through a few of the astonishing events that have taken place in there over the last 600 million years. If you find that you gain a deeper sense of caring, humility and love for this tiny part of the planet, perhaps engendered somewhat by insights and understanding which I have triggered, then I've done my job as a writer should.

Leo Tolstoy wrote (in *War and Peace*) 'All, everything I understand, I understand only because I love.' My feeling is that understanding something of how our planet works sows the seeds of the caring and love so desperately needed today. Don't you agree?

Like *Lakeland Rocky Rambles*, I want this book to be fun. I want to help you feel the excitement which I always do when I start 'reading' the rocks beneath my feet in Nature's own classroom: the great outdoors.

I'd like to thank...

Chiefly my wife, Val, whose slender form decorates both the cover and several figures in this book. She – on your behalf – has checked out almost all these rambles ... by doing them. She gets her left and her right, her north and her south hopelessly mixed up and so I could be sure that if my directions weren't good enough, she'd root them out in no time. I was right. So now if my directions aren't clear, it's probably because someone has built a new stile or put a fence where there wasn't one before. This happens all the time. When Val checked the Moelwyn ramble late in 1995, we found that an entire footpath had been rerouted on the other side of the valley. I'd only done the work 10 months earlier. She has also checked this text from cover to cover. Now there's devotion for you.

My old colleagues and friends Malcolm Howells and Adrian Rushton have helped me greatly by updating me on the latest ideas and literature and have patiently answered all my questions. Geoffrey Haggis of Totnes Environmental Unit kindly commented on parts of the text for me.

Meantime, have fun!

Bry Lynas

Contents

Introduction

Why you need this book . . .

Snowdonia's rocks and scenery can tell us a story more extraordinary than any Tolkien fantasy but most of us haven't learnt to read the words. Because we know how to read written words, we can read books and understand their messages. Rocks are a bit like books though you have to look at the pages in rather different ways. To make things difficult, Mother Time has ripped out some of the pages and screwed up others. Even so, a curious group of humans called geologists (or earth scientists) have learnt to read rocky books, more or less, and to understand something of the greatest tale of all time: the history of our planet. The purpose of this book – made of paper and with all its pages – is to help you to grasp the story hidden away in the rocks and scenery of this wonderful area. I feel that this sort of understanding opens perspectives 'conventional' education doesn't begin to touch though don't let me give you the impression it is easy. The message in Snowdonia's rocks has been so difficult to read in detail that it has taken many people many years to piece together the meaning of this giant Rosetta Stone. The job is mostly done and we now have a unique insight and understanding of this ancient landscape and its story, better than almost anywhere else on Earth.

When you do these rambles, please keep your eyes peeled. I've noticed that many people don't. They just talk and make a lot of noise and go crashing down the mountainsides and *see* nothing except the quickly-snapped photos at the top – when the prints come back. This book will, I hope, help open your eyes to the wonders around you – there for all of us to see and marvel at but seldom appreciated fully. This rocky library we call Snowdonia makes no admission charge and there's nobody to tell you not to touch the fine old volumes. You can even scramble over them and pick some small ones up.

When I reach the top of a fine mountain, I experience feelings of awe at the silent grandeur around me. I often avoid the summit because I don't like to feel I've 'conquered' the mountain. Rather, I feel humbled and privileged to be there. Sadly when you reach poor Snowdon's summit, properly called Yr Wyddfa, you experience hundreds of people, most of whom have taken the railway to the top. The awe is lost amongst the noise and the soft-drink cans. People rush to clamber onto the trig for the photos. They don't have a clue what they're walking on to get there and perhaps they don't care either. When I was there researching this ramble, a noisy group appeared (to be fair, I think they had walked up) who, after the usual 'I conquered this' rituals of standing on the trig point and photos, instead of admiring the view, phoned mother on the cellphone. 'Hello Mum ... What? ... Oh yes, it's me. I'm on the top of Snowdon ... get the kettle on ... yak yak yak.' Nothing about the mountain scenery. Nothing about the views. Nothing about what the mountain is like or what it can tell us.

Early next morning, I was at the summit again and spied a young woman fell-runner, far fitter than I have ever been. She ran direct to the summit, touched the trig, gasped and was off back down the way she'd come – all within a few seconds. For myself, I 'm settling for the lesser fitness which inadvertently slows you down so you at least have no excuse for not looking around you as you climb or walk. So I thoroughly recommend that you give yourself time to *look* at things; time to read this book; time to think about what I'm showing you; time to think about what it all means. To really appreciate nature and scenery, you must give yourself time to look ... and to think. My feeling is that most of us *do* care; we just need a little guidance. That's why I've written this book.

I deliberately avoid explaining any more about the hows and whys of geology than you'll find in the next few paragraphs. The rambles themselves will show you, little by little, how the rocks formed and were later moulded into the landscape of today. You don't have to know any geology at first, but as you both see and think for yourself – with a little guidance from me – the ideas involved should fall into place for you. If you find some parts heavy going (what I've written; not the walking), don't hesitate to skip bits. There's no exam at the end and I've tried to achieve an even balance between 'not enough' and 'too much'.

All the processes I'll be talking about next have at some time been active in Snowdonia. My rapid description just gives you a quick grounding in the sort of things you will actually see there. Sometimes I have to use technical words because there simply aren't equivalents in everyday English. You'll find these explained in the Glossary at the end. All the rock units have names for the same reasons that you and I do. You'll find these all summarised in a special Timescale diagram in the Appendix to this book. There's also a simple geological map and information about other books and maps which offer more detail.

Towards the end of the book, I 'm sure you'll be 'reading the rocks' for yourself.

Cakes, layers, beds, time-travel and squeezes

Imagine yourself making a layer cake. You prepare the ingredients for the layers and assemble them into a cake. Where did you start the layers? At the bottom of course. Obvious, you say. Yes, it is obvious but who stops to think about that? The first layer is, in a sense, the oldest. It was the first layer you laid down and has been there longest. The icing on the top is the youngest layer; it was the last thing you did. So why this cookery lesson? ...

... Because most rock strata are, or were, formed like gigantic layer cakes. The rocks you find at the bottom of Arizona's Grand Canyon are, obviously, the oldest. The Kaibab Limestone (which forms the plateau into which the Colorado River has cut this stupendous piece of natural architecture) forms the top and so is the youngest rock. Riding down on a mule to the bottom of the canyon is veritably a journey backwards in Time.

Time travel: Here and there in this book, I ask you to use your imagination (= picturing images in your head) to take rapid trips back through Time. It may help to picture yourself climbing onto your own time machine like that of H.G.Wells' Time Traveller which could whisk you back thousands or millions of years at the touch of a lever. I help you along by describing what you might see. I think you'll find this a useful tool for helping you visualise how things formed or used to be in Snowdonia.

This principle is geology's most basic: the deeper down you go, the older the rocks become. So when you do a ramble up a mountain, you'll be walking across ever-younger rocks; going up in Time. But in Snowdonia, there's a catch. The rocks have been pretty strongly squeezed by powerful earth movements which occurred after the layers of the rocky cake had formed. If you squeeze your layer cake, it buckles up into a series of folds (and to actually do this could be very instructive, especially since you can eat the mangled results of your experiments). So the layers of rock – the beds or formations – are often tilted and forced up into great folds, making the whole thing more complicated. But sometimes, you can actually see the folds in the rock quite plainly – at Cwm Idwal for example. This helps you understand how the land really lies. Fortunately, we can find other clues to unravelling the complexity: some formations – like layers of cream filling – are easy to recognise and so form the key to the less obvious structures, many of which are covered in screes or rubbish left by the glaciers. One such marker which you'll see several times on these rambles is called the Pitt's Head Tuff.

But what exactly do the layers mean? Back into the kitchen for a moment. Consider your lowest cake layer. You made it out of flour, sugar, fat and so on and mixed it up. Then you spread it out on a baking tray. This was 'an event' – a short period of time in which the layer's ingredients were formed and deposited or laid down (on the tray). It's just the same with rocks. Each layer, some of which may be only paper-thin whilst others may form half a mountainside, represents a 'happening', an event way back in the distant past. This is another basic principle: each rock layer tells its story of an event. That event may have been a storm, an earthquake which triggered other events, or a volcano erupting. Gradually, many layers built up on ancient seafloors, just as they do today. An 'event' like an earthquake or storm, can trigger powerful currents which can hoosh a lot of loose material out into the deeper sea. As the current loses its energy, all the lumps and rubbish it carries within itself drop out onto the seafloor – forming a bed, the basic building block of sedimentary rocks. You can try this yourself by adding some soil to a jar of water. Put the lid on and shake. Whilst you supply energy by shaking, all the soil remains in suspension. When you put your jar on a table, what happens? The coarsest grains like gravel fall out first followed by sand and, ever more slowly, finer and finer particles. It may take many hours for the clay and mud to settle.

Alternatively, a volcano might erupt and send a vast cloud of ash and dust into the stratosphere. As the updraft from the eruption loses energy, the cloud begins to rain ash over a huge area. Some may fall into the sea and be washed about by currents before coming to rest as a bed. Ash beds are very distinctive. When hardened into rock, they become tuffs or tuffites. Incidentally, most eruptions worldwide are below the sea and so, for obvious reasons, are almost never seen by humans.

What I've just described are called sedimentary rocks. Another class of rock – igneous rocks – start life as red-hot liquids (magmas) and don't always conform to our simple cake model. Magmas can force their way into the 'layer cake' after it has formed – or sometimes during its formation. This may cause a volcanic eruption if the magma bursts out at the surface (giving lava or ash eruptions) or it may not. To visualise what happens, imagine filling a syringe for decorating a cake with nice sloppy icing – our magma. But instead of writing 'Happy Birthday' on top of your cake, you plunge the business end of the syringe deep into its inside layers and squeeze the plunger hard. The pressure you exert forces the liquid icing magma into the inside of your cake. You have created an intrusion of icing which will shortly become solid as the sugars in it crystallise. If you then cut your cake in half (it's going to be quite a mess by the end of this experiment), you'll find a large blob of solid icing where it shouldn't be – right in the middle. It will also have disrupted the layers of the cake, either breaking them vertically to form a dyke or, more likely, forcing two of the layers apart to form an icing sugar sill. The Snowdonia rocky layer cake is riddled with such intrusive rocks almost everywhere. Most of them were linked intimately with the vast volcanic outbursts whose tough rocky end products are, together with the intrusions, the prime reason for the rugged landscapes of today.

As you'll see, the reality is far more complex than my simplistic layer-cake concept, but then if it were easy, you wouldn't need this book to guide you. Even so, the principle is sound and is worth bearing in mind as you walk: the younger rocks are on top of the older ones, even when they're tilted quite steeply. The real problems start when the tilting makes them vertical. Which is on top then? But that's another story and, for the most part, the Snowdonia rocks are not so steeply tilted.

From cakes to plates

Our planet would be a dull place indeed if erosion finally had its way. Erosion goes hand in hand with deposition (like love and marriage?). You can't, in the words of the old song, 'have one without the other'. If the planet wasn't the live and active place it is, there would be no mountains and probably no land. Every high part of the planet would have been eroded and redeposited under the seas. All the deep parts of the oceans would have been filled up. It would be quite boring really. But thanks to plate tectonics, the planet is indeed a dynamic and continuously changing place.

You've probably heard about the great geological theory of plate tectonics. This was important in Snowdonia, as in Lakeland, because it provided the power for the theatrical performances which we'll be looking at and which built today's mountains. Our planet's crust exists as two different types: continental crust (which is thick – 40 kilometres or so) and oceanic crust (thin – a mere 10 kilometres). The rocks which form them are totally different but both move about, floating like a skin on the hot plastic mantle which forms the bulk of the inside of our planet. It is gigantic convection current plumes in the mantle which push the thin surface plates around – but in an irregular way so that some crash into each other (see Figure 1), some slide sideways past each other (as, for example, in California: the infamous, earthquake-causing San Andreas Fault system) and others tear apart allowing magma to well up and form new crust (as along mid-ocean ridges, one of which surfaces in volcanic Iceland). It's almost as if the crustal plates are riding on a great conveyor-belt system.

If you fly over the Labrador Sea in winter, you can see smaller examples of this process in the form of sea ice. The ice floats, like crustal plates, on the water surface, subject to the vagaries of the currents beneath which drag the ice with them. Where currents meet, the ice buckles into pressure ridges = mountain ranges. (It was pressure ice which crushed and destroyed Shackleton's ship '*Endurance*' during his 1914 expedition to the Antarctic, resulting in one of the most extraordinary stories of adventure in extreme adversity of all time.) When the sea currents diverge, they tear the floes apart and new ice forms in the opened leads of water = new crust as at the mid-ocean ridges.

The 'crash' or collision plate boundaries, as you'd expect, can mean crumpling and buckling: mountain ranges. They can also mean volcanoes of the sort which existed in Snowdonia. These developed here hundreds of millions of years ago because one plate – weak oceanic crust (the floor of a long-gone ocean called Iapetus, Fig. 1) – was forced down under the thicker continental crust of another plate called Avalonia (part of the ancient super-continent of Gondwana).

You can mimic this with your hands. Hold each hand out flat, palms down, and bring them together, fingertip to fingertip. Keep moving them, like the moving crustal plates, relentlessly together. Something has to give. Assume that one hand is strong continental crust which is less dense (lighter) than the other oceanic crust hand. Only one thing can really happen: your lighter strong hand ramps up over the weaker oceanic crust hand, forcing it to slide down underneath. This sliding is subduction. If you push very hard, you find that you generate heat by friction between your two hands. This happens too along subduction zones; enough heat is generated by the relentless, irresistible motion to partially melt some of the rocks. Hot pods of melted material (magma) are relatively light and so ascend – like hot air balloons – through the crust above, melting or forcing their way ever upwards. If they make it to the surface, you get volcanoes; if they don't, you get intrusions. This simple 'hands on' model explains why many of the world's volcanoes exist, from New Zealand to the Andes; from Japan to the USA. All these are above subduction zones (though that is not true for all volcanoes).

It explains too why Wales and Lakeland had volcanoes hundreds of millions of years ago. The vanished Iapetus Ocean lay some distance to the northwest of Snowdonia which existed as what geologists call a marginal (or backarc) basin, well behind the leading edge of the Avalonian plate (which included the Lake District and was partly land). Eventually, all the

Iapetus Ocean disappeared under Avalonia which then collided with another continental plate, formerly the continent on the opposite side of Iapetus: the Laurentian plate (Scotland is a fragment though most of it is now part of eastern Canada). This mighty collision marked the end of subduction and the beginning of a tremendous climax of mountain building called the Caledonian orogeny. This created most of the folds and other structures which screwed up the layer cake of sedimentary rocks in Snowdonia.

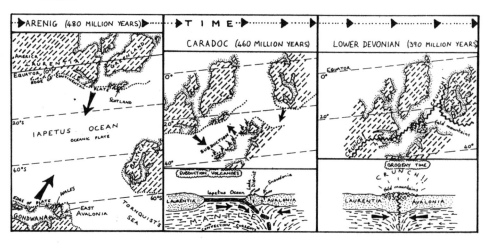

Figure 1: *The destruction of the ancient Iapetus Ocean. The left drawing shows the continents 480 million years ago with the ocean lying between. What would become Wales lay at about 60 south of the equator at that time. The centre drawing shows how after 20 million years or so, the continent plates had come quite close and most of the ocean and adjacent Tornquist's Sea had disappeared along subduction zones. The cartoon below shows an imaginary section (northwest-southeast) through this. Notice how the thin and dense ocean plate ramps down under the Avalonian continent edge. Great rafts of this cold, dense crust break off and sink ever deeper into the mantle, drawn down by the descending convection currents. Above the subduction zone, pods of magma rise slowly through the crust to erupt as volcanoes at the surface. The right hand drawing shows the Big Crunch – the climax of the Caledonian orogeny about 390 million years ago. All the weak ocean crust has gone and the two continents crash into each other, welding to form a suture (heavy zigzag line) and ranges of fold mountains.*

Real ice on the cake: the great Ice Age

We now know that what is loosely called 'the Ice Age' was a whole series of long, bitterly-cold deep freezes of which the latest finished about 11,500 years ago – at around the time agriculture was beginning to be developed in what is now Iraq. For tens of thousands of years before this, most of Britain (and northern Europe and Canada/northern USA) had lain frozen beneath thick sheets of ice which, in Snowdonia, were probably at times over 1000 metres thick. The actual start date for the big freeze in Britain was less than 2 million years ago (called the Quaternary Sub-Era), though we know that there were many periods after this time in which the climate bounced back and forth between warm and bitterly cold. At certain times, hippos wallowed in the Thames and monkeys swung in the trees of southern England. Yet at other times, mammoths roamed the ice fringes and only the hardiest creatures survived. Ice Ages would not have suited nationalists because what we now call Britain was just a northwesterly extension of Europe. The Channel was dry land until 8,000 years ago!

But from research conducted by deep sea core drilling, we know that ice sheets covered most of Greenland 2.4 million years ago and glaciers in Alaska and northern Canada had been around for several millions years before that. The Antarctic was already ice-bound 36 million years ago and continues that way. So in some senses, the Ice Ages are still with us. There's no reason to suppose they've ended though our own climate tinkering (I mean our casual outpouring of greenhouse gases from vehicles, heating and factories) could change this – for good or, more likely, for ill. The questions on every climate researcher's lips are: why did the Ice Ages occur? and will they come again? We know much of the answer to the first question but haven't a clue about the second.

The cake cut ... noble ruins

The rocky cake has been fairly bashed around by Time. It lies today partly in ruins, the mountains torn and ripped apart by the talons of past glaciers. But these ruins have a special beauty which appeals to us all.

Since the glaciers melted, many other events have taken place in the Snowdonian theatre. The most obvious was the arrival of human beings over 6000 years ago. Since then, people have been making their mark on the landscape. What we see today is not natural: apart from obvious scars left by slate quarries, mines, roads and towns, the vegetation which clothes the rocky mountains is largely the product of the nibbling of countless sheep introduced, of course, by people. If this landscape was pristine, everywhere except for the higher mountain areas would be covered in mixed forest. Trees used to grow high up on the mountains but, partly because of climate change though mostly because of people, these have now gone. They cannot regenerate because of sheep and cattle.

So although mountains are dominated by the rocks which build them, the plants and animals which live amongst them are part of the whole scene. The mountains would be dull indeed without the splash of colour in late spring given by purple saxifrages or the *krrronk* call of the ravens. So, as in my first book, *Lakeland Rocky Rambles*, the companion volume to this, I've put in notes and drawings about some of the natural wildlife you will encounter. The rambles will take you over some abandoned quarries and mines so I've touched on the industrial archaeology of the district too.

The rambles: where they are and what they're about.

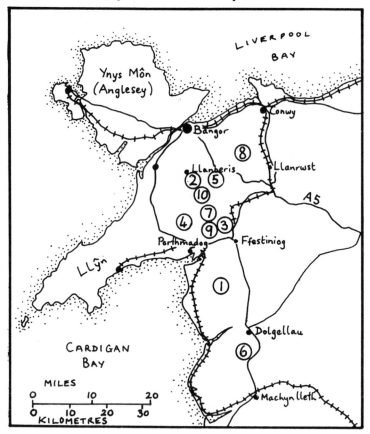

Figure 2: *Location map showing where each ramble is, together with the principal roads, towns and lakes.*

1. Cwm Bychan and Rhinog Fawr
Here I introduce you to the older sedimentary rocks of Snowdonia. We consider some basic geological ideas and look at evidence for former ice sheets.

2. Llanberis and west Snowdon
On this ramble, we meet some of the great players on the ancient Snowdonian stage of Time. We take a first look at some of the violent volcanic events which took place over 450 million years ago here and see more evidence of ice.

3. Cwm Orthin and Moelwyn
Here we look at some huge slate quarries and some older volcanic rocks.

4. Moel Hebog and Moel yr Ogof
This ramble takes you in some detail through the remains of one of the great eruptions. You can marvel at the giant 'cannonballs' as I did. Later, you see extraordinary lava flows.

5. Cwm Idwal, Y Garn and Glyder Fawr
Charles Darwin first realised that the mounds of debris in Cwm Idwal were the result of glaciers. We look at these and imagine how it must have been then. Later, we examine all of the great Snowdon Volcanic Group which builds Y Garn, the Devil's Kitchen and most of the Glyderau range. There's an exciting descent.

6. Cwm Cau and Cadair Idris
Here we venture into a less-visited part of the Snowdonia National Park. Cwm Cau and Cadair Idris formed during an earlier period of volcanic activity – all beneath the sea.

7. Llyn Dinas and Moel y Dyniewyd
Though in the heart of Snowdonia, people don't often do this easy ramble. We visit Sygun copper mine and cross volcanic rocks which formed at the edge of an enormous submarine crater.

8. The Crafnant country
This is the easiest ramble. We look at some of the youngest of Snowdonia's volcanic rocks which were deposited in fairly deep water. We peep into an underground slate quarry.

9. Cwm Croesor and Cnicht
After looking at the remains of an underground quarry and tramway, we examine some odd sedimentary rocks and thick sheets of igneous rocks.

10. Cwm Llan and Snowdon
I kept the toughest ramble for the last. Here, we cross through the entire Snowdon Volcanic Group of rocks and find something remarkable on Snowdon's summit. From the summit, I try to build for you a picture of the view in the depths of the Ice Age.

As you'll see, I've selected rambles from all around Snowdonia. My basis for the selection is that the rambles are well known or especially interesting. Almost all the paths are public rights of way and each walk offers a variety of fascinating things to see, ending back at the starting point.

Getting around the rambles and what you should take

I know not everyone has their own transport so in every case, I have given information about bus or train services which get you nearest to the ramble start points. Car owners will have no problem. Most carparks are free but don't leave valuables in your vehicle.

Although you'll have no trouble finding most of the localities, some are less easy to describe. So I include full National Grid References for all, always in square brackets (e.g. [6097 5438]: the summit of Snowdon). All Ordnance Survey maps explain how to use grid references if you are not familiar with them. The 8-figure reference theoretically gives you the point to within 10 metres of its precise location, so a scaler helps. Most compasses include a perspex scale of some sort. 'Eyeballing' the location of the reference should be quite adequate in most cases.

Always take a compass for I often refer to directions. Some compasses include a dip needle which can be helpful for measuring the inclination of strata. Also essential is a x10 magnifying hand lens for examining rocks and minerals – and small plants too. Hang it round your neck on a strong string. Binoculars are great for birds but also for examining inaccessible rocks or plants. A camera is obviously worthwhile. Although geology is traditionally associated with hammers, such tools are frowned upon nowadays – banned in many places – and you simply won't need one for what you will be looking at. Because of the notorious weather, it's useful to have some means of protecting your map and this book. There are several different styles of map cases available with clear plastic windows so that you can look at your (dry) map or book in the worst weather. Some people, speaking of my *Lakeland Rocky Rambles* book, told me that because of its bulk, they ripped it apart into its component rambles. This inelegant bit of lateral thinking makes a lot of sense, especially if it means you buy a second copy 'for best'. If that grabs you, get ripping ... then I get more royalty money!

I've arranged the text for the walks so that the **directions** are set in a different type style from the descriptions – in order that you can see at a glance which you are dealing with. Each ramble has its own map, with a scale showing distances in both kilometres and miles. The rambles are based on a series of **localities** at which I hope you'll stop and take a little time to look around you and see what you make of what I've described. Some of the localities are optional extras: spurs off the main ramble. You can take them or leave them according to the weather and how you feel. For this reason, I'm deliberately vague about how long a ramble may take. In fact, most are almost certainly full day excursions if you are to have time to take stock of what you see – and enjoy yourself.

Where to stay?

Bed & Breakfast accommodation is widely available and there are quite a few campsites, mostly marked on the OS Outdoor Leisure Maps. There are reasonably convenient YHAs at Bryn Gwynant [640 514], Snowdon Ranger [565 550], Llanberis [574 597], Ogwen Cottage [649 604], Capel Curig [726 579] (all on Map 17); Llanbedr [586 267] (Map 18); Abercorris [754 080] (Map 23). For information about hotels, guest houses or self-catering accommodation, call the free information and booking service at 0800 834820.

A little common sense: country codes and mountain weather

You will have read, time and again, about following the Country Code, so you won't need reminding that it applies in the Snowdonia National Park as much as anywhere. It is equally important to remember that most of the rambles take you through quite high mountain country, so be aware of likely weather conditions – and be prepared for rain and cold winds. Indeed, I wouldn't recommend that you attempt any of the walks in poor weather. You wouldn't be able to – or want to – 'read the rocks' in rain and gale-force wind, let alone read the notes for each ramble. And of course being on the mountains in bad weather can be downright dangerous.

As you'll notice, erosion is not only a natural process. The constant pounding of mountain paths by myriads of walkers' boots is a severe problem. The plants, which normally protect the underlying soils from erosion by rain, are destroyed. The National Park authorities have rebuilt many of the more popular paths by laboriously cobbling them, so please keep to these as much as possible – and don't take short cuts.

Some of the walks take you around old quarries and mines. Beware! Mines and quarries are by their very nature unstable. Rock falls do occur and entering mines is dangerous, even if you're experienced.

Do take with you the appropriate copy of the Ordnance Survey (OS) Outdoor Leisure Maps. There are three: 17 (Snowdon and Conwy valley areas), 18 (Harlech and Bala areas) and 23 (Cadair Idris area). All are at 1:25,000 scale; 2 1/2 inches to one mile; 4 centimetres to 1 kilometre. They cover the whole district (with no overlap, which is a nuisance but you can't have everything) and they are indispensable. You may find it helpful, before attempting a walk, to pencil onto your Outdoor Leisure map the route I show on my own maps of each ramble. Most are on well-defined footpaths clearly marked on the OS maps. My maps cannot, without becoming hopelessly cluttered, give the route-finding detail you may need. So be sure to take *both*. The OS maps are also highly accurate representations of the mountains and have for years been metric so that all heights (contours etc.) are given in metres above sealevel. I too have followed the metric scheme.

It's a good idea to take a smaller-scale map if you want to identify the more distant mountain summits.

How science works: facts and theories

I not only want to help you to 'read the rocks' but also give you the confidence to make up some of your own ideas about how a particular structure or formation came into being. It is a cornerstone of science that an idea or theory of something, or some event, should be testable. So if a gardener goes down to her vegetable patch and finds all her cabbages full of holes, she'll want to know the cause so she can stop it happening again. Looking around, she sees small green caterpillars on the plants and develops a theory that it is they which made those holes. She can test her theory by observing the caterpillars. If she actually *sees* them eating holes, she knows her theory is correct and can either pick the caterpillars off or spray them with poison. If her theory was wrong (yes I know it's unlikely) and the caterpillars were just passing the time of day, the holes having been eaten by snails, then she'd be wasting her time killing the caterpillars.

Geology is a slightly odd science because many of its ideas are not directly testable. We cannot travel backwards in time to see what actually happened to create those oddball markings in this or that rock. Instead, geologists have to look for similar things forming now – and make an assumption that the same process operated way back in time. This gives rise to the rule that 'the Present is the key to the Past'. It works well for rocks like lavas where you can see features in 450-million-year-old rocks just like those in lavas spewed out yesterday by an active volcano (Fig. 3).

Figure 3: *Active White Island volcano, New Zealand. A visit to this brooding and sinister place is both frightening and wonder-full for a geologist. Val, my wife, peers gingerly down at the boiling lake and roaring steam vents of the central crater. If you get a chance to see an active volcano, grab it. There's no better way of making sense of ancient volcanic rocks than to see brand new ones which have just been formed. And there's nothing on Earth so humbling as the insignificant powerlessness a tiny human feels before these awesome natural wonders.*

This principle doesn't work when the process has never been seen operating in the present – or cannot be seen owing to its extreme violence or inaccessibility. Such an example is the type of volcanic eruptions which created rocks called ignimbrites, now known to have been produced by colossal eruptions never witnessed by man.

In similar fashion, it has not been possible until very recently to see processes happening in the deep oceans. Today we can 'see' either directly (via specially designed submarines) or indirectly (by means of sophisticated sonar and remote probes). As a result, we now know about huge seafloor slumps and slides and bottom-hugging turbid currents which can, over time, fill deep-sea basins with thousands of metres of sediments. It is our understanding of these processes that can help us to make sense of peculiar structures in ancient sedimentary rocks. Even deep-sea volcanoes have now been seen pouring out lavas onto the seabed.

But there's another problem to grapple with and that is 'secondary' alteration: changes in rocks which happen sometimes long after they have been formed. These changes can be small scale – for example when water gets squeezed out of sediment (dewatering) – or they can be very large scale indeed, such as those produced when crustal plates collide (see above). Many of these things no one could ever see, but we can model the high temperature and high pressure processes on a tiny scale in modern laboratories. So generally we can be pretty sure we are correct in our ideas about why, for example, cleavage forms in some rocks.

So you'll find that I may offer more than one explanation for the curious rocks you see – and offer you the choice of how the rock actually formed. Interpretation of the meaning – 'reading the rocks' again – is fraught with difficulty, for in many cases the 'language' is ambiguous. You'll see the evidence, you'll maybe talk it over with your companions, and you'll come to some sort of conclusion. You may be right ... you may be way off; you just cannot be sure in some cases. Remember, geologists themselves have often turned out to be quite wrong. The theory which now underpins the whole of Earth science – plate tectonics – was once regarded by scientists (in its earlier guise as 'continental drift') as crackpot baloney. Alfred Wegener, its proponent, was ridiculed in his day but now would have the last laugh. In Snowdonia, geologists are – I believe – getting close to the truth about what went on here countless millions of years ago. But arriving at this near-truth was a stormy process, usually propelled by the odd characters (some of whom it has been my privilege to know and work with) who were ready to chance their reputations and suggest something unorthodox. In some cases they were right; in others, wrong. This is the stuff of science which doesn't just drift; it bounces!

A Welsh glossary and notes on pronunciation: easier than you'd think.

Welsh, despite what you may think, is a phonetic language ... unlike English. You only need ten minutes to be able to make quite a reasonable stab at the musical words. After a few days, you should be able to amaze your friends by pronouncing 'Llanfairpwllgwyngyllgogerychwyrndrobwll-llantisiliogogogoch' all in one go. This is the famous railway town in Anglesey (Ynys Môn), the longest place name in Welsh. It's also a lesson in how it and many other seemingly complex names are really just simple short words stuck together.

The vowels a, e, i, o, u, w and y all have one sound (unless changed by a ^ to a longer sound): 'a' as in 'back', 'e' as in 'bent', 'i' as in 'skin', 'o' as in 'office', 'u' (like the French 'u' as in 'une') which you say by making your mouth into an 'o' and saying 'ee', 'w' as in 'boon' and 'y' as in the 'er' in 'mother'. This sound (phoneme), common in English, is called the *schwa* in the phonetic alphabet. Most consonants are as in English except for the doubled

consonants 'll' and 'dd': 'll' approximately as in the '-ch' of 'lo**ch**' followed
by an 'l' (chl, sometimes murdered by the English as 'thl'), 'dd' as 'the'. The
'ch' in Welsh is as in the Scottish 'lo**ch**'. The 'c' is always hard (like a 'k') and
one 'f' always sounds like a 'v'. There are also masculine and feminine forms
of words (*bach* and *fach*, for example).

Following are the commoner words you'll find on the maps.

aethnen	aspen tree
afon	river
allt	hillside
arddu	dark
bach, fach	little
bedd	grave (burial place)
betws	chapel
beudy	cowshed, byre
blaen	end, summit
bleiddiad	ferocious warrior
braich	arm
brân, fran	crow
bras	bunting (bird)
brwyn	rushes
bryn	hill
bwlch	pass, col
bychan	little, small
cadair	cradle, chair, throne
carnedd, garnedd	cairn, mound, tumulus
carreg, cerrig	stone, rock
castell	castle
cath	cat
cau	enclosed hollow
ci	dog
cigfran, gigfran	raven
clogwyn	cliff, crag
clyd	snug, cosy, sheltered
cneifio	shear (as in sheep)
cneifion	clippings
coch, goch	red
coed	wood, trees
cnicht	knight
craf	garlic
craig	rock, crag
crec y garreg	stonechat
crib	crest, summit, ridge
croes	cross
cwm	valley, glen
cŵn	hound
Dafydd	David
dinas	fort
drws	doorstep, door
du, ddu	black
duo	to blacken, darken
dwy, ddwy	two
dysgl, ddysgl	dish, cup
eithin	gorse

eryr	eagle
Eryri	Snowdonia
ffridd	mountain pasture
ffynnon	well, spring
gafr	goat
gallt (=allt)	hill, a slope
geifre	flock of goats
glas	blue, green
gloyw	bright
gorsedd	throne
gribin	crest of a hill
gwartheg	cattle
gwyn	white, holy
gwynt	wind
hafod	summer dwelling
hebog	falcon
hwyad	duck
hydd	deer
Iago	James
isaf	lowest
llan	church
llech	slate
llethr	slope, steep
llwyd, lwyd	grey
llyn	lake
Madog	Maddock
maen	stone
mawr, fawr	big
mochyn	pig
moel, foel	bare hilltop
morfa	sea marsh, bog
morwyn	girl, virgin
mynydd	mountain
Myrddyn	Merlin
nant	stream
newydd	new
ogof	cave
pen	top, peak
pibydd y mynydd	meadow pipit
plas	mansion
porth	harbour
pysgod	fish
rhinog	threshold
rhyd	ford
saeth	arrow
traeth	beach
twll	hole
tŷ	house
tyddyn	smallholding, small farm
uchaf	highest
wen	white
ynys	island
Yr Wyddfa	literally 'place of presence' owing to Bardic meetings thought to have taken place on the summit
ystrad	vale

Rocky Ramble 1:
Cwm Bychan and Rhinog Fawr

How to get to the start of the ramble

In Llanbedr, between Harlech and Barmouth (Abermaw), turn east along a series of
progressively narrower roads right into the heart of the wild moutainous area known
to geologists as the Harlech Dome. Your road is well signposted to Cwm Bychan
and you follow it until you reach the carpark at Cwm Bychan farm. This is a large
flat field on the right just after Llyn Cwm Bychan. Parking currently (1996) costs £1
and you can, if you wish, camp here. There are no facilities except the clear stream
but it is a lovely spot not prone to flooding.

Sadly, you can't get near this area by bus or train though both run through Llanbedr:
Bus No. 38, Blaenau Ffestiniog – Harlech – Abermaw (Barmouth) (Crosville Cymru,
tel.01492 596969 or 01248 370295). For train times (Pwllheli – Porthmadog – Llanbedr – Barmouth – Machynlleth), call 01492 585151. From Llanbedr, you have a 9-
kilometre walk to the start of this ramble. But you can camp there, so if you've a
tent, backpacking is a solution. Or hitching a lift.

The ramble: needs, distances and times

The ramble is 9 kilometres (5½ miles) with 680 metres (2230 feet) of climbing.
You'll need a fine day for it because the views are excellent and route-finding is a
bit tricky on part of the return. If the clouds come down, it may be sensible to retrace
your steps because the paths to Rhinog Fawr summit are fairly clear. Cwm Bychan
is quite remote and so just getting to the start of the walk can take an hour or more
out of your day, so it's best to give yourself a full day. Then if the weather is fair, you
can linger at pretty Gloyw Lyn ... maybe even swim. You'll need OS Outdoor Leisure Map 18.

Introduction

If you're familiar with Snowdonia's scenery, you'll already be aware that this
district here, part of what geologists call the Harlech Dome, is quite unlike
anywhere else. You can see lines of rock outcrops everywhere and it all looks
much the same. It's characterised by endless small crags but few larger ones.
The reason, as you'd guess, is that the rocks are somewhat different from the
'usual' in that they are amongst the oldest in Wales and have quite a different
origin from those in other parts of Snowdonia. Everything you will see today
formed at the bottom of a shallow sea into which 'events' elsewhere caused
powerful currents to surge, carrying within their turbulent selves heavy
loads of sands and sometimes even gravels. These were turbidity currents,
so called because the turbid and chaotic but highly energetic currents were
powerful enough to hold vast quantities of sediment in suspension whilst
they travelled down sub-sea slopes into deeper water. The steeper slopes fed
energy into the moving current just as slopes give you energy – because of
gravity – in the winter when you ski down hill. Only when the currents lost
energy as the slope flattened out, did they begin to shed their load of debris
and lay down a new bed of sand and gravel. The finer material like silt or

mud would have continued on further because it needs less energy to keep in suspension.

The currents were actually triggered by 'events' like hurricanes or earthquake shocks. How could these 'events' trigger currents? Simply because masses of loose material were being constantly stored up by river deltas building out into the shallower seas. This store of debris remained stable until some trigger event generated large waves and began to destabilise the whole pile of stored sediment. Then part of the pile collapsed, a process called fluidisation, gaining energy as it hooshed down into deeper water forming a turbidity current. We now know that such currents are both powerful and remain extremely common processes today, just as they have been since the oceans first formed perhaps 4 billion years ago. They are difficult to see because we live on the land! But they can form huge thicknesses of what eventually becomes rock. You'll be looking at a fossil example of such an accumulation all around you in the Harlech Dome rocks, dating back well down into the Cambrian Period; around 530 million years or so. The rocks are called turbidites (or greywackes) and are part of the immensely thick Harlech Grits Group: the Rhinog Formation, also called more simply the Rhinog Grits.

One final point: You are probably wondering how it was that such huge thicknesses were able to develop. Where did they come from? Why didn't they fill up the sea completely? These are good questions and help show us just how mobile what we think of as static – mountains and seas – really are. One lesson of earth science is that nothing is permanent. Mountains come and go. Oceans, even, come and go. Everything everywhere is always changing. To achieve this kind of pile of grits, you had to have two things happening: one was that the source of the sediment – mountainous land – was rising steadily and so continually being torn at by unusually catastrophic erosional forces like rain and rivers; the second was that the trough occupied by the sea would indeed have filled up if it hadn't been constantly subsiding. This subsidence may have been triggered by the weight of new sediment or may itself have triggered the constant new influx by creating unstable steep submarine slopes, liable to generate turbidity currents. Which came first? The chicken or the egg? Such subsiding sea basins have been common throughout our Earth's history. Recognising old ones can be of great economic importance for almost all the world's major oil deposits are found in them. The North Sea basin is a fine example. That has kept Britain self-sufficient in oil and gas for two decades so far.

As you walk, keep your eyes open for the small flocks of wild goats which roam these mountains. They have long black, brown and white hair, and slightly curved dark horns. I've seen them nibbling young bracken fronds so probably no one has told them about the cancer scares associated with this member of the fern family.

To the Roman Steps

Walk up to the top of the carpark field and through a gate or over a stile

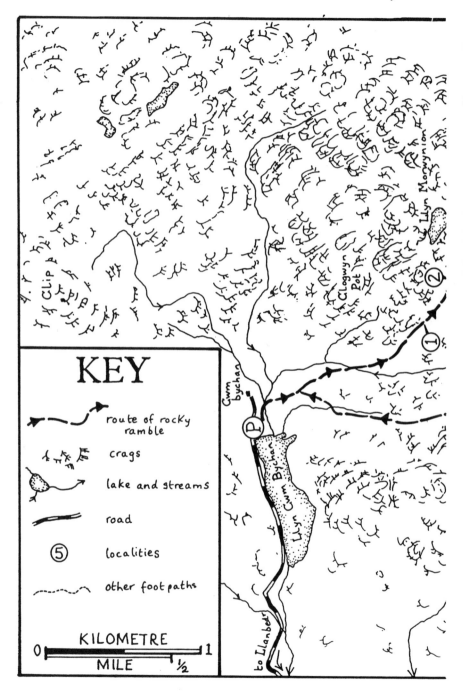

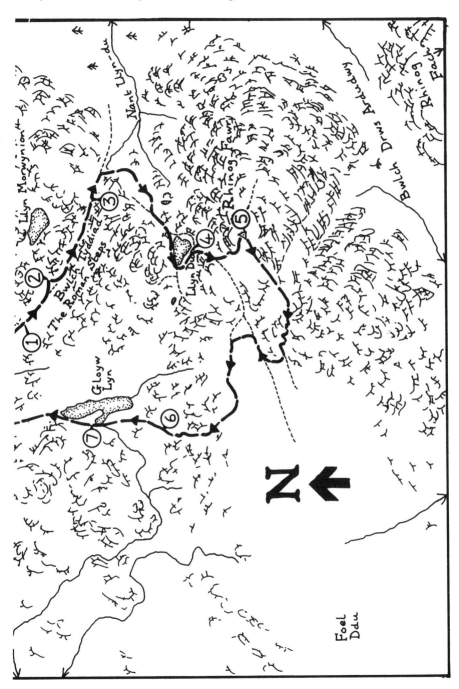

at a newly-constructed wall to turn right onto a freshly-gravelled track over the stream. All around are rowans, oak trees, a few sycamores and hawthorns and even crab apples. Mostly, it's sheep-nibbled pasture. Everywhere too is a litter of huge boulders.

Shortly, the path runs between a fence on the right and a huge slab of rock dipping towards you on the left. This is a tilted bedding plane inclined – dipping – at about 30° to the west. Formerly and briefly, it was part of the surface of the ancient seafloor before being buried by another turbidite. Much later, it and all the other rocks were crushed by unimaginable forces and deformed into huge folds. This plane is the western side of an enormous upfold – anticline – called the Harlech anticline. You'll see many more examples of bed surfaces, starting at Locality 1.

Cross a ladder stile into oak and birch woodland. Wood sorrel grows amongst the mossy boulders and ferns. In spring, this wood is alive with birdsong, notably summer visitors like cuckoos, chiffchaffs and willow warblers as well as the usual residents like titmice (Fig. 1.1). The two warblers are almost impossible to tell apart save by their song, the willow warbler having a delightful descending song. **Shortly, you come out of the woodland, crossing another ladder stile into more open country with scattered birches and the rocky, heathery wilderness of the central Harlech Dome. Behind is the conical mountain Clip (actually a ridge). In front is the beginning of the Roman Steps, Bwlch Tyddiad, a track paved with flagstones from the grit beds around here.** Tradition tells us that these 'steps' were fashioned by the Romans to allow easy access for sentries, but they appear to be Medieval – quite old enough to be fun to walk up.

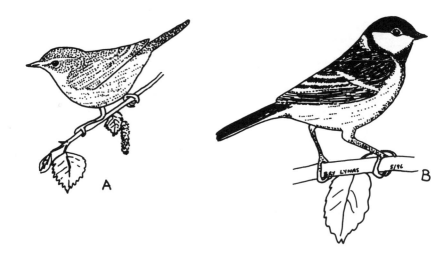

Figure 1.1: *Willow warbler (A) and great tit (B), two of the birds you're most likely to hear in these woods.*

Old arts lost? The path carries plenty of foot traffic so much effort has been put into bringing it into good repair. One stream was, for a short time, crossed by a tiny stone-arched bridge which was newly-built in early 1995. By June, it was in bad shape though still standing. By September, there was nothing left of it. You wouldn't have known it was there. Is the art of arch-construction using keystones lost, like the Roman Steps, in the mists of time?

The dominant plants around you are now wiry grasses and sedges, tormentils (perhaps the commonest mountain flower), polypody ferns, bilberry, milkworts, foxgloves and even violets ... and heather. The heather used to be notoriously deep on this walk but the paths are now well used and you rarely have to wade through knee-deep heather as you once did. But this is not easy country to walk through if you aren't following a path and you can see why.

As the valley narrows, the steps run close to the stream where a few willows grow. Then it ascends a little, curving this way and that, and you cross big slabby surfaces – bedding planes again. Ahead is the pass of Bwlch Tyddiad, a dry stone wall and a large mass of outcrops – Clogwyn Pot – to the left. In this, you can see that the beds are nearly flat-lying.

In front is a well-made dry stone wall which is where the best of the Roman Steps begin. There's a wooden gate through the wall. Stop just before the gate and double back to the right. This is the first locality.

Meeting ancient seafloors ... and cleavage: Locality 1 [6513 3040]

Right in front of you is a large dipping bed surface which you can walk out along. You are, in reality, walking across part of an ancient seafloor which has been buried for hundreds of millions of years, but is now exposed once again, this time to the forces of destruction: erosion.

As you walk to the west end of the tilted slab, the dip steepens. Scramble off the end to look at the third dimension – depth – which you don't normally see except in eroded sedimentary rocks.

This repetition of unit after unit, each comprising a massive layer followed by a bedded top, is the building block for all the mountains around here. Each bed – some quite thin, others thick as you will see – represents a single 'event' after which there was a period – perhaps months or years – when nothing much happened save that sea-floor currents played around with the finer top layers, reworking them a little and redepositing them to give the laminations you can see here. What is striking in the Rhinog Grits is the near-absence of any fine mud or silt material ... though not total absence as you'll see at the next locality.

As you walk back to the gate in the wall, you should spot riffles – linear irregularities – which intersect this bed plane, trending slightly east of north. These are due to a structure called cleavage which you'll see a great deal more of.

In the marshy hollows near the path, you should find a tiny purple-flowered member of the snapdragon family: lousewort (*Pedicularis sylvatica*). Also here are milkworts and sundews (*Drosera rotundifolia*) (Fig. 1.2).

Time dimensions and weird languages ... When you walk across a sandy beach like that at Mochras or Traeth Bach (Harlech), you can see the sands stretching out before you in all directions (at low tide). That's the equivalent of the bedding plane you've just walked across. What you can't see is what it looks like in depth. There could be hundreds of metres of sand underneath – or almost none. You don't have any clues to go on – unless you dig or bore a hole. But here, natural erosion offers you the chance to see this third dimension everywhere. This dimension represents Time: the time taken for repeated beds of sands to be flushed in and laid down and so build up beds, cluster of similar beds (usually called Formations) or different ones (like muds or volcanic debris, both of which you will see on all the other rambles). The study of sequences of beds is called stratigraphy and is one of geology's great cornerstones. By looking at beds like these and building up your understanding of the stratigraphy, you can perceive a great deal about the way things were when the rocks formed way back in time. Here, the stratigraphy is simple: Rhinog Grits everywhere, and these serve to illustrate how beds piled on beds, turned into rocks, folded and exhumed by erosion hundreds of millions of years later, can tell us the story of what was going on. The rocks are no longer just grey hard things; they're like pages of a book written in a strange language, a cipher, with only bits of the pages visible. But, with care, you can de-cipher more than you might expect. That's what stratigraphy – and geology – is all about: telling the story like it was. In this section through the third dimension, you can see the different size ranges of the sediment which has built this rock. Most of the grains are quartz, the commonest rock-forming mineral in sedimentary rocks like these because it is, like Levi jeans, immensely tough and long-lasting. It is one of the hardest minerals and won't oxidise or dissolve in normal acids or alkalis. The grains here reach the size of peppercorns but most are smaller giving, at the top, a medium to coarse sandstone or grit.

Figure 1.2: *Sundew, one of the two common insect-eating plants in these mountains. The plants exude sticky droplets from the hairs on their leaves. These trap tiny insects and then digest them, giving the plant the nutrients it needs to flourish.*

Sundew

Walk through the gate to confront a large vertical outcrop to the right of the steps. It is covered in grooves from top to bottom (Fig. 1.3). These grooves were gouged out by the passage of thick, heavy glaciers and are called striae. Like everywhere in Britain, save the far south, these mountains were covered many times with enormously thick ice sheets. You'll see more of their effects later today and on every other ramble in this book.

The Roman Steps are now a delight to walk over as you continue on up the pass. Look over to the low crags on the left side of the valley, directly above an old wall which the path intersects. These crags seem to have whitish-grey bands. Don't worry. You don't have to scramble over to them. They will come to *you* presently because they are almost horizontal. So as you climb higher, you are bound to walk over this particular set of beds. You are, in effect, walking up in time, for beds that rest on top of others must obviously be younger.

Figure 1.3: *Glacial striae (I've emphasised these) which are almost parallel to the bedding, though bedding is only noticeable at the top of the outcrop. This is a particularly thick massive bed unit. The slightly curvy vertical fractures are cleavage (see next locality).*

Almost at the skyline at the top of the outcrops with the grey-white bands, you can see a sort of bulging moulded projection of rock ... and it is moulded too: by ice. If you look at it through binoculars, you'll see that it's covered in beautiful striae just like those you saw by the gate.

As you continue, shortly in front you see another large dipping bed surface just to the left of the path. About 25 metres *before* this bed, you should find a tiny path (up to Llyn Morwynion) off to the left. Follow this across a little stream and within 30 metres, you reach the banded outcrops I mentioned. This is Locality 2.

Funny structures and squeezes: Locality 2 [6544 3023]

Here you can see that the pale bands are finer grained beds: muds and silts sandwiched within the normal coarser sandstones (Fig. 1.4). Each siltstone represents a different 'event' – or rather, non-event, since muds and silts usually settle out onto the seabed when nothing much else is happening. Every so often, another sand-laden turbidity current flowed briskly over, dumping some of its load as it lost energy. Sometimes, they only dumped the coarsest pebbles, having enough energy to keep the finer grit grains from falling out of suspension. Result: thin pebbly layers that geologists call 'lag' deposits. Some of the beds were heavy enough to sink slightly into the underlying bed. This produces load casts which are very common in alternating sequences of finer and coarser sediments. Remember, because these sediments formed under the sea, they were much more mobile and sloppy than you might imagine.

Figure 1.4: *This shows the obvious nearly flat-lying beds of siltstones and sandstones, cut by the later cleavage (which I've enhanced in the right centre). Notice how the cleavage is refracted (see text) between the softer silt beds (where it is well developed and dips from left to right) and the tough sandstones (where it forms widely-spaced fractures which are almost vertical). I've also marked a slump.*

Here too you see cleavage rather well (Figs 1.4 and especially 1.5). Cleavage is a difficult concept because there is no direct analogue (like a sandy estuary when talking about beds, for example) which we can see today. The processes which create it only operate after the rock has been deeply buried by thousands of metres of later sediments. We now understand quite well that cleavage is a by-product of the immense forces which Nature employs to thrust up mountains and squeeze what to us look like unsqueezable rocks into huge folds. It develops as a response to powerful stress fields which affect deeply buried rocks during orogeny: mountain-building. Mountains are usually formed when two of the great crustal plates of our planet collide. It's rather like putting a lump of putty in a vice. Apply force and the putty gets squeezed and deforms – it becomes strained – to accommodate the force. This happened here and everywhere in Snowdonia during the great mountain-building episode at the close of the Silurian Period: the Caledonian orogeny. At that time, all these rocks were deeply buried and became quite hot, because of their depth. The heat coupled with the powerful roughly horizontal stress field – the jaws of the vice – caused some minerals to 'change their skins' like insects which change – metamorphose – from (say) a caterpillar to a butterfly. New minerals like micas began to grow, replacing others like clays (which is what mudstones are largely made of). But micas are naturally platy minerals and always grow with their platy faces at right angles to the direction of the squeezing stress field. Snowdonia's rocks were subjected to immense but roughly horizontal forces squeezing from north-west to southeast. So almost all of the folds and their associated cleavage trend at right angles to this former force field: that is, northeast-southwest. And almost always, the cleavage dips steeply and the folds are mostly upright (not of high moral fibre, but with their limbs tending to become parallel to the cleavage as the tightness of the fold increases). The story is very much more complicated than this in detail, because different rocks behave differently and we know of several periods of mountain building which were all subtly different too.

If this is all a bit baffling, don't worry. You will over the course of these rambles see many examples of alut other timescahich will help you make

sense of it. In Figure 1.5, you can see how the cleavage angle is determined by the rock type it cuts. It is 'refracted' (like a beam of light passing at an angle through a glass block), being shallower in the finer-grained sediments and almost vertical in the sandstones. The sandstones, being tough, were highly resistant to having cleavage planes formed in them. So usually, the cleavage ends up as a series of widely-spaced joints called fracture cleavage.

Figure 1.5: *Close-up of the top end (left) of this outcrop. Here you can see beautiful cleavage refraction as cleavage planes pass between mudstones and siltstone beds (M) and sandstones (S). C – points to the lower angle cleavage in the mudstone-siltstone bed. F-F is a tiny low angle fault which disrupts the siltstones here.*

Slates. Everyone knows what a roofing slate is. But few know how they form. They were all originally muds or silts which, as always, built up on an ancient seafloor. They became slates because cleavage formed in them long afterwards by the processes I've just described. Because they are so fine grained, the cleavage is often perfect, a quality long exploited by Welsh quarrymen for roofing slates. You will see many examples of slates and the quarries from which they came on later rambles. Cleaved mudstone or siltstone = slate.

There's one more thing to see at these superb exposures of rock: a slump (Fig. 1.4). This bed has actually slipped and folded round within the otherwise normal sequence of more or less parallel beds. It tells us that this bed must have been laid down as more of a soft, squishy sludge, a bit like sloppy mashed potato. But to form the slump, the sea-floor must have been sloping slightly to give it the vital gravity energy.

Return to the Roman Steps and continue on up to the col. The glaciers have dropped many large boulders especially for you to examine as you tramp past. Some of these are on their sides or upside down, but offer you easy glimpses at more sedimentary structures like slumps, wavy beds (probably fossil ripples) and the alternation of various sandstones and thin siltstones. The glaciers have left their mark too. The rock walls to your right are smoothed and rounded with striae.

You will certainly hear the vigorous song of Britain's tiniest and probably hardiest bird: the wren. Wrens are just as at home in remote rocky mountains as in hedgerows and woodland. They 'bounce' in and out of cavities or cracks in rocks like tiny feathery balls on springs; hence their Latin name *Troglodytes* (cave-dweller). Apart from the heather, bilberry and cowberry are quite common here (both species of *Vaccinium*). Both are edible though bilberry is much the better of the two.

The top of the pass is marked by a large pile of stones and big, flat glacier-polished bedding surfaces. This is Locality 3.

Top of Bwlch Tyddiad: Locality 3 [6590 2997]

This locality gives you your first views to the southeast, across large areas of conifer forest plantation. Much of this rather desolate area below is covered over by thick piles of rubbish – till – left by the last decaying ice sheets. Beneath the till are even older rocks; the core of the region. The whole area is drained by the Afon Eden which later unites with the Afon Mawddach and runs into the Mawddach estuary.

The narrow valley of Bwlch Tyddiad was actually carved out by the ice sheets. The ice came from a vast ice accumulation well over 1000 metres thick to the east, and headed for the Irish Sea to the west. Usually valleys coincide with faults – lines of weakness where the rocks have broken and moved either up, down or sideways. Bwlch Tyddiad is obviously a line of weakness picked out by the moving ice, but here the weakness was a dyke of an intrusive rock: dolerite. You'll see dolerite many times on other rambles, though you can't readily see it here. But its existence explains this gorge-like valley, for although dolerite is fairly hard, it's nothing like so hard as the Rhinog Grits.

From here you have to continue on the Roman Steps and drop down a little to pick up the path to Rhinog Fawr. It isn't far and you can't really miss it as it splits off to the right, heading south, just before you come to an obvious dry stone wall. The Roman Steps continue on down (east). This is where the ramble stops being like a Sunday stroll! The path leads you on through heather and peaty areas up a shallow valley towards Llyn Du, passing after a bit through a ruined wall. Now for the first time you begin to see the forbidding rocky north face of Rhinog Fawr. After crossing the wall, watch out because a little after this, the path seems to double back to the right. This is actually another path (a short cut from Bwlch Tyddiad which is not easy to find) coming in to join this one. You keep straight on up over some boulders and so up to Llyn Du.

Llyn Du, Black Lake, is a fairly wild and desolate place (as I know having camped here alone one night when preparing this ramble). But here you can see many fine bedding planes formed of grits which have thin siltstone beds separating them, the alternating rock types showing cleavage refraction (as in Fig. 1.5). The lake basin was carved by ice – as indeed are all natural lake basins in Snowdonia. In some instances, the lakes are held in place by a dam of glacial debris: moraine. In others such as this, the ice has simply scooped out a basin within the solid rock which later filled with water. There are no moraines here at all.

Looking across the lake to the southwest, you can see the path you'll be following: a steep rocky scramble to the right of a gully full of loose boulders, between two buttresses. It isn't as steep as it looks. You can walk round either side of the lake, though the southeast side (where there is a tiny path) involves some scrambling. The northwest path is certainly easier and more used. Head for Locality 4, a rocky bluff overlooking the lake.

Dastardly deeds done by the Destroyer: Locality 4 [6553 2936]

From here, you can see right across Cardigan Bay to Llŷn and look back down to the lake. The rocks themselves are dishevelled (Fig. 1.6). They need to pull themselves together! You can see how part of this large gently inclined grit bed, some of which contains distinct quartz pebble layers, seems to have fallen apart, such that you could almost push the pieces back together again. Why has this happened? It was, as I'm sure you've guessed, the movement of the destroying glaciers below the north face of Rhinog Fawr which did this dastardly deed. Pre-existing joints, mostly due to fracture cleavage, made these tough rocks easy meat for the ice sheets. They plucked, pulled and ripped the guts out of this lake basin, heaving huge boulders miles away down to Cardigan Bay and leaving this desolation of rock. At this locality, the ice hadn't finished its business; it had broken and prised apart these outcrops, rather like the Polynesian peoples on Easter Island who abandoned some of their 45-tonne statues half complete as their culture declined into chaos. The incomplete Easter Island statues will never now be taken from their quarries but who knows when the ice will return here to continue its unfinished business?

Figure 1.6: *Well-bedded grits with thin siltstones and pebbly layers, broken apart along joints by ice sheets as little as 14, 500 years ago.*

Climate change: We've all heard about global warming. But what about global cooling? What causes ice ages? This is a question to which we still don't have a sure answer. What we do know is that ice ages have been waxing and waning for nearly 2 million years in our hemisphere. The last, called the Weichselian (Devensian in Britain) finished just 11,500 years ago, ushering in a warmer period we call (wishfully perhaps) the Post-Glacial or Holocene (see Appendix, Timescale). If much of the last 2 million years has been glacial, why should we expect it all to be over now? We have short memories – a few decades at the most. But we know from careful studies of deep sea sediment or ice cores from Greenland and the Antarctic that Earth's climate can flip from one 'stable' state to another in as little as a decade. The last great interglacial period, the Eemian, seems to have been characterised by constant change. Why should we expect any different now ... especially with our unintended grand global experiment of atmospheric pollution with car exhausts and industrial filth? What tricks does our planet Gaia, our only home, have up her sleeve?

Now head towards the gully I mentioned. This starts as a right turn off the path which continues around the lake, up towards a bit of stone wall on the right into the stony gully. The path sometimes divides as you scramble over the boulders and through the heather, but you end up in the same place. Shortly, you emerge at the top to continue on a clear path around the northwestern shoulder of Rhinog Fawr. Your views north to Snowdonia become better and better. Almost immediately, you come to a junction where you take the left fork up the mountainside (another path continues on to the southwest). Again the path splits and rejoins. You end up scrambling up a scree slope and up a small stream gully. Finally, you reach the rounded summit plateau and the trig point: Locality 5.

Rhinog Fawr: Locality 5 [6568 2900]

The grits on the summit plateau are much broken up, making a good home for English stonecrop (*Sedum anglicum*). For sure, the glaciers at one time flowed right over here too, accounting for the mountain's rounded humpy form. At other times, the summit would have been exposed to the intense arctic cold and periglacial (meaning a process happening at the edge of the glaciers) effects. Such periglacial processes were dominated by the astonishing power of repeated freezing and thawing to prise apart rocks and then to move them about to produce 'patterned ground'. This continues in the present in the high Arctic lands of Siberia and northern Canada where the ground is permanently frozen, often to hundreds of metres depth. But for a brief period during the summer, the surface layers melt in the 24-hour sunshine of places north of the Arctic Circle. Soon, it all freezes again.

Time and ice: How can ice (not including glaciers) so influence a landscape? Water when it freezes, expands. That's all it takes. Fill a crack in the rock with water and, on a frosty night, the crystallising ice pushes relentlessly and prises the crack a little further open. The same thing happens the next night. Eventually, the rock breaks apart and pieces roll away down slope to accumulate as scree. If you doubt the power of ice to do this, try leaving a car out on a very cold night with no antifreeze in its coolant. Well maybe you shouldn't do this because the repairs you'll need could run into four figures. The radiator will almost certainly burst and, much worse, the thick, tough cast iron (sometime aluminium alloy) cylinder block may crack. Iron broken by a bit of water turning to ice! So freezing and thawing, repeated tens of times each year, every year for thousands of years, has astonishing power to remould entire landscapes. Vast tracts of the prised-off debris can slowly 'flow' down shallow slopes to accumulate in valleys. You can see remnants of this having happened all over Britain, and especially in Snowdonia. It's hard to imagine all this happening on a fine summer's day but on a freezing winter's day, you feel very different. It's also very hard for us to visualise the unimaginably long time during which these processes continued. If a rock is moved just one centimetre (very conservative estimate) each winter, but you have 100,000 winters, that's 10 kilometres! Measurements from the Arctic show that you can get movements between a few centimetres to 35 centimetres each winter – and on slopes as low as just 1 degree.

From this summit, you have wonderful views both near and far. To the south, across the astonishingly deep pass of Bwlch Drws Ardudwy (nearly 400 metres below) is Rhinog Fach with Y Llethr behind, all made of the same Rhinog Formation grit. Bwlch Drws Ardudwy is, as you'd expect, the result of glaciers picking out a line of weakness in the grits caused by a fracture – a fault – which underlies the pass. The ice has also carved out the rock basins now occupied by Llyn Hywel and Llyn Cwmhosan.

A brief Welsh lesson: *Drws* means doorstep and *Rhinog* means, in this context, pillar or doorpost. So you can see how these mountains and this pass came to be named.

On both mountains, the dip everywhere is to the southwest. The core of the Harlech Dome lies about 3 kilometres to the east (known to geologists as the Dolwen Pericline, a boat-shaped upfold). No one knew what rocks were underneath this since they are never exposed at the surface, so a borehole was drilled to find out. This boring passed through sandstones into a thick volcanic formation, named the Bryn-Teg Volcanics. These *may* be the equivalent to the Precambrian age Padarn Tuffs at Llanberis (Ramble 2).

Further to the east, the rocks dip east and so become younger again. The Arenig mountains are Ordovician in age, mostly formed from volcanic rocks. Likewise the Aran ranges to the southeast, Cadair Idris (Ramble 6) and the high central Snowdonia mountains: Moel Hebog, Snowdon, Cnicht and Moelwyn Mawr. The last four, also visible from here, are the subjects of some of the other rambles in this book.

A much odder thing happens to the west. A borehole was sunk at Mochras to see what happened just a matter of 3 kilometres from the nearest outcrops of almost the oldest Cambrian rocks. These known rocks were dipping (=getting younger) to the east, so as you go west, you would expect to encounter even older rocks. The borehole was an astonishing surprise for everyone. Instead of finding even older rocks, or at least Cambrian rocks, it passed through over 2,000 metres of young sediments dating back to the time of the earliest dinosaurs some 220 million years ago (Triassic). So these rocks were well over 300 million years younger than you might have expected. How could this have happened? It seems that a really huge fault, now called the Mochras Fault, has moved down thousands of metres on its western side, forming the east margin of Cardigan Bay. This is a wonderful example of how deep basins (which I've talked about in the Introduction) can form with 'walls' and 'floor' made of much older rocks. For somewhere down there must be the equivalents of the rocks you are standing on here! How deep, no one knows. Perhaps 3 or 4,000 metres? It says something for the size of the Mochras Fault.

To the southwest is Moelfre in which – with care – you can see things have changed: the dip is different. At its north end, you can see quite clear big bed surfaces like those you've crossed on the way up ... but these are dipping *east*. (Everything you've seen so far has been either flat-lying or dipping west.) You get the sense of more east-dipping beds in the heathery precipices of Moelfre too. If you then scan further towards Y Llethr, you soon pick up beds dipping, like those underfoot, to the west. This geometry can mean only one thing: there's a big downfold – a syncline – in the rocks between the Rhinog mountains and Moelfre. So the Harlech Dome isn't quite the simple structure it sounds to be.

The entire west flank of Y Llethr is made of younger rocks which overlie the Rhinog Grits. You can see a clear change in outcrop style from nearly bare rock (grits) to mostly grass with hardly any crags at all (younger siltstone formation – the Hafotty Shales).

To continue, head from the trig towards the sand dunes at distant Llanbedr – southwest. The path is clear and marked on the OS map. After an easy descent for about half a kilometre, you come to a slight rise with

a pile of rocks on top. Just below is a dry stone wall with a ladder stile. To the northwest is the pretty lake of Gloyw Lyn, and your route will (in due course) be around its west shores. Drop down to the ladder stile and cross the wall. From here, it is a good idea to look fairly carefully at the route to Gloyw Lyn. You can see paths quite clearly in the expanse of heather below. None is marked on the OS map, though they are on mine. You can't easily go directly down this steep slope towards the lake. It is much easier to follow the definite path down towards the southwest until the slope shallows out at the base of the steeper descent (about 300 metres past the stile). Watch out for a tiny path which turns off to the right. If you find yourself approaching some ruined sheepfolds and Cwm Nantcol, you've missed this path! The tiny path, about 100 metres and really no more than a sheep track, cuts across heather and boulders and disappears. But by then, you're only a few metres from another prominent path onto which you turn right (east again). So it doesn't matter if you don't find the tiny path. You only have to plough your way north for 100-150 metres to meet the next path.

Tornado alley? Not quite perhaps. Tornadoes are not something we associate with climatically-gentle Britain. Yet in September 1995, Val and I were checking out these rambles so that I wouldn't confuse you as I have her by ambiguous directions and cranky, half-baked explanations. The weather was poor and black-looking clouds were gathering over to the southeast. The Rhinog summits sometimes vanished in banners of cloud and sometimes they were clear. The outlook was not good. Indeed it chucked it down about an hour later. But whilst watching this cloud over towards the Aran mountains, I noticed a ragged tatter of cloud apparently descending from the cloud base. I said, jokingly, 'Look, a tornado.' And as we watched, spellbound, so it turned out to be. A more and more obvious dark swirling funnel of cloud dropped further from the cloud base, sometimes apparently touching the distant mountain tops and then dissipating a little. It seemed to be getting closer and larger when the clouds enveloped us definitively. And that was that!

Another 150 metres back towards Llyn Du along the new path, you come to a junction in a hollow with a jumble of boulders. Turn left here to head north across the moorland. (A third path ascends back towards the north-west shoulder of Rhinog Fawr.) The northward path isn't much used and is not always clear, though it's easy walking. After about another 150 metres, you cross a marshy patch (and the path becomes vague) and begin to see Gloyw Lyn and descend slightly. Almost as soon as you see the lake, you intersect yet another prominent path onto which you turn left (west). Now, at last!, it is straightforward. The new path contours round high above Gloyw Lyn, descending gently and traversing round the south end of a small but deep valley. On the west side of this valley, there's a wall with a ladder stile. From here, you can see where the path picks its way through the heather along the west side of Gloyw Lyn.

Shortly, there's another path junction and you bear right, down to the wall and stile. Then the path continues its descent towards Gloyw Lyn crossing odd boggy patches. Half way down the steep bit, just past a ruined dry stone wall, is Locality 6.

Figure 1.7: *These bulgy rocks have so obviously been moulded and grooved (S – striae, enhanced on one part only) by the ice that they almost scream it at you. The sticking-out bits are the harder grit beds and the grooves, the softer parts.*

Figure 1.8: *Perfect example of a perched block, a lump of rock dumped on this broad bedding plane when the ice melted. It's been sitting there unchanged for around 14,500 years. It's even protected the glacial striae right underneath it. The only difference is the vegetation. This block is a little further down the slope than Fig. 1.7.*

Glaciers as artisans: Locality 6 [645 295]

This locality is not one single place, but a number of places through which the path takes you as you descend. The idea is to look around a bit at the extraordinary sculpting and moulding of the grits by the passage of the ice (Figs 1.7 & 1.8).

Glacial artisans need tools and sandpaper ... Ice – pure ice – is soft. Try scratching a rock with ice. You can't. So how come the glaciers were so destructive? How could they have the power to gouge, chisel, cut and polish in the way that you can see they have around here? The answer is simply that they used tools, just like any other artisan from Henry Moore to a carpenter. Unlike human artisans, glaciers were not intelligent. Their 'tools' were accidental. Any rocky material which became incorporated into them, by avalanches or ripping up loose stuff at their bases, became part of their toolkit. Go to any melting glacier snout today and look at the ice. It's often completely covered in the rocky material it was carrying, and the ice itself always contains lumps of rock. When these lumps of rock – the 'tools' – ended up at the bottom of the glacier, they could gouge into the similarly hard rocks underneath. The more damage done by ice and freeze-thaw, the more tools that glacier had to grind and polish everything it flowed over. It became a giant version of sandpaper, the 'sand' being rocks which in many cases might have weighed tens of tonnes. The 'glue backing material' was the ice itself. This was a powerful combination for rapid erosion, and the more rocks the glaciers carried, the more erosive they became. We can admire the results of their craftsmanship around here, for some of their carving is very beautiful. Andy Goldsworthy, the renowned modern sculptor who uses natural materials for his outdoor creations, would love this!

The rock itself – Rhinog Grits again – is made of really thick individual beds around here. Some are several metres thick and massive (meaning that they have no internal structures). These represent what must have been powerful turbidite 'events' indeed.

Just before the lake is a boggy patch and you cross a small stream. As you skirt a round inlet, another path joins your path from the left. Continue on to the north along the west side of this attractive lake: Locality 7.

Gloyw Lyn 'Bright Lake': Locality 7 [645 300]

Shhh! If you're quiet and there's no one about, you may spot some water birds: ducks such as teal, snipe and moorhens, all of which I've seen here though they're quite shy. The southern sector with its shelter of water plants is alive with little birds going about their private business, mostly hidden away from inquisitive humans.

This lake was made by moving ice, excavating a slightly softer bed: it is exactly parallel to the strike – the horizontal trend – of the bedding. The eastern shores are almost continuous west-dipping bed surfaces just like that you saw this morning at Locality 1. The ice didn't quite chisel enough away at the north end to let the water run out that way, but the watershed is only a few metres higher than the lake. Instead, the outlet is to the west.

And like all lakes, it is gradually filling in. A stream at the south end is slowly but surely building out a cone of alluvial debris into the lake. So the south end of the lake is almost entirely silted up and is filled with rushes, water horsetails and bog cotton.

Bright Lake; Magic lake? There's a good place to swim at the south end of the small peninsula. Once after I had done so and was enjoying the warm, midge-free late spring sunshine, a curious noise made me look around. It sounded as if someone or something had jumped into the lake. But there wasn't anyone around. Was it a monster or ghost? Then I spotted it ... a sight I have never seen before. An old Welsh mountain ram with double-curled horns had not only taken the plunge but was happily swimming slowly across the lake through the cotton grass and horsetails, nibbling off mouthfuls here and there. Somehow he'd discovered that these plants offered a good bite to eat; worth his heavy, waterlogged fleece. Normally, sheep *hate* to swim. I had never before seen one do so despite many years of being in mountains.

Your path crosses the low watershed. From here, you have your final views of Moel Hebog, Mynydd Mawr, Snowdon and the Glyder Fawr. Another track joins from the east lake shore. Now you descend to a wall with a ladder stile and continue on towards Cwm Bychan. In some of the marshy bits, you may find common butterworts (*Pinguicula vulgaris)* growing. These, like sundews, are insect-eating plants with sticky leaves which trap and digest small flies. Here you also begin to find blue milkworts, violets, wood sorrel and hawthorns trees.

In some of the gently sloping marshy areas beyond the ladder stile, you see numerous low shrubs growing. This is bog myrtle (*Myrica gale*) which has wonderful fragrant leaves (like other real myrtles that you find around the Mediterranean). There's more to this humble plant than meets the eye. It may even become the salvation of the tourist industry in western Scotland where midges drive people mad on the long summer evenings. It seems that an extract of the oils from bog myrtle is loathsome to midges. So if midges bother you, try rubbing yourself with bog myrtle leaves.

Keep straight on down with Clip dominating your view overlooking the head of Cwm Bychan. Soon you cross a broken down fence and have a good view of the whole of Cwm Bychan and its lake. At a modern wire fence, the path bends round to the right to go down through some woodland. Follow the fence down to the bottom, crossing some boggy bits. Then you meet another fence coming in from the right, and the two fences funnel you in to a steel gate. Just before the gate is a huge smooth bedding plane dipping moderately steeply towards you. **After the gate, turn right for a few metres, towards the ladder stile you crossed this morning. Rejoin the Roman Steps track crossing a barbed wire fence with some large rocks placed conveniently so you can readily step over. Turn left and return the short distance to the carpark.**

Afterword to Act I ...

So ends your first rocky ramble. If you're new to the ideas of vast amounts of time, how sedimentary rocks form, mountain building, rock folding, cleavage and how glaciers work, I hope you will now have some practical understanding from today's walk. This should have prepared you for the following rambles which build on this understanding, introducing you to more rocks and – in particular – to those formed in the most violent events of which our planet is capable: volcanic eruptions. As you can see, this lovely scenery has a terrific tale to tell.

Rocky Ramble 2: Llanberis and West Snowdon

How to get to the start of the ramble

The ramble starts in Llanberis where you can park on the streets though there are also public car parks. The town in served by a number of buses. The YHA (tel. 01286 870280), Llwyn-celyn, is well-sited for this ramble which begins at the narrow tarmac road to the waterfall and pottery [5796 5956]. There is nowhere to park just here so approach on foot from the main street, turning by the church.

Several buses serve Llanberis: Bangor – Llanberis No. 76 & 77 (Williams; tel. 01286 870484); Caernarfon – Llanberis No. 88 (KMP; tel.01286 870880); Llan-dudno/Porthmadog – Llanberis No. 95 (KMP) and No. 97 (Express; tel. 01286 674570).

On poor days, there are other things to do in Llanberis: the Llanberis Lake Railway (tel. 01286 870549); Snowdon Mountain Railway (tel. 01286 870223); the Power of Wales Museum which can include a visit to the largest pumped storage power sta-tion in Europe – underground at Dinorwig (tel. 01286 870636). The Welsh Slate Mu-seum is a must.

The ramble: needs, distances and times

The ramble is about 14 kilometres (8¾ miles) and you'll be climbing about 850 me-tres (2800 feet). This is a full day walk for there's plenty to see. You need to do a lit-tle simple route-finding during parts of the ramble. Beware of loose scree and climbers dislodging rocks at Clogwyn Du'r Arddu.
You need OS Outdoor Leisure Map 17.

Snowdonia: All the world's a stage ...

I like the parallel between theatre played by humans and theatre played by tireless Nature. Our Hamlets or King Lears occupy the stage for a couple of hours. Nature's actors have been performing continuously since the Earth formed 4,600 million years ago. Not all Nature's performances grip your attention in the way that Shakespeare or Dylan Thomas does. Frankly, some of her performances are rather dull. But on this ramble, you'll begin to see what she can offer in the way of super spectaculars as I introduce you to players with odd names like Pitt's Head. This ramble does encompass a vast range of time. You start amongst the oldest rocks, here in Llanberis – roughly the equivalents of the Rhinog Grits you saw during the first ramble. Then you climb up, both in Time and in altitude. For mostly, every step up that you take means you're stepping on rocks which are younger than those underneath. For parts, each step you take could represents thousands of years of slow accumulation of muddy sediments; not very exciting. But things get hotter as you get to Clogwyn Du'r Arddu, the famous climbers' precipice which adds a sombre impressiveness to the west flank of Snowdon.

The noisiest players today are the RAF and the engines of the Snowdon Mountain Railway which is now over 100 years old. Sadly, the old puffing

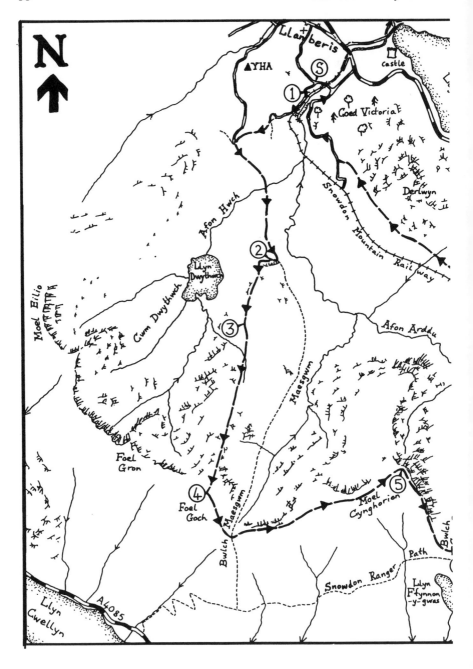

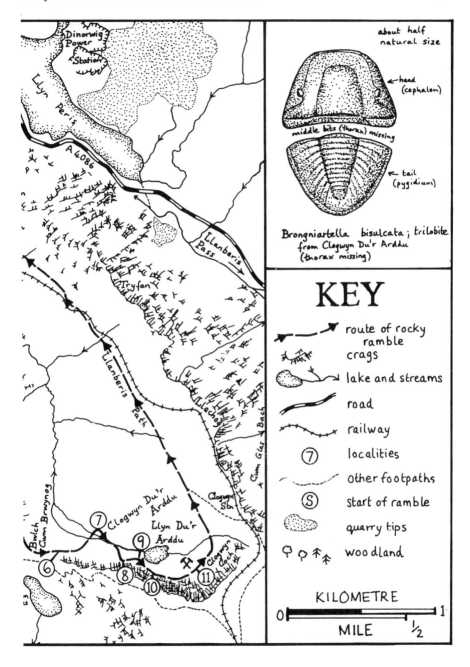

about half
natural size

head
(cephalon)

middle bits (thorax) missing

tail
(pygidium)

Brongniartella bisulcata ; trilobite
from Clogwyn Du'r Arddu
(thorax missing)

KEY

route of rocky ramble

crags

lake and streams

road

railway

⑦ localities

other footpaths

Ⓢ start of ramble

quarry tips

woodland

KILOMETRE

0   1

MILE   ½

Map labels: Dinorwig Power Station; Llyn Peris; A4086; Llanberis Pass; Tryfan; Llanberis Path; Llechog; Cwm Glas Bach; Cwm Glas; Bwlch Cwm Brwynog; Clogwyn Du'r Arddu; Llyn Du'r Arddu; Clogwyn Coch; Clogwyn Stn.

steam engines are being replaced by noisy boring diesels. But all these are dwarves by comparison with the age-old mountains which have such a tale to tell

This ramble is an introduction to most of the principal actors in this vast theatre and you'll meet all of them again, sometimes in different guises. But I shall unmask them for you if I can ...

> *I could a tale unfold whose lightest word*
> *Would harrow up thy soul, freeze thy young blood,*
> *Make thy two eyes, like stars, start from their spheres,*
> *Thy knotted and combinèd locks to part,*
> *And each particular hair to stand on end,*
> *Like quills on the fretful porpentine...*

(spoken to Hamlet by his father's ghost in **Hamlet** by William Shakespeare)

If I can excite you just a little in such a way, then I shall have succeeded in my writing!

Dolbadarn Castle: a brief history. This tiny castle perched on a *roche moutonée* above Llyn Padarn held Owen, the imprisoned brother of the famous Welsh chieftain Llewelyn ap Grufydd, for 22 years – before Edward I (builder of castles like Harlech, Conwy and Caernarfon; Harlech cost £8,190 two shillings and fourpence-farthing to build!) came to the English throne. Llewelyn led a violent life and met a violent end – beheaded by two English knights.

Llanberis, the start

From the main street, take the turn to Ceunant Mawr (waterfall) opposite the Castle Gift Shop. There's a service station on the corner of the narrow street which runs past the church on the right. Take the second footpath (actually along a road at first) off to the right a little before the Snowdon Mountain Railway viaduct. This is marked 'To the waterfall' and to Llanberis Pottery. Another road just goes to a coal merchant. Before this right turn, do look into the beautiful garden on the left where natural outcrops of rock have been tastefully incorporated into a semi-natural giant rockery with rambling roses spreading along the walls. The road climbs steeply up the hill through oakwoods. At the top of this first short climb, the road curves round towards the Snowdon Railway and there's an open space to your left between the wood and the railway. This is the first locality.

Meet the Bronllwyd Grit: Locality 1 [5790 5948]

Walk off a few metres to the left to the top of the bank here. The railway is just a few paces away.

This is the oldest rock you will actually stand on today though you can see from here the great Dinorwig Quarry opposite which worked slate that underlies and so is older than the rock here. I'll say a little more about the quarry and the slates later on this ramble at Locality 4.

Dinorwig Quarry whose vast open workings span a vertical height of nearly 550 metres, closed in 1969. In 1882, it employed 2,757 men and produced over 87,000 tons of finished slates. The Bronllwyd Grit overlies the slate formation, forming the summit of Elidir Fach.

The Bronllwyd Grit, as you can see in the outcrops around you, forms thick slabby beds which dip quite steeply (Fig. 2.1). Separating each of these thick, quite coarse grey sandstone beds are much thinner siltstone beds. You can see siltstone sticking to the top surface of the bed in the centre of Figure 2.1. The siltstones show a strong, almost vertical, cleavage which doesn't affect the tough sandstone beds at all (almost entirely hard quartz grains up to small lentil size). Do these beds look familiar? They are very similar to the Rhinog Grits of the first ramble and were probably deposited at about the same time. We can't be sure because there's no way of dating them accurately.

Figure 2.1: *Typical outcrops of Bronllwyd Grit, dipping steeply southwest in big slabs. The massive sandstone (S) beds can reach 2-3 metres thickness. They are usually separated by thin cleaved siltstone (Si) such as that sticking to the dipping plane of grit in the centre-right.*

English stonecrop (it should be Welsh!) grows in nooks and crannies on these slabs.

As you walk on up the road, you pass a real tree house perched in a weeping birch tree. A little further on is a short diversion to visit the waterfalls for which there's a viewing point after crossing the railway via

a kissing gate. Having seen the rocks at Locality 1, you'll immediately recognise these as Bronllwyd Grit again, the waterfall being constrained by the big slabby bedding planes of the sandstone which, as before, dips steeply southwest. The woodland around the gorge is rather more varied with ash, sycamore and birches as well as oak.

A little further up the road, there a fork. The right hand fork goes to the pottery – a public footpath and your route; the left is a private road. A few paces along the left fork, there's another railway crossing point, with gates, if you wish to visit the top of the falls. At Crochendy (the pottery, built on a *roche moutonée* of Bronllwyd Grit), **you walk right between the houses up a grassy hillock between two dry stone walls to a kissing gate about 20 metres from the house. Now follow the high dry stone wall on your right. Don't be seduced into walking up the obvious farm track (not a right of way). Ahead, you'll see a twin gabled house (Hafod Uchaf) with larches and sycamores surrounding it and Moel Eilio behind. Walk towards this and shortly, you should see a galvanised steel kissing gate which you go through. Now you follow a small stream on your left across some rough pasture dotted with clumps of soft rush and boulders. Pass through another galvanised kissing gate.** Just after this, there's a big ice-smoothed outcrop on your right made of the formation – called the Marchlyn Flags – which overlies the Bronllwyd Grit. This is well laminated fine sandstone dipping gently west. **Another 50 metres brings you to the tarmac road. Turn left onto it towards Hafod Uchaf and then turn left again after crossing a ladder stile, onto the unsurfaced road which continues to the southeast, shortly bridging the Afon Hwch that flows out of Llyn Dwythwch.**

The second locality begins where the walking track passes through an old gate with a ruin and hawthorn tree on the left. To the right of the gate is the remains of a wall which angles back (west) up the steep hillside with a few iron posts marking its course.

The little cottage of Ty'n-yr-aelgerth is another 100 metres further along the track to Maesgwm. **If you want, you can skip the next three localities and continue straight on up Maesgwm and then up Moel Cynghorion.** Following this route, you see some of the quartzitic sandstone of Locality 3, though the outcrops are less exciting. You also see the great landslip (Locality 4) from below.

Mud and funny black rock: Locality 2 [5760 5812]

Immediately after the gate, you encounter outcrops of strongly cleaved mudstones and siltstones (part of the Marchlyn Flags again) which formed exceedingly slowly in fairly deep sea conditions. The sediments washed in from distant rivers or were stirred up by great storm waves on the shallower undersea areas closer to land.

Time that passes understanding. By now, you'll have got the idea that I bandy around inconceivably vast periods of time – like a few millions of years – as though it were a mere flick of the fingers. Well in a sense, it was. We humans, for whom even an hour can seem like an age, have a rather prejudiced view of time. Because we only live for 70 years or so, we think of that as 'a long time'. To a worker honeybee which may only live for a few weeks before exhausting herself from endless work, 70 years would be inconceivable too. Even our documented history only goes back about 3 millennia. As far as the Earth is concerned, bees and humans are insignificant. Like some bright and noisy firework, we've occupied the stage for a few seconds and may fizzle out and be forgotten before much longer if we continue as we are at present. So in geological terms, a million years is indeed a snap of the fingers. It's even more so in cosmological terms; all the chemical elements except hydrogen, helium and lithium – including those that make these rocks and you and me – formed inside ancient stars which exploded as supernovae billions of years before our planet and solar system even started to form.

Follow the old wall as it angles back up the hillside. A vague path runs between it and the rock outcrops on the left. In places, you can make out thin sandstone bands which represent rather more vigorous events – perhaps due to earthquake shocks or violent storms which triggered the flow of sandy beds 'stored' in shallower waters, down into the deeper sea. The final outcrop just before the top of the wall, one pace to the left of the path, is odd. Though covered in lichens and mosses, you can see the slate is cut by many irregular veins and knots of a hard black mineral, in places as thick as your forearm. These are broken and gashed by later white quartz veins.

What could they be? These black veins confused me when I geologically surveyed this area in the mid-70s. It wasn't until I was able to look at a transparent slice with a special microscope that I found they were made out of a silicate mineral called tourmaline, a complex substance which includes the element boron. You usually find it near granites (as, for example, around the granites of Devon and Cornwall) and later work showed that there is indeed granite underneath this area. This is a northeasterly underground extension of the microgranite intrusion which forms the great rounded boss of Mynydd Mawr. Tourmaline often forms beautiful crystals and is sometimes used for jewellery. Here it's far too fine grained; the gem quality stones come from Brazil.

The ruined wall dog-legs back south to join another ruined wall – clearly marked on the OS map – and you head south up the ridge to the right of a pile of light grey boulders on the skyline about 100 metres beyond where the two walls meet. What do you make of this very different rock? Since you'll see it much better shortly, **continue on for 500 metres, contouring around – with Llyn Dwythwch in view – towards the sheepfolds (on OS map) which mark the next locality.**

Big ripples and coarse grits: Locality 3 [5735 5760]

Have a look at the rock around and behind the sheepfolds. This rock is strikingly different from the drab siltstones you saw at the last locality. It's made up of rounded quartz grains, some as big as peas, 'floating' in a grey mud-like matrix (which may contain tourmaline) whilst others are tightly packed together to form a rock which looks like solid granulated sugar. This is a quartzite, one of the hardest of all rocks. Now look at the tilted outcrops close to the wall (on its southeast side) (Fig. 2.2). This coarse sandstone is known as the Carnedd-y-Filiast Grit and is the highest representative of the Cambrian Period in this area. It forms the craggy summit ridge of Elidir Fawr, the high mountain to the northeast of Llyn Peris. The mudstones and siltstones you saw at the last locality (the Marchlyn Formation) lie underneath this, separating it from the much older Bronllwyd Grit of Locality 1. So with each step you take on the first half of this ramble, you are walking up the sequence of rocks and up in time because younger rocks almost always lie upon older ones. The younger rocks which lie upon the Carnedd-y-Filiast Grit are a thick but boring sequence of slates, The Nant Ffrancon Group. Because they are mostly softer than the other rocks you'll see later, they don't crop out much and form the smooth grassy slopes of Foel Goch, Moel Cynghorion and Moel Eilio.

Figure 2.2: *These large ripples of clean grits tell of shallow seas with strong currents and big waves. The ripples here are symmetrical and so formed due the rocking back-and-forth action of passing waves. By contrast, current ripples have one side much steeper than the other. You can see ripples like these in several parts of Snowdonia, especially at Carnedd y Filiast itself (p. 119). You can usually see both ripple types at any sandy beach. The thick beds here dip southwest.*

You would never know it here, but there is a huge time break between the top of the grits at this locality and the base of the overlying slates. A chunk of time – about 20 million years – is, as it were, missing. Other rocks may have formed during this vast time break but ancient uplift and erosion removed them before the area subsided again to become the relatively deep sea in which the Nant Ffrancon Group muds slowly settled out. This time break – an unconformity – occurs all over Snowdonia beneath rocks of the Arenig Epoch of the Ordovician Period.

Heavy going? To help you, I've summarised all rock names and ages in the Timescale (see Appendix).

Cwm Dwythwch and its quiet lake, seldom visited because it's not on any walking track, was carved by glaciers as was every other cwm in the area. You can also see smaller 'hanging' cwms below the crags of Foel Gron. Since the ice melt, screes have grown below Moel Eilio, partly covering the older humpy glacier debris. The screes are, oddly, pink because the slates were 'cooked' by the underlying microgranite which squirted iron minerals into the rocks as well as tourmaline veins. More difficult to see in the heathery patches surrounded by pink screes are several tight folds in the same grit as you are standing on. This grit also forms the lower slopes of Braich y Foel on the opposite side of the lake, but it's hard to make out, being masked by scree patches.

The great mountain-building forces which caused all these rocks to deform into folds – or to break to form faults – had a real ball around here: a series of highly irregular folds and large faults slice through the rocks forming bizarre and unpredictable structures which only show up in detailed surveys. These structures pass through the mountain to emerge on the steep slopes above Betws Garmon, but are always hard to see. You really need to be in a hot air balloon with a pair of binoculars. To get some idea of what they look like, see Fig. 5.8 (p. 131). The reason these folds are so irregular is because the tough units like the grit are quite thin by comparison with the muddy sediments both above and below them. These muddy rocks make easy meat for the mountain building forces. They are ductile and just squeeze and deform like toothpaste to accommodate the stresses. The tough, brittle rocks like the grit tend to snap or buckle into tight folds with straight limbs. This 'style' of folding is quite different to what happens when great thicknesses of tough rock are involved as you'll see later today at Clogwyn Du'r Arddu.

From the sheepfold, head up the slope for 30 metres to a ladder stile and then aim for Foel Goch summit, slightly west of south. This is an easy walk with a fence off to your right. You'll see some more quartzite outcrops as you cross a small stream. Then comes peaty moorland and ahead is a bend in the fence and a ladder stile at the point where the slope steepens for the final long ascent to the summit. Don't cross the stile; just keep on the left side of the fence all the way to the top; Locality 4.

Landslip and a journey through Time at Foel Goch: Locality 4 [570 583]

At the top, you see no rocks underfoot; just grass and sedge. But the view is superb. This is a place to sit, rest and think for a few minutes. One striking feature you may have noticed on the way up is the northwest face of Moel Cynghorion. It looks almost as if a great chunk of this has slipped down into Maesgwm and that is indeed what happened. This entire face has land-slipped, or started to landslip. You'll see more of this as you walk along the ridge later. This is an old landslip which probably occurred at the end of the last glacial period when there was a good deal of freezing and thawing to help things along. Later screes have partly covered the landslipped area. The slips occurred because the dip of the cleavage was roughly parallel to the dip of the steep mountain flank, oversteepened by earlier glacier action as the ice flowed through Maesgwm. The ice tore out the base support for the millions of tonnes of rock, so down much of it slipped, probably quite slowly, along existing planes of weakness – the cleavage – lubricated by water.

To the north, you can see Anglesey, separated from the mainland by the Menai Straits. These straits represent one of the really big zones of faulting in Snowdonia: the Menai Straits Fault System. These faults have certainly been in existence since the late Precambrian when they were actively involved in controlling what rocks were laid down where. These faults caused some areas to be high and probably land (called 'horsts') whilst others were low and flooded by the sea ('grabens'). This pattern of horsts and grabens, by controlling whether rocks were laid down or not, dominated much of what happened in our Snowdonia theatre for tens of millions of years – right up to and spectacularly including the Snowdon volcanic rocks as we shall see. The grabens formed a series of separate stages onto which the actors, rock-forming 'events' (such as volcanic eruptions or turbidites), strutted and blustered for a fleeting period before being buried under the products of later 'events'. But importantly for us, seeking to understand the past, each event on the graben stage left a buried record of itself, lying there waiting to be deciphered by you and me hundreds of millions of years later.

No such thing happened on the elevated horst sectors (see box, p. 70). Because they were either shoals or actual land, erosion was the main actor. Erosion is destruction; the tearing out and 'shredding' of some of the topmost rocky 'pages' which the horsts were built of. The destroyed rocks, of which there is now no trace, had once recorded the passage of even earlier time, so erosion's wanton destruction meant great time gaps that geologists call 'unconformities.'

Ancient movement along many of the large northeast-trending faults in Wales, such as the Menai Straits faults and the Bala Fault (p. 152), may have been partly sideways – strike-slip. Later movements seem to have been mostly vertical rather than sideways. Movements continued intermittently over at least a 300-million year period.

Earthquakes in Wales. Earthquakes are uncommon in Wales and the borders to the east – but they do happen. Almost certainly these are connected to these ancient fault systems which are still slightly active.

The processes you see operating all around today – rivers, wind, rain, gravity (and some you don't see like ice and chemical weathering) – are slowly tearing Snowdonia apart. But where does all the material torn from the mountains end up? Some was dumped by ice sheets as glacial till; some as river deposits in valley bottoms; a little as screes. But the vast majority ends up in a natural sediment garbage can: the Irish Sea and Cardigan Bay. This sea area is a modern graben – a sedimentary basin – gradually being filled with sands, silts and muds brought in by the rivers.

Past climates, big bangs and dinosaur mega-deaths. Below the bottom of the world's seas and oceans, we find an almost perfect record of each year's storms, volcanic outbursts and climatic changes. It is this record too which tells us of the asteroid impact 65 million years ago (in Yucatan, Mexico) which probably killed the dinosaurs and many other life forms. This is why deep sea sediment cores and careful examination of rock sequences (which mostly formed on old seafloors, now uplifted) can tell us so much about past climates ... if we can interpret them. We *are* slowly learning to 'read' these sediment records like the pages of a history book, extracting more information as we learn the language and all its subtleties. And so we piece together the detailed history of Earth's climate, especially over the last few tens or hundreds of thousands of years. Such understanding could help us to predict what the future may hold: warming or freezing?

Now for some serious time travel. From here, you can see the bare and heavily glaciated rocks which form the low hills at the north and west end of Llyn Padarn. These are the oldest rocks in Snowdonia, dating back to a huge eruption in the Precambrian Period about 625 million years ago. They are extremely hard volcanic rocks: welded rhyolitic ash flows. You'll see many younger examples of such rocks during the next few rambles and, like their younger counterparts, they too were erupted in and mostly confined to deep grabens associated with the Menai Straits faults. Overlying these with a large time break – unconformity – are the oldest Cambrian rocks which make a complex sequence including the thick and world-famous purple and green slates (the Llanberis Slate Formation) which were once quarried on a vast scale. One great source of these slates, Dinorwig Quarry, scars the southwest slopes of Elidir Fach right down to Llyn Peris (see Box).

The Cambrian Slate Belt of Snowdonia. These hard and perfectly splittable slates, mostly purple though often sporting vivid pale green oval spots, crop out in a northeast-trending belt between Nantlle and Bethesda. Everywhere where they outcropped, the quarrymen made use of them, excavating giant holes from which they extracted these attractive and long-lasting slates. Only Penrhyn Quarry (Bethesda) continues in production today though the slate industry is undergoing a modest revival, especially around Blaenau Ffestiniog (see Ramble 3). There, the slates are grey and Ordovician in age. Most of the Cambrian slates came from 'terraced' quarries (Penrhyn, Dinorwig) or deep holes (Penyrorsedd, Cilgwyn and Dorothea quarries at Nantlle) whereas much of the slate at Blaenau came from underground. Cilgwyn Quarry was the oldest having started as long ago as the 12th century. Dinorwig Quarry may be dead now but deep inside the mountain, a new power surges into life every 24 hours: the Dinorwig pumped storage hydroelectric power station. You can visit this as you can also visit the Welsh Slate Centre, located at the junction of Llyn Peris and Llyn Padarn.

The slates started life as muds and silts, slowly laid down in deep water, far from the land. Their distinctive colour comes from an abundance of ferric iron. The green spots, some of which are the diameter of a large marble, formed where the iron oxides reduced from the ferric to the ferrous state: reduction, the opposite of oxidation. Millions of years later, long after they had been buried by all the later rocks which form Snowdonia, they were strongly squeezed by the same mountain-building forces which caused the folding I mentioned at Locality 3. Perfect cleavage planes formed parallel to the traces of the folds, all of which trend northeast-southwest (as do most of Snowdonia's structures). Hundreds of millions of years later, erosion cut through all these tilted and folded layers and allowed the quarrymen to get to work ... and you to imagine all the exciting events which took place here so long ago.

Following the purple slates came the Bronllwyd Grit which you saw at the beginning of this ramble. And later today, you'll walk right up into the much younger Ordovician volcanic rocks of Snowdon so on this ramble, you really get to see a pretty good cross section of all Snowdonia's rocks – a 200-million year journey through time from the oldest (Precambrian) to the youngest (late Ordovician).

Meanwhile underfoot are the soft Nant Ffrancon Group siltstones. In total, they are well over 1000 metres thick and although themselves rather boring, had one important role to play: they acted as the backdrop for all the exciting events which occurred later on. They began to form about 480 million years ago but it wasn't until 25 million years had passed that things began to happen around here. So if you divide the thickness of these mud and silt rocks by the 25 million years during which they formed (there may, of course, have been breaks or some might have been removed and redeposited somewhere else), you get 4 millimetres of mud and silt being laid down every 100 years! Later today, in total contrast, you'll see thick rock units which screamed out of volcanoes as fiery hurricanes and were laid down in a few days or months.

To the west, you can see the great rounded mass of Mynydd Mawr. This mountain is entirely composed of the microgranite I mentioned earlier. This rock, like that at Tanygrisiau (Ramble 3), was forced up into the crust like a giant fist to finally solidify (and so setting the radiometric clock ticking – see Appendix) some 438 million years ago. It represented the final stage of the volcanicity, that most charismatic player which intermittently strutted the Snowdonian stage from the Precambrian to the upper Ordovician periods – perhaps around 200 million years.

Riebeckite, curling stones and asbestos. The Mynydd Mawr granite contains a rather unusual blue mineral called riebeckite, an amphibole. You can also find this in the granite which forms Ailsa Craig up in the Firth of Clyde, famed for being the source of fine curling stones. This mineral can occur in a fibrous variety, crocidolite, better known as the highly dangerous blue asbestos. Mynydd Mawr is *not* a health hazard and should not be removed!

More to the south, you can see Moel Hebog and Moel yr Ogof, subjects of

Ramble 4. A large downfold – a syncline – affects the volcanic rocks and trained eyes can make this out from here. Moel Hebog is at the south end of this remarkable structure which you'll also see today and again on Ramble 5. More distant are the Harlech mountains, also of Cambrian age, part of which you've already seen on Ramble 1.

Head down to Bwlch Maesgwm, a steep but grassy slope. At the col, you cross a ladder stile and walk up a faint path to the right of the wire fence. As you walk, you'll pass many boulders left here by melting ice sheets about 15,000 years ago. Most of the boulders – called glacial erratics or perched blocks – haven't travelled far for they come from a series of small intrusions of igneous rock which have pushed into the slates hereabouts. Some rest on small pedestals of slate.

As you get higher up onto Moel Cynghorion (Bwlch Carreg y Gigfran), you see more and more evidence of the large landslip I mentioned. The fence runs roughly along the backscar of the slip (Fig. 2.3), much of which has only moved a few metres though parts seem to have slid down much more than this into Maesgwm.

Figure 2.3: *Top of the landslip at Bwlch Carreg y Gigfran. I've marked the backscar, landslip mass and direction of movement.*

Like Foel Goch, the summit of Moel Cynghorion is flat. The fence runs round the top but there are stiles so that you can cross as needed. This is Locality 5.

Moel Cynghorion and Cloggie: Locality 5 [586 564]

Step over the stile so as to be on the northeast side of the fence. At last you have a striking view across to Snowdon's famous northwestern cwm, Clogwyn Du'r Arddu, known to climbers as Cloggie. You can't quite see Llyn Du'r Arddu on whose haunted shores fairies and goblins dance according to legend. Today, you're more likely to find rock climbers' tents.

This cwm was gouged out by ice during the Pleistocene ice ages and today you can see a great spread of glacial debris – moraine – dotted liberally with boulders which hitched a ride in or on the ice as it moved down towards Llanberis, only to be dumped when the climate warmed and the ice melted. The cwm filled with ice again during the cold spell known to climatologists as the Younger Dryas. This came after the earlier Devensian ice sheets had melted away completely and began quite suddenly about 12,500 years ago (see Appendix and Timescale). It also ended suddenly 11,500 years ago. No one knows quite why though there are plenty of ideas. During this brief cold period, small glaciers formed again in cwms like this throughout Snowdonia and you can see below you two boomerang-shaped fresh moraine ridges the glacier formed before it finally melted away. On one of these terminal moraines, you can easily pick out a vast erratic boulder (apparently labelled Maen-du'r Arddu on the OS map) which forms Locality 7.

After the huge boulder, your route picks its way around the base of the great precipices, via several exciting localities, to join an old miners' track which eventually joins the Llanberis Path from Snowdon, the return route. You can see from here that there are several ruins and an old incline which ran down to the (invisible) lake. In the crags high above, you'll notice several signs of workings looking like irregular black slots in the precipice. These are called stopes – the space left after the miners removed the mineral-bearing vein. Here, as at Britannia mine on the other side of Snowdon (p. 241), they sought copper. To me, it's quite astonishing how the miners were able to get at the most inaccessible veins high in the rock faces without the benefit of all the climbing clobber we have available these days, and which you will probably see in use later as people make their slow ascents up the vertical slabs of Cloggie.

If you walk north for about 20 metres from the bend in the fence, you have a fine view down to Llanberis and a tiny secret cwm half way down the mountainside below. Here you can see that there obviously was once a small lake, now completely clogged with sphagnum mosses and other bog plants. This is the fate of all lakes, no matter how big. They all become filled in eventually as the streams which supply their water gradually wash in more and more sediment in times of flood.

The rocks forming Moel Cynghorion are all part of the thick Nant Ffrancon Group slates which continue as far as Bwlch Cwm Brwynog where, as you will see at the next locality, there is (at last) a change.

Make your way down to Bwlch Cwm Brwynog, staying on the east side of the fence. As you descend, you have a good view into Cwm Clogwyn with the great screes of Snowdon and Llechog behind. This cwm contains several lakes, all impounded by moraine dams, the closest being Llyn Ffynnon-y-gwas. **At the col, a fence runs down Cwm Brwynog but there's a stile over this onto a vague path which runs east, skirting below the craggy outcrops at the start of the ridge of Clogwyn Du'r Arddu. Follow this path to the next locality. If you've had enough, you can return to Llanberis by a small path along the west side of Cwm Brwynog. At Helfa-fawr, there are ladder stiles though the path becomes a bit lost. You then join the Maesgwm track, keeping north of Helfa-fain.**

Rocks which herald a big change: Locality 6 [5924 5576]

The rock at the col is still slate as you'll have noticed. But as soon as you start along the path after crossing the stile at Bwlch Cwm Brwynog, you can see that the rock outcrops above you on your right begin to be different. You can see the bedding which dips steeply northeast, picked out by thin bands of sandstone (Fig. 2.4). Continuing on for a few metres (going up in time), the siltstone of the Nant Ffrancon Group disappears being replaced entirely by sandstone. This sandstone has a curious scalloped honeycomb weathering pattern which you'll see again (e.g. Ramble 4). Some of the sandstone beds are quite thick and massive: with no internal structures. Others are coarse and quite striking to the eye.

Figure 2.4: *Sandstone beds with pitted surfaces (S) with thicker siltstones (Si), dipping steeply to the left, both cut by cleavage (C) which is almost vertical. Just a few metres further left, the sandstone has taken over completely.*

What does this change of rock type mean? This is a geological 'Ides of March' – a trumpet heralding the entry of great actors on our Welsh stage of Time. What those actors will be you'll soon see ... but for now, consider what you're seeing here as you walk up through this locality. The coarsening grain size tells us that the sea was shallowing, for sands like these need nearby rivers and deltas to produce them. (Ramble 4). One possible reason for the shallowing is that the whole area was becoming uplifted so that part of it not far away became land. Careful studies show that the land lay a few kilometres to the southwest, not far from where Moel Hebog is today. The uplift may have been along faults bordering the horsts and grabens which had for so long dominated this part of the crust. It was probably caused by molten magma forcing its way up from deep below in the mantle to form a magma chamber, a necessary prelude to any sort of volcanic event (see Box).

A DIY magma chamber: inflation and calderas. If you want to see what can happen when magma moves up into the crust, head for the beach with a football-bladder or beach ball with no air in it, a spade, a hand pump and connecting tube. Dig a hole in the sand, connect the pump tube to the ball or bladder, bury the ball and flatten it all down. Now start pumping magma (air in this case). What happens? The ball (magma chamber) inflates though all you can see is the surface of the sand swelling into a dome as the expanding ball pushes its way upwards. This is exactly what happens before volcanic outbursts – on a grand scale. Imagine that you kept on pumping way past the safety limit. What happens next? Eventually the ball will burst at the point where there is the least confining pressure – the top of the dome where most of the sand cover has, by now, slipped off. Bang!! A volcanic eruption!. Then what happens? The ball 'magma chamber' erupts all its air and collapses completely ... and so does the sand above and around it, partially filling the hole but leaving a large central 'crater'. This also commonly happens when real magma chambers vent all their spleen to surface eruptions. Suddenly, the weakened roof over the chamber has lost its support, so it collapses forming a caldera (Spanish, meaning a cauldron). Caldera collapse is very common after major volcanic outbursts and the calderas can be huge – tens of kilometres wide. Lake Taupo in New Zealand is a fine example. I shall refer to calderas many times on later rambles because they were important in the volcanic history of Snowdonia. Note: if you want to make your experiment more true to life and more spectacular, use tomato ketchup instead of air ...

Growing on these damp crags you can find a number of little plants including parsley and other types of fern, bilberries, clubmosses, foxgloves, bedstraws and golden rod (*Solidago*).

As for birds, wheatears are common in the summer and you'll probably see or hear choughs. Choughs, like their raven cousins of the crow family, are black but have curved orange bills and orange legs. They are, also like ravens, superb aerial acrobats. Their call is a brisk 'cheeaww', quite different from the raven's guttural 'kronk' or 'prruk prruk'. They usually nest around sea cliffs or crags though I once found a nest in an abandoned slate quarry. Another unrelated black bird you may see or, more likely, hear, is the mountain blackbird or ring ouzel. These birds are like their lowland relatives, all members of the thrush family, but with a distinctive white bib. They are summer migrants from Africa.

Continue along the path crossing a ruined wall onto the boulder-strew

moraine. Head over towards the huge boulder I mentioned earlier. The path is one of those 'now you see it, now you don't' affairs but who needs a path with such a landmark? At first, it makes its way across scree but then emerges onto the moraine.

Stone age man woz 'ere ... In the screes above to your right, I found a perfect polished stone axe head years ago, when I was surveying this area for the British Geological Survey. This is one of my treasured possessions. It is fascinating to think that the last person to hold it before I picked it up was a man who lived perhaps two thousand years before the Romans who founded Caernarfon (Segontium) around AD75. He must have dropped it and later cursed loudly when he realised his loss. Archaeologists have found stone axes made from the granite at Penmaenmawr around 4000 years ago – the Graig Lwyd axes [715755] – at over 40 locations in Britain.

Remember as you pick your way towards the giant boulder that the boulders underfoot have come from the precipices high above and so show you rather well the different types of rock which form them. See what you can make of them. They're very different from anything you've seen so far. At first, most are grey-green sandstones like those you've just seen, from higher up the ridge. But what of the increasingly bizarre-looking things, some of which are streaky, some concertina-ed as though once the consistency of treacle, some full of lumps?

Figure 2.5: *Giant boulder with Val for scale.*

Giant Boulder: Locality 7 [5958 5595]

This is one of the biggest glacial erratic boulders in Snowdonia (Fig. 2.5). Several chunks have broken off since it fell onto the Younger Dryas glacier for its 700-metre piggyback ride from its source at Clogwyn Du'r Arddu. It gives you some idea of the power of these glaciers; they really can, over time, move mountains.

The boulder is made, as you can see, of much the same material as the smaller ones hereabouts. It's a breccia, meaning that it's made up of big angular lumps of other rock. This is part of the enormously thick volcanic sequence you'll be walking through shortly. The blocks and lumps it contains consist of several different types of volcanic rock, mostly pale-coloured rhyolite.

Continue on up (southeast) over the successive mostly grassy moraine ridges (on which you can find three different types of clubmoss) towards the precipices. You have to cross the stream which runs partly underground to make your way to the next locality which is at the start of the main precipice where it overhangs somewhat.

Introducing Pitt's Head and Lower Rhyolites, two principal actors: Locality 8 [5978 5571]

This huge mass of rock above you is the base of a unit which tells us a dramatic story of sudden volcanic violence. Meet the Lower Rhyolitic Tuff Formation, something of a mouthful we can shorten to LRTF. You'll see a great deal more of this on later rambles so I won't go into details about the eruptions which produced it at this point. Here you can see many of the classic hallmarks of this common and excessively violent form of eruption, tiny versions of which were first witnessed by humans after the destruction of St Pierre town in Martinique by one small outburst from Mont Pelée volcano in 1902. French geologists called these types of eruption *nuées ardentes*, glowing clouds. On a grand scale, never yet seen by humans (fortunately) are ignimbrites (literally 'fire cloud rock') which can be vast and so hot inside that the individual bits of ash and pumice which make up the flow can glue themselves together after they have settled, welding to a dense streaky rock in which the pumice lumps have squashed to become pancake-shapes.

You'll see many examples of this, one of which is the Pitt's Head Tuff, the earliest of the volcanic players in this part of Snowdonia, forming the lowest rock unit in the great Snowdon Volcanic Group. The Pitt's Head crops out about 100 metres southwest of this locality, above the scree slope. The outcrops are rather more subdued than the huge crags formed by the LRTF but you'll see much more of this exciting and distinctive rock on Ramble 4. Many boulders lie about on the screes just to the west of here.

The LRTF is rather more complex, a thick unit involving varying modes of eruption. You can see rather well here that part of the tuff contains short columns (Fig. 2.6). This is a sure sign that it was once hot and, like lava, it cooled and shrank in on itself, contracting as it did so and breaking along regular cooling joints. Below the columnar-jointed part, the actual base is a tuff with fragments of other volcanic material – volcaniclasts – up to marble-size. The LRTF in the Snowdon area reaches 600 metres in total thickness and as you'll see as you continue on to the next locality, it's pretty thick here. It formed as the result of a series of massive ignimbrite eruptions which seem to have been entirely under the sea. This contrasts with the earlier Pitt's Head eruption which was on land further southwest, though the flow you see here actually rolled its way down across the ancient coast (between here and Moel Hebog) and into the shallow seas which at that time deepened to the north and east.

Figure 2.6: *Columnar joints at the base of the LRTF. The Pitt's Head forms the outcrops at the skyline from centre to right, underlying the LRTF. Both dip steeply east here.*

You can find various alpine plants in crevices on these crags: parsley fern, thrift, roseroot, starry saxifrages, golden rod, wood anemone.

Contour round a slightly loose scree towards an obvious ice-smoothed rock ridge ahead. As you scramble, notice the boulders which have fallen from the LRTF crags high above. Many of these are made up entirely of quite large blocks of volcanic material. You can see which part of the crags these came from if you have binoculars or good eyesight. This rock was the product of violent smashing up – brecciation – of solidified volcanic material which then became part of a massive coarse pyroclastic flow, carried along by a hot hurricane of finer ash blasted out of a vent somewhere quite close by. This is the same material as the huge boulder back at Locality 7.

After crossing some large boulders, you reach the top of the smoothed rocky ridge, a *roche moutonée*. This is the next locality.

> **How do we know what was land and what was sea?** Most of this knowledge comes from looking rather carefully at the sedimentary rocks in the area. If a volcanic rock overlies a sediment like mud or silt which was laid down in deep water, and is in turn overlain by more of the same, the simplest explanation is that the volcanic rock was either erupted under the sea – a very common occurrence, even in the deep oceans – or flowed into the sea. The sedimentary rocks poignantly illustrate the 'background' environment of the time. Mud rocks usually mean deep water; sandstones mean shallow water though certain distinctive sandstones form on the land: desert sands. These are often red-tinged and actually cover much of parts of Britain, dating back to two separate periods when much of Europe was desert. Careful examination of sedimentary sequences can tell a detailed story of how seas gradually infilled to become river deltas and dry land – or the reverse. The sandstones back at Locality 6 were telling us of a major shallowing event. For more on this, see p. 98.

Clogwyn Du'r Arddu: Locality 9 [5993 5570]

Below to the east you can now see Llyn Du'r Arddu. The lake basin and smoothed rock ridge you are standing on, a *roche moutonée* (named 'sheep rock' by French geologists because they look a little like sheeps' backs), were both carved by the glacier which existed here until about 11,500 years ago. Typically, the thawing ice dumped its load of boulders everywhere and many remain stranded on the *roche moutonée*.

From this vantage point, you can see the whole cwm and that the dip of the rocks changes to the east. At the last locality, the LRTF dipped steeply east. As you can see, the rock units above also have this dip. But if you follow them through the precipices towards Clogwyn Coch, the dips slackens, becomes flat and then steepens up again – but this time dipping to the west; the opposite direction. You are, then, looking at a huge downfold – a syncline – which affects the whole sequence here. The trace of this great fold continues both to the northeast and to the southwest: you'll see it again on Rambles 4 and 5. Try and imagine the scale of the forces needed to buckle these thick, tough rocks! And this is just a gentle fold. You should see what can happen in some other mountain ranges.

The LRTF is now clearly exposed for you in all its splendour. The blocky section you can see is many tens of metres thick but passes up into a bedded upper part, some of which forms the rock underfoot at this locality. A curious notch-like bed defines the top of the LRTF and runs from lower left to upper right, to the top of the precipice. The 'notch' bed is a different and softer rock type altogether and you'll see blocks of it when you cross the next scree. Overlying the 'notch' bed is another very thick and massive unit with great cooling joints. You'll see these at the next localities.

Continue on across and slightly up the next section of rather unstable scree – beware! Keep your eyes open because some of the blocks on this

active scree are loose and could cause you to fall. Keep your eyes open too for blocks (Fig. 2.7) of the 'notch' bed. This is interesting for two reasons: firstly, it has an odd weathering pattern with rows of elliptical hollows, very much like the Coniston Limestone in the Lake District (see p. 71 *Lakeland Rocky Rambles*). And very much like that limestone, this rock contains fossils. If you're fortunate, you might spot parts of quite large trilobites such as the *Brogniartella* I found here in 1995 (I've sketched this above the Key for this ramble's map). This robust animal, the largest trilobite found around Snowdon, lived along with other shelly creatures like brachiopods on or near the seabed here during the brief interlude in volcanic violence which this limy sandstone bed represents. So this is good evidence that the LRTF 'event' took place beneath the waves. Geologists have found this trilobite in Shropshire and as far away as Cross Fell in the north Pennines. It quickly became extinct and so finding it in rocks in other parts of the country tells you that those rocks formed at about the same time as this bed here. This is the basis of stratigraphic palaeontology (see Appendix).

This limy 'notch' sandstone provides a tiny oasis for lime-loving plants such as the loose-cushion-forming vernal sandworts (*Minuartia verna*) and purple saxifrages (rare). You'll almost certainly find sandworts growing on some of these blocks.

Figure 2.7: *'Notch' limestone block with cavities where the lime-rich parts of the rock have been dissolved away by slightly acid rain. The top of the LRTF has been slightly eroded by water currents – reworked – to give the more resistant paler bands of tuff which stick out like ribs.*

Folds and thrusts. The syncline here is an open fold. If the squeezing — 'crustal shortening' — had continued, the limbs of the fold would have continued to rotate, gradually approaching vertical to form a tight U shape. This extreme form of folding is called an isocline and does indeed occur in Snowdonia (see Fig. 5.8). In certain circumstances, the folds may flop over to lie down flat — recumbent. In even more extreme folding, such folds can rupture so that one limb slides as a sheet of rock right over the other separated by a flat-lying fault called, for obvious reasons, a thrust. In the most extreme cases, you can get stacked piles of thrust sheets. Many of the world's mountain ranges show examples of these. In the Alps, many folds are recumbent and many have become broken by flat-lying thrusts to form nappes. Although less obvious, you can see old and deeply eroded remnants of this sort of extreme tectonic style — the type of folds and faults in an area — in the highlands of Scotland.

As you approach the edge of the scree, look out for a mossy cave below the central crag. Above this is an obvious small fault which slashes right through the precipice at about 45° from the upper left to the lower right where it intersects with the limy sandstone bed before both are covered in scree. The mossy cave which usually has dribbles of water running down inside is the start point for the next rather extended locality.

Weird structures and sticky toffee: Locality 10 [6003 5558]

This locality is more of a traverse than a point. You start below the mossy cave where you will find a path much used by climbers getting to their pitches. Walk along to the right for a few paces. The rock on your left which overlies the limy sandstone (about underfoot here; you'll see it again shortly) is a geological wolf in sheep's clothing. It looks at first sight like some sort of bedded tuff. You can see the beds, can't you; flat-lying and parallel? But look more closely and what do you see? Some of the 'beds' double back on themselves. They are minute examples of recumbent folds – folds which are literally lying down flat – which I briefly mentioned at the last locality. How can you have recumbent folds in an ordinary bedded tuff? What's going on here? Have a think as you continue.

Roseroot, starry saxifrages and foxgloves grow around this grassy shelf, especially where the inclined plane of the fault intersects a few metres to the right. Along here too is a short trial excavation made by miners in an unsuccessful search for minerals. From here, you have a good view up the 'notch' formed by the softer fossil-bearing sandstone. **Beware of falling rocks. This scree is still actively forming and going further up here is potentially dangerous.**

Return past the mossy cave and drop down a grassy cone for some 15 metres until you come to the brown-weathering 'notch' sandstone on your right. Scramble on around to the right where you quickly pick up the same climbers' path again.

You are, more or less, following the contact between the 'notch' sandstone and the overlying weird rock with folds. Have you noticed how the dip has changed from east to just about flat here? This is almost the core of the downfold. The contact between these two rocks is dramatically clear just above the path all the way along here.

Figure 2.8: *This is one of the clearest contacts between two different rocks that you'll ever see. Below is the limy sandstone which is a mixed ragbag of sediments. This has a fairly strong cleavage which dips from left to right at about 40°. The contact dips gently west, meaning that you're now on the northeast limb of the synclinal fold. You've crossed the core – the axis of the fold.*

> **Folds, cleavage and shear: a simple experiment.** Folding isn't as simple as it seems. If you fold a stack of photocopy paper, have you noticed what happens to the edges? When the block is flat, the edges are straight, perpendicular to the block as you'd expect. If you fold the block into a U shape, the edges end up at about 45 degrees to the top and bottom of the block. This is because in folding this paper block, each sheet slips slightly relative to its neighbours to accommodate the new shape you're forcing them into. This slip is 'simple shear'. When you release the force (stress) you're applying, the sheets all slip back over each other to return to the way they were at the start.

Exactly the same happens when rocks become folded and you can see the effects here: the cleavage. At this position in the fold, the rocks on top (Fig. 2.8) have slid up to the left slightly relative to the softer sandstones with silty layers below. The sand and silt being more squashable (ductile) have accommodated the movement (strain) and the cleavage developed as a response to this shearing motion.

Now to consider the rock which contains these extraordinary folds. This is the same unit as you saw to the right of the cave. It's a type of volcanic rock, a rhyolite, which was forced (intruded) whilst molten into the rocks here just after they were laid down. Because the rhyolite has intruded older rocks parallel to the beds, it is called a sill. You can tell it was liquid because of the extraordinary folds it contains. It would have been about the consistency of hot sticky toffee, though about 700 degrees hotter. Rhyolite lavas and shallow intrusions (such as this) are usually very sticky (viscous) and slow-moving. Some of the intrusions in the Snowdon Volcanics formed great domes (like pumping up a ball buried in sand) and in places, their tops became exposed due to instability and collapse. In such cases, broken masses would slough off the side of the growing domes and accumulate at the base as rhyolite breccias.

If you look carefully at the contact here (Fig. 2.9), you can see that the base of the rhyolite has chilled to a rather dark rock because of contact with the cold sediment underneath. This dark edge was probably a glass, for lavas, when rapidly quenched, tend to be glassy because the crystals which normally form as a rock cools have no time to do so. In Figure 2.9, you can see a perfect example of how one of these folds formed as the rhyolite tongue slowly forced its way from right to left. As it did so, the base chilled and glued itself to the underlying rock whilst the tongue of liquid dragged ever further to the left, leaving clear flow bands. This is a fabulous place to see flow bands and flow folds. Have a look. Some of the folds are astonishingly complex and beautiful all around here.

Figure 2.9: *Perfect recumbent fold in rhyolite which glued itself to the substrate as it moved from right to left.*

The path continues upwards slightly, roughly following the dip of the rocks which is now gently northwest. You should spot butterworts in some of the damper places and masses of saxifrages and thrift growing on ledges of the great rhyolite precipice above. A few violets hold out here too as do common columbines (*Aquilegia vulgaris*). The path climbs a little more steeply and then turns away from the precipice to cross the scree towards Clogwyn Coch and the old copper mine. The path is reasonably obvious though some of the scree is loose, so take care. If you have binoculars, look back at the rhyolite. You can see that flow folding continues until at least half way up. The upper part shows quite good cooling joints which, seemingly unclimbable, give the rock climbers the challenges and adrenalin-surges they seek. Sooner them than me.

Just past the miners' incline top, the path runs over the back of a *roche moutonée*. This is the final locality.

Clogwyn Coch copper mine: Locality 11 [6040 5563]

From this vantage point, you can see very clearly the northwest-dipping limb of this great synclinal fold and gain an overall impression of it. But the rocks underfoot are different from anything else you've seen today. This is another type of intrusive rock – dolerite. Dolerites are, like their extrusive lava equivalents called basalt, basic igneous rocks. The LRTF and rhyolite intrusion you've just seen are richer in silica: acid igneous rocks. Acid rocks are usually pale; basic are dark or even black. Acid rocks, when erupted, are sticky and the eruptions can be violently explosive (as at Mount St Helens in Washington state, USA). Basic lavas are the hottest known with temperatures several hundred degrees higher than rhyolites and are often almost as mobile as water. Their eruptions are generally quiet and gentle affairs as in Hawaii.The dolerite underfoot has cooled slowly so that the minerals it's made from had time to grow into a network of obvious crystals giving it a speckled appearance. You'll see some beautiful dolerites on Ramble 9.

Above the crags, the rock is different. Suddenly, vents opened and began erupting basalt lavas and tuffs. This became the Bedded Pyroclastic Formation (BPF). There's a small patch of this preserved in the core of the Clogwyn Du'r Arddu syncline where it overlies the intrusive rhyolite at the top of the precipice. You'll meet the BPF on Ramble 4.

The miners found their copper minerals in veins cutting the dolerite and the LRTF which forms the steep crags of Clogwyn Coch. The rocks are stained red around here (coch = red) because of oxidised iron minerals, probably from the mineral veins. The mine operated at the end of the 18th century but only in the summer months, though who'd have been a miner working in this inhospitable place? Imagine having to go to work up these screes and then into the slot-like stopes high above. They must have used the incline you've just passed to tram the ore down to the ruins near the head of the lake where it was crushed and sorted using water from the small stream, dammed in a couple of places. The debris from this process has built an orange delta out into the lake. The miners would have hauled the cleaned ore back up the incline to be loaded onto pack animals for the journey to Llanberis and beyond. The track out – which you shortly follow – contours easily round from here to join the Llanberis Path.

Walk on round the easy track, passing another ruin on the right and crossing more ice-smoothed dolerite masses. In front of this old building you'll notice piles of clinker. Did the miners actually try smelting the ore right here? Or did they bring up coal to keep themselves warm? Both possibilities seem unlikely.

Before joining the Llanberis Path, you may like to branch off to the left and walk out onto the boulder-strewn moraines overlooking Clogwyn Du'r Arddu for a final synoptic view of the entire folded volcanic sequence you've just traversed (Fig. 2.10).

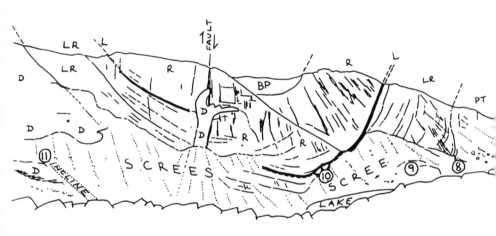

Figure 2.10: *The great syncline of Clogwyn Du'r Arddu. I've marked localities 8-11. D – dolerite; BP – Bedded Pyroclastic Formation; LR – Lower Rhyolitic Tuff Formation; L – limy sandstone. The limy sandstone (black on my drawing) serves as a marker bed and you can see how it has been cut by a fault, since invaded by an odd-shaped dolerite intrusion in the centre of the syncline. The fault has dropped the sandstone down from high in the precipice on the left to much lower down on the centre and right: Locality 10).*

Join the main path and return to Llanberis. As you walk below Llechog (the rocky ridge to your right [606 569]), you cross back down through the LRTF (buried underfoot by glacial moraine) followed by the Pitt's Head Tuff and then the sandstones of Locality 6. After that, you're back onto the Nant

Ffrancon siltstones until you're opposite Tryfan [598 579]. Here, you cross back over the Carnedd y Filiast Grit and the Marchlyn Formation. Before Hebron Station, you're back on the Bronllwyd Grit (though, again, it's mostly covered over with moraine). Things become a little complex because of folding and faulting, though you are rarely far from the Bronllwyd Grit. And near Llanberis, you can see the familiar slabby outcrops of this hard gritty rock.

This ramble has introduced you to most of Snowdonia's major actors and you've seen something of what they can do. You'll see them again on most of the remaining rambles when I'll go into a little more detail about their roles in this great theatre of Time.

Rocky Ramble 3: Cwm Orthin and Moelwyn

How to get to the start of the ramble

You start from Tanygrisiau, just over 1 kilometre southwest of Blaenau Ffestiniog. Follow signs to the hydroelectric pumped storage power station visitor centre. The turning to this (shared with one to Tanygrisiau village) is off the A496, easily accessible from the south or north. You start from the free car park and power station visitor centre at the north end of Tanygrisiau reservoir. You could theoretically get to Tanygrisiau by using the Ffestiniog Railway (tel. 01766 512340). Otherwise there are both buses and trains which go to Blaenau Ffestiniog giving you a 2-kilometre walk to the start: No. 1 bus Caernarfon – Porthmadog – Blaenau (Express; tel. 01286 674570); regional railway from Llandudno via Betws y coed (01492 585151).

On a poor day, you can always visit the old slate mines of Gloddfa Ganol (tel. 01766 830664) or the astonishing Llechwedd Slate Caverns (01766 830523) in Blaenau Ffestiniog.

Needs, distances and times

Unfortunately, this ramble falls upon the very edges of two of the OS Leisure maps: sheets 17 and 18. If you are fortunate enough to have the older 1:25 000 'Harlech' (No. 19) Outdoor Leisure map published in 1982, this has the entire walk on it. Otherwise you have two choices: use the two OS maps, which offer no overlap at all, as best you can in conjunction with mine, or do as I have done many times: make a photocopy (colour is better but pricier) of the relevant part of each sheet and make up your own map by cutting them and carefully joining the two along the 45 gridline. Sorry about that.

The full distance is about 11 kilometres (under 7 miles) with 760 metres (about 2500 feet) of climbing. Since there's plenty to see, allow a full day.

The start ...

Walk up a small flight of steps, past some picnic tables and turn right onto a tarmac road to immediately cross the Ffestiniog railway heading (both you and railway) towards Tanygrisiau. Just about 20 metres past the level crossing, there's a large outcrop of banded and striped rocks: Locality 1.

Hot rocks and spots: Locality 1 [681 449]

Look at these banded pale grey to pink-coloured rocks carefully. Notice something? They're spotty, as if they caught measles long ago. They didn't catch measles, of course, but something far more unpleasant happened: they got cooked. The sediment formations of which these are part were intruded by a large, hot granite, long after they were laid down. The granite itself crops out not far to the south and east of here, forming the low rugged hills you can see on the other side of the reservoir. Because the crystals that form it are quite small, geologists refer to it as the Tanygrisiau microgranite and to date, the forces of erosion have only exposed the very top of what we know is a much larger body that extends far to the east, right under the Manod mountains and slate quarries east of Blaenau Ffestiniog.

You may wonder how we know this. In fact we have two lines of evidence. Many years ago (horrors! It's over 27 years ago!), I was geologically surveying a bleak area of mountain and moorland to the east of here called Migneint (Welsh for 'quagmire' and well named!). One day, down in the bottom of a deep valley called Cwm Hafod-y-rhedrwydd, 6 kilometres east of Blaenau Ffestiniog, I found rocks just like those in front of you: they were hard, bleached-looking and full of spots too. This seemed to me to be good evidence for the existence of a long eastward extension of the Tanygrisiau microgranite, an obvious idea which geophysicists later confirmed by surveying the gravity and magnetic anomalies of the district. So what we see really is just the tip of the iceberg (although icebergs and granites don't really mix well).

Geologists call cooked rocks like these 'hornfels', a word taken into our eclectic idiom from the German, meaning 'tough rock'. And so they are. The spots in them are the remains of (here's a good one) porphyroblasts. Just as osteoblast cells build our bones (with osteoclasts unbuilding them again), porphyroblasts were crystals which actually grew in the rocks as a response to the heat from the nearby intrusion. This happened, and always happens, because different minerals have different forms at different temperatures. Minerals like quartz are very stable over a wide range of temperatures but other minerals, like the clays in muddy sediments (which these once were) change – metamorphose – into another form which is stable at a higher temperature if they get cooked as these rocks have. This is how metamorphic ('meta' = change, 'morph' = shape) rocks form. The spots were once crystals of a mineral called cordierite ... but they aren't now. Why not? you might wonder.

The reason appears to be that after the rocks had been really roasted and the new high temperature minerals had grown in them, they slowly cooled as the granite itself cooled. Granites are often very 'wet' meaning that they contain an abundance of volatile fluids like water. These fluids forced their way up through the overlying metasediments (sediments changed by heat) and, being still quite hot and charged with salts and ions of various elements, were highly reactive. They caused the high temperature porphyroblasts to return to a lower temperature suite of minerals, just leaving that tell-tale trademark of the spots you see here. We call the spots, as you might guess, pseudomorphs ('false shapes').

What of the rock itself? It was, as I've said, a sediment though because of the metamorphic effects, it looks quite unlike the normal dark grey rocks you see in Snowdonia. Here, the coarser bands have turned a yellowy green colour and the whole effect of the cooking seems to be to make the bedding stand out very clearly. There are loads of outcrops of this metasediment around here and in all of them, the bedding is prominent, dipping gently northwest. The sediment was laid down on a shallow sea floor during the Tremadoc Epoch, around 490 million years ago. The term 'Tremadocian' is used by geologists all over the world for sediments of this age, but Tremadoc village is only a few miles away (now spelled Tremadog) north of Porthmadog.

Around you as you walk on along the road, you see the impressive remains of former industry plus the modern pump storage power station.

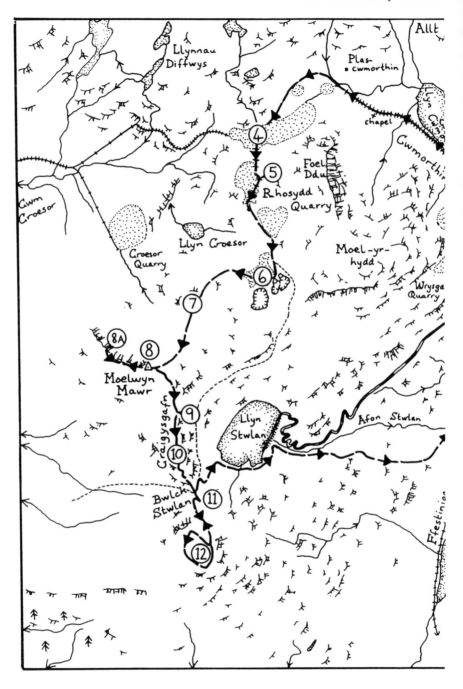

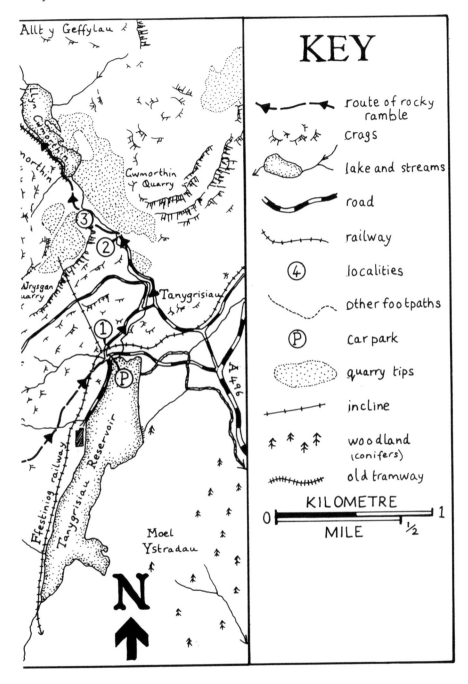

KEY

route of rocky ramble

crags

lake and streams

road

railway

(4) localities

other footpaths

(P) car park

quarry tips

incline

woodland (conifers)

old tramway

KILOMETRE

0 _____ 1

MILE ½

Like all pumped storage hydroelectric stations, this one has two reservoirs. The lower one you've already seen, but the upper one is invisible, impounded by a great concrete dam: Llyn Stwlan. The idea of pumped storage is to use off-peak electricity to pump water from the lower reservoir back up to the upper one. When there is a sudden demand for electricity, the pump turbines reverse as water is allowed to flow back down the huge pipes from the upper reservoir. The pumps now become generators and within a few seconds can start pushing power back into the electricity grid. This station is relatively small, able to produce around 300 megawatts of electric power for a couple of hours. Britain has several others like this, the largest of which is at Dinorwig (p. 45). You can visit this power station if you wish. Call 01766 830310 for information.

Over to your east is Blaenau Ffestiniog, a sombre place on the best of days, surrounded by its huge slate tips and quarries, some of which you can visit. Indeed around here above you are inclines coming steeply down the mountain, one coming straight out of a tunnel (Wrysgan incline). These come from slate quarries, some of which you'll see later in Cwmorthin. As you approach Tanygrisiau with the stream on your right, you come to a concrete weir where there is the most beautiful ice-smoothed *roche montonée* you ever saw. Take stock of the scene from this point, looking back behind you.

You can see that all the outcrops are *roches moutonées* with steep plucked downslope sides and smooth sheeps' backs on the upslope side, just as you'd expect with the glaciers moving down the valley towards Cardigan Bay.

Shortly after this, the road to Tanygrisiau crosses on a new bridge. Take this right turn over the bridge and into the top end of the village where you turn left up towards Cwmorthin. The tarmac road goes very steeply up with the stream on the left and on the right, a large slate tip from the Cwmorthin quarry. From now on, you begin to get good views. You can see the great incline I mentioned on the lower slopes of Moel-yr-hydd, and Moelwyn Bach further away to the southwest. In the foreground, several large glacial erratics bedeck the gently dipping glacially-smoothed bedding surfaces. Pass through a gate which says 'Chwarel Cwmorthin Quarry' on it (this is a public footpath) and up the steep slate quarry road. Immediately on your left is a lovely cataract, cutting down into the striped metasediments like those at Locality 1, for the granite's heat penetrated here too. Now you can see the contrast between these cooked sediments and the younger and higher grey slates in the tip on your right. The slates weren't affected by the granite. At the top of the cataract with the entrance gate still just in sight is Locality 2, where you see the highest waterfall. After this, there are buildings to both left and right of the road.

Lower Cwmorthin: Locality 2 [682 457]

Turn left off the track towards the stream to find a huge erratic boulder resting atop a perfect *roche moutonée* whose top surface is polished and grooved by glacial striae – particularly obvious here. The 'down' side forms the highest waterfall.

Figure 3.1: *Ice once rode over this smooth outcrop. It also dumped the large boulder on the right. The beds dip gently from left to right.*

The top surface is inclined – a bedding plane. Around here, because of the low dip angle of the beds, the ice tends to have exploited this structure in carving the *roches moutonées*. The sediments are still pretty much cooked and well banded, like those back at Locality 1.

Walking on, you suddenly find yourself in Cwmorthin with much quarry devastation all around with tips and old buildings. A beautifully arched tunnel conducts the Afon Cwmorthin under some of the old and new quarry processing buildings and a large flat area formed by slate debris. The footpath (new in 1995 because of quarry operations and so not corresponding to that marked on the OS maps) branches left and crosses to the southwest side of the Afon Cwmorthin, passing through new slate gardens with small ponds, streams and ornamental shrubs (many of which had died when I last saw it in November 1995). Fortuitously, the new path allows you to look at some fine outcrops: Locality 3.

Cwmorthin Quarry has had a chequered career. Having worked most of last century, it closed in 1900, opening again in the 1920s, failing again and now, as you see, it is working again. It had a nasty reputation for being a killer and was known to the quarrymen as 'the Slaughterhouse' (in Welsh).

Meet the Moelwyn Volcanic Formation (MVF): Locality 3 [6800 4570 to 6788 4585]

These rocks are great! You can't miss the striking bulbous masses rearing just to the left of the track here, all heavily smoothed by ice (Fig. 3.2).

Figure 3.2: *Ice-smoothed Moelwyn Volcanics. But what do the rocks tell us?*

If you examine the rocks here, you find that they are a real mix of fragments: volcanic debris and flow-banded rhyolite. You can hardly see the bedding at all which is typical of rocks laid down by a process called mass flow (debris flow) in which an unstable pile of rocky material of any size, hot or cold, water-saturated or not, suddenly starts to behave like liquid: it flows. To start it needs some kind of triggering shock like an earthquake or volcanic eruption. For the process to continue, gravity is all you need; it energises the moving flow. So you also need a slope because mass flows, like water or lava, won't move without.

Slides, waves and catastrophes. One of the best studied mass flows, a rock avalanche, overwhelmed the small mining town of Frank in Alberta, Canada, on 29 April 1903. Half the town was wiped out as a huge mass of broken rock crashed down from high up the valley side (640 metres vertical fall). The astonishing thing is that when the rock mass came to rest 100 seconds later, it had travelled 4 kilometres across the valley floor and actually *climbed* 140 metres up the other side. This was a tiny flow by comparison with those which geologists have only recently come to terms with around the Hawaiian islands. We now know that monumentally vast sectors of the Hawaiian volcanoes regularly (perhaps every 100,000 years) collapse. Most of these slides have been under the sea and have swept out across the ocean floor for hundreds of kilometres. The scary thing about this for the people living around the Pacific Ocean is that such events can set up diabolically powerful tsunami waves (often incorrectly called tidal waves, though they have nothing to do with tides) which travel right across the ocean, losing none of their energy, to ramp up coasts as far away as Australia. If such a slide occurred today, it would reach Sydney by tomorrow – and wipe it out.

And don't be complacent! A smaller version called a storeggaslide involving hundreds of cubic kilometres of rock broke off from the Norwegian shelf 7000 years ago, flooding Scotland's east coast with giant waves.

The rock here arrived where it is now by mass flow. This is why it is unsorted – a jumble of different fragment sizes. When rocks are well bedded, like those laminated sediments of localities 1 and 2, they are sorted into sands and silts or muds either by falling out of water suspension or because bottom currents rework the seafloor. A strong current winnows out the finer, lighter particles like wheat chaff in the wind during threshing, leaving coarser beds where the grains roll or bounce along the bottom. You'll see more of these volcanics later on this ramble. They were erupted millions of years before the Snowdon Volcanic Group and lie well down in the Caradoc age rock sequence.

If you're particularly observant, you'll have noticed that my explanation can't be wholly right because there are oddities. Some large parts of this outcrop (e.g. **turn left off the path just before the start of the big bulbous rocky mass of Locality 3, crossing a ruined wall through a gap. Walk on another 5 metres**) are flow-banded for many metres and seems to be either rhyolite lava or intrusion. Huh! How can these fit in to what I've just said? Explain that one! Easy ... These rocks are messy. They don't fit into neat compartments of classification. This isn't 'a rhyolite intrusion' or 'a debris flow' but a jumbled up mix of both. Imagine the incoming liquid rhyolite magma inflating the seafloor like a tyre inner tube. The higher it built and flowed, the more unstable it became. So parts collapsed to form debris flows. Other parts remained fairly coherent masses of rhyolite. It's quite easy to picture, isn't it? And this simple picture explains rather well the complex relationships in the MVF: sometimes it seems to be intrusive, sometime lava, sometimes mass flow, sometimes tuff or tuffite. By invoking submarine eruptions, you can even imagine small short-lived islands or sea-stacks being built up, with vigorous wave erosion forming the rounded cobbles you often find in parts of the MVF flows. Later when activity was dead, it all subsided beneath the waves again to be covered in more mud and silt .

The mystery of the missing rock: Time gaps. Somewhere between Localities 1 and 3, a huge chunk of time has vanished. What? How can time vanish? Well it wasn't the time exactly, but evidence of the passing of time. If you imagine time like the tape on a cassette onto which someone has recorded a slow dance (Dance of Time!), you'd notice if you were listening to it and suddenly, the music skipped from one part to another, missing out a long passage which should have been there. You have two possible explanations for this missing chunk: someone stopped the recording, effectively stopping our tape of time; or someone or something cut out several metres of tape and spliced the cut ends together seamlessly ... except that we know that some of the music is missing when we listen carefully. This is exactly what has happened in this part of Wales. Between the Arenig and the Caradoc epochs (see Appendix Timescale), the rocks that were laid down during that 13-million year interval (if there were any) have gone missing. Geologists call this time gap the 'pre-*gracilis*' unconformity. The 'gracilis' is a type of graptolite (*Nemagraptus gracilis*) found in the older Caradoc age mudstones and siltstones (Nant Ffrancon Group). Careful work over many decades shows us that the area of Cambrian rocks to the south (Ramble 1) then, as now, formed an early Harlech Dome. This was probably dry land for much of this time break so not surprisingly, no sediments could be laid down. To the north, a deep-water trough – graben – foreshadowed the future centres of the Snowdon Group volcanic eruptions, more of which you'll see on later rambles.

If you wish, you can make a diversion up a small cobbled track to the Wrysgan quarries from just past these first outcrops. The path wends its way up the slate tips to a flat area where the quarry buildings once stood. To the left is the dramatic incline (accessible) which starts steeply down the mountainside through a tunnel, emerging high up on Craig yr Wrysgan. More inclines continue on up, following a bed of good slate between the two thick MVF units. (You've just seen the lower one.) This involves over 100 metres of climbing (not included in my estimate for the ramble) but, if you have the time and energy, is well worthwhile. You can see a large collapse of one of the chambers but several other huge underground chambers, which have the lower volcanic unit as floor and upper as roof, are accessible. I wouldn't recommend entering them as there have been roof falls. You'll see plenty of the MVF and the slate too. This slate, formerly a slowly-formed accumulation of mud settling out on the seafloor, tells us clearly that the Moelwyn volcanicity occurred beneath the sea.

Wrysgan Quarry. The quarry opened in 1844 and closed as recently as 1972.. At its peak in 1901, it employed 107 men and produced about 2,600 tons of finished slates each year. The incline was built from 1844-5 but cost a damaging amount to the company.

Walk on around the old tips overlooking the new slate processing plant below. About 200 metres after the start of this locality, at its north end, you'll see many more outcrops, mostly to the left of the track. These are part of the upper unit of the MVF. Some (Fig. 3.3) are well bedded tuffites but contain distinct beds of cobbles indicating a mix between pyroclastic (mass) flow origin and current activity laying down beds at a much slower rate (though far faster than the slate-forming 'background' muds and silts which were completely swamped by these vigorous but short-lived volcanic events).

Figure 3.3: *Well bedded coarse volcanic debris, reworked and sorted by currents on the seafloor but originating as debris flows. That's why they contain some large cobbles. I've outlined some of these.*

The track continues directly to Llyn Cwmorthin. Immediately to your left is a *roche moutonée* of the same massive pyroclastic material, with a row of sombre-looking windowless and roofless cottages built on top, well sited for a great lake view and out of the damp boggy surrounds. Some of the rhyolite blocks incorporated in this upper MVF reach the length of an outstretched arm. The crags to your left which form most of Moel-yr-hydd are entirely intrusive rhyolite, commonly with beautiful flow-banding and folding (p. 58).

Everywhere here you see slate tips and the remains of large quarrying operations. Fortunately the north side of the cwm isn't spoiled by quarrying. You can see quite clearly the strong features that the thicker beds form where they crop out of the steep mountain slopes (Allt y Ceffylau). Most of the rocks that form these slopes are siltstones and mudstones, now slates. You can quite easily pick out some hard thick units that are sills of intrusive dolerite or rhyolite.

Continue on along the track on the west side of the lake, heading northwest. On the eastern lake shore, there's a boathouse and a small cottage built in a small group of trees, one of which is a monkey puzzle. In the quarries above, you can make out a series of large white quartz veins that cut through the upper quarry walls and obviously made much of the slate worthless by screwing up the otherwise perfect cleavage. Above the quarry and its quartz veins, you can see two units of strongly cleaved but well-bedded volcanic rocks that overlie the older quarried slates.

Llyn Cwmorthin was scooped out by the huge glacier which once filled this valley, leaving a rock bar (MVF) which dammed the lake behind. At one time, the quarrymen raised the lake level slightly by augmenting the natural rock dam with one of their own, but this is no longer in use.

In the lake just beside the track, you can see some water plants growing as well as the ubiquitous soft rushes at the edge. In one place, you can see water horsetails (*Equisetum*) and white water lilies (*Nymphaea alba*).

As you come round into the head of the cwm, you can see that there are yet more quarries up on Bwlch Cwmorthin. These explain this track that once had a narrow gauge tramway laid along it. The tramcars were horse-drawn. Here and there, as you walk, you can see the remains of wooden sleepers and iron rails, now mostly covered in peat and mud which have slumped down from the soft moorland on the left. There remains a low stone embankment just to the left of the track that kept the tramway out of the marsh. Much of the track was probably taken up as well. Waste not, want not (or its Welsh equivalent) was a principle followed by the hardy quarrymen. You come to an iron kissing gate through which you continue. Shortly, on the right, you pass a fine example of a slate fence, something which farmers used everywhere locally as an alternative to dry stone walls, before wood and wire fences became common ... and whilst quarries could easily produce them as a by-product. As you can see, just an interwoven double strand of tough wire kept the fence vertical.

Now look left up into the cwm below Moel-yr-hydd. On the left, there's almost nothing but ice-smoothed rock outcrop. These are MVF. To the right, precipices and heather terraces of Foel Ddu give the general impression that all the rocks are uniformly dipping to the northwest at just over 20°. There's nothing complex about any of this thick rock sequence. Look now slightly to the right of the track into northwest corner of the cwm where there's another deserted house – Plas-cwmorthin – surrounded by a group of larch and deciduous trees. Between you and it is a large area of near flat, very boggy ground indeed. Obviously this was once lake, now filled in with flood deposits from the abundant streams (which look very different after a few days of persistent winter rains). Directly north is another ruin – Cwmorthin-uchaf – with a steeply descending stream behind whose alluvial cone you can see.

After a little more walking, you come to another slate fence on the right of the track. On the left is a ruined chapel, minus slates. The existence of this little chapel, with two miserable pine trees outside, is a reminder that Cwmorthin was once a flourishing community. People lived, worked all their lives ... and often died in these slate quarries. Many had smallholdings too to supplement the meagre quarry wages. At Cwmorthin in 1845, a quarryman would be paid £2 18s 6d for making 3,780 slates!

Above the chapel, the rough ground below Foel Ddu is entirely occupied by moraine: jagged angular boulders, some quite large, scattered around on the moraine humps.

It's common to see and hear ravens flying around here, as in most mountainous places; their gutteral croaks punctuating the constant distant roar of rushing streams.

Now you are approaching the old Conglog quarries. Dead ahead are three holes, a bit like the cones which form in an egg timer as the sand runs out. The quarries were underground, but obviously part of the roofs collapsed so that the scree and glacial debris on the surface ran down into the openings. These emphasise, once again, that much of the quarrying was underground (sometimes the entire operation as you'll see at Croesor Quarry on Ramble 9), the only other evidence for their existence being the massive waste tips. Plas-cwmorthin was quite possibly the quarry manager's house, set aside from the quarrymen's cottages off to the left of the track. All are now sad ruins.

You might want to make a diversion off to the right to Plas-cwmorthin. It's an interestingly built quite large house with cellars and two floors, each having massive slate lintels forming the chimney piece. Every room had a fireplace – 9 in total including the kitchen range with an oven. You can see where the floorboards used to be, and there's little left of the roof. Still, enough remains as testimony to its former elegance with its collection of sycamore, ash and conifer trees and garden surrounded by a slate fence. Some of the dressed corner stones used to build the house are huge, perhaps weighing up to a ton. They're volcanic rocks and must have been brought in from one of the slate quarries which happened to have a volcanic unit cropping out in it. The network of railway tracks would have made this comparatively easy. The entire west wall was once slate-covered to make it more weatherproof when the wet Westerlies blew.

As you approach the start of the inclined track, our route up to Cwmorthin, there's a gate with a kissing gate. Go through this and look at the ruins on the left of the track which shows how the quarrymen used rails rather than traditional timbers to hold up the roof of huge slate slabs.

If you look back beyond the manager's house, you can see how the entire sequence along the skyline, bed after bed, dips clearly northwest. At one place, there's a perched block silhouetted against the sky.

Now begin your ascent up the roughly cobbled track. Ahead are the first tips of yet another quarry: Rhosydd, which opened in 1840. To your left, you can't miss the large quartz boulders that have rolled down after breaking off from quartz veins high in the crags of Foel Ddu. Also on the left are neat stone pylons which must once have carried a small rail track down to the slate splitting sheds, little of which remain (now converted to sheep folds) below. You can see the remains of an inclined track coming down the valley side just below this track. This must have intersected the stone pylons.

A bit further up the track, look out for a curving slate tip coming out from the three holes I mentioned earlier. Twenty metres higher, there's a sharp turn back to the right. This leads you on to a grassy platform with a couple of ruined sheds and the main entrance into the underground mine (of which the three holes and curved tip are the only surface sign).

It's a sobering thought as you puff up the track (which tries its hand as a stream in wet weather ... quite successfully) that these mountains of slate all around are all the product of muscle power: men just hauling little trucks, using winches and hoists, levers, black powder and skilled strength.

Lower Rhosydd Quarry: Locality 4 [665 462]

As you approach the top of the incline, be prepared to have your mind blown by the sheer scale of the quarrying operations you'll start seeing in this high, inhospitable place: try being up here in driving rain and cloud if you don't believe me.

The first sight is a huge wall that might almost have been made by the Incas of Peru. Stone 'steps' project from the outside of this, for the adventurous only. What purpose did they have? A powerful stream from Clogwyn Brîth gushes down the rocks from your right just before the strange walls. The lower wall, built of dressed slates, must have supported a large waterwheel inside it. The stream must have been channelled to the top of the wheel, but of the waterwheel itself, you'll find no trace at all.

Continue on to the pass (Bwlch Cwmorthin) to enter a vast flat area of desolation. Once, hundreds of men worked here. Today, the ruins remind you of this industry in no uncertain terms. For here a century ago were the splitting sheds, bunkhouse and workshops ... today, there are just wind-haunted ruins, twisted iron, broken rail cars, nuts and bolts and old engines. There's still plenty to see (Fig. 3.4).

Rhosydd Quarry. Like all the slate quarries, this great enterprise started in the late 18th century and was worked from Croesor. By the 1820s, a whole series of tramways and inclines, including the steepest in Wales (Ramble 9), connected Rhosydd, via Croesor, to the port of Porthmadog. Conglog, Wrysgan and Cwmorthin all connected to the Ffestiniog railway which opened in 1836. This part of Rhosydd, called New Rhosydd, was entirely underground as was Croesor Quarry (Ramble 9). The older, partly open quarry you'll see shortly. Croesor and Rhosydd connect through underground and there are stories of quarrymen nipping from one to the other for a smoke or a doze whilst they should have been working their shifts! Today, there is talk of re-opening the upper workings but these lie within the National Park boundary. What will happen? Which is more important? Jobs and 'wealth creation' or landscape?

Figure 3.4: *Not many buildings remain at Rhosydd but this beautiful arch was still standing in 1995.*

From here, you get your first view of Cnicht and Moelwyn Mawr and yet more tips higher up from the upper parts of this once great quarry. If you look at the rock outcrops around the quarry, you see that they're just as strongly ice-smoothed as the ones you saw lower, showing us that the ice sheet flowed right over this pass at 400 metres above sea-level. Pass-breaching by ice is called transfluence.

The entrance to, and drain from, the underground parts of the quarry is behind the buildings, a large tunnel with a fair-sized stream draining from it. The main incline from the upper workings descends to the right of the tunnel. Inside the entrance is the usual chill dank air and the sound of rushing waters. It's quite large, wide enough for two rail tracks side by side, though today all you can see are a few chunks of timbers and lengths of twisted rail.

The next part of the climb starts up the incline, right by the tunnel. The lower part has been cut through the slate outcrops. You can still see the drill holes into which the quarrymen rammed gunpowder to blast this rock out. The higher part of the incline has been built up to an even gradient. At the top of this incline, again cut into the rock, there's a nice ice-polished surface just to the right of the track bed. If you look carefully, you can see the striae which show (as you'd guess) that the glacier ran northeast-southwest, over the pass. At the top of the incline is the old winding house that would have once held a drum and cables to control the rail cars' ponderous descent.

From here, a raised causeway of slate continues on round to the left to cross a marshy area with rock outcrops to the left and slate tips to the right. This then runs up to the base of a second incline to the higher parts of the quarry. Before this, some 20 metres after the winding house, you'll notice a rock outcrop projecting half out into the track. This is Locality 5.

Riddle in the rocks: Locality 5 [6652 4604]

The rocks to the left of the track are clearly bedded sediments with distinct packets of laminae up to finger-thickness (Fig. 3.5). But what really strikes you here is the strong north-dipping cleavage. If you look carefully, you can see that the coarser beds are actually broken up into small sigmoid (flattened S) shapes. Each sigmoid chunk is separated from its neighbours by a cleavage plane. The finer sediments in between have simply become true slates: the cleavage is so total and penetrating that as it formed, it destroyed the finer siltstone laminae which must have made up this mud-silt and fine sand rock that once formed the sea-floor.

About 50 metres behind (east of) these outcrops, across a small stream and boggy patch, you'll find a number of other outcrops, quite different in appearance to what you've just seen. Here, they are cut by joints which typically form in hard brittle rocks because of the stress which causes cleavage: this is fracture cleavage. But what do you make of the rocks? They have no structure, unlike the sediments; they're coarse grained and shot through by many highly irregular veins that stick out of the surface and so must be made of some harder mineral, perhaps quartz. But some 'veins' look like beds, mimicking the dip of the bedded rocks above. What's going on?

Figure 3.5: *Strongly cleaved Nant Ffrancon Group fine sandstones and siltstones. You can see how cleavage disrupts and, at an advanced stage, destroys the original bedding structures in the rock. The finer grained the sediment, the more easily the destruction and overprinting by the metamorphic event which gave rise to the cleavage. Tape recorder at bottom right gives scale.*

By now, you know well enough that there are no easy answers to this sort of riddle in the rocks. The structureless rocks with the irregular veins aren't sediments at all, but are intrusive dolerites that were injected as very hot liquid into these sediments not long after they were laid down. The dolerites of Snowdonia are almost all associated with the various bursts of volcanic activity that went on during the Caradoc Epoch. In some of the outcrops here, you can see actual junctions between the sediments and the dolerite bodies (Fig. 3.6).

Figure 3.6: *My penknife rests on the dipping junction between the coarse dolerite (below) and sandstone above. The strong near-vertical joints are fracture cleavage.*

Some musings on Time

To-morrow, and to-morrow, and to-morrow,
Creeps in this petty pace from day to day,
To the last syllable of recorded time;
And all our yesterdays have lighted fools
The way to dusty death. Out, out, brief candle!
Life's but a walking shadow, a poor player,
That struts and frets his hour upon the stage,
And then is heard no more; it is a tale
Told by an idiot, full of sound and fury,
Signifying nothing

(Macbeth lamenting the death of his wife, from the play of that name by William Shakespeare)

The sediments you've just been looking at are part of the enormously thick Nant Ffrancon Group which formed the theatrical backdrop in the great theatre of Ordovician Time. The time span represented by this group of sediments was around 30 million years (Arenig to Caradoc; see Appendix Timescale). Most of the events on this stage were but walking shadows and poor players (like alternating beds of muds and silts) betokening nothing more than seasonal changes or storms that churned up the sea-floor a little, or pumped out more sediments from distant rivers flowing from nearby islands or larger landmasses. Each bed, each rock type is in this metaphor, a 'syllable of recorded time'. The volcanic formations and dolerites were once major players, Macbeths and Hamlets belching their fiery and violent presence across this stage of Time. Today, the mountains remain – like tattered programme notes – as silent testimony to their performance. We can read those programme notes and piece together something of the original performances, and imagine what they would have been like had we been there to see them.

And now we too are major players on this same stage. But our brief candles have only just flared into life. How long will it be before they too are snuffed out? In a few million years will another intelligence be looking at the dirty and still slightly radioactive strata which represent our fleeting appearance on this eternal stage? Will this intelligence piece together the significance of the mass extinctions associated with our bones, what remains of our buildings and realise our devilish ability to create weapons for killing life on a vast scale?

On that sombre note, hammering home our long term insignificance on the world stage, let us continue on our ramble. **Return to the track to begin the ascent of the second incline up towards the slate tips.** At the base of the incline, the rock is really screwed up with great contusions of quartz veins, splurting in all directions. **At the incline top, you have fine views north and west: Cnicht and the main Snowdon range (Y Lliwedd, Crib Goch and Yr Wyddfa – Snowdon's summit). Further west is Moel Hebog. And just as you thought you were reaching the end of the slate quarries, you find there's even more higher up.** It really is an astonishing monument to the persistence and sheer hard work of the Welsh quarrymen. It's also clear that there must be some big holes underneath the ground below your feet somewhere because (apart from what you'll see shortly), a colossal amount of slate has been taken out of this mountain.

Ice smoothing and sandy lumps: Locality 5 [6654 4601]

Midway between the incline top (where the cable drum used to be) and some ruined buildings (with another adit entrance to the upper workings), just to the left of the flat area, you can see more ice-smoothed outcrops of the intensely cleaved sediments we saw back at the last locality. Here you can see dark grey sandstone lumps demanding an explanation, within a much finer sequence of sediments. What do you think? Maybe the sandstones tell us of a great hurricane or a powerful earthquake shock, either of which might have triggered unstable sands in shallower waters to slump down and fan out into a more or less continuous thin bed upon the muds below. I' d guess that they've been fragmented into separate lumps as part of the squeezing and shearing associated with the cleavage formation. The still slightly plastic muds and silts seem almost to have squeezed between the sandstone. The beds dip quite gently northeast (about 20°), whereas the cleavage dips steeply west.

Continue on across the gentle grassy moorland, heading slightly east of south, up towards the highest quarries, keeping the slate tips on your left all the time. To your right, with a great grassy flank, is Moelwyn Mawr (which you'll visit later).

The exit level from the upper quarries (whose tips you've just climbed) is just to the right of the small path. Inside the dark and damp tunnel entrance, you can hear water gushing. **Once you've reached the top of the tips on the small path, you can see the two great holes that represent the highest part of Rhosydd Quarry, almost 550 metres above sea-level. You can walk along the top of the tips on a broad causeway across the featureless peaty moorland hereabouts, towards the two big holes.**

Big holes; big collapse: Locality 6 [666 453]

The eastern hole is remarkable. It's as if a bomb had exploded, leaving piles of boulders and foundered rock masses in a large crater. What actually happened here was that the roof of the underground quarry collapsed completely so there are great subsidence hollows and huge crevasse-like cracks as masses of rock weighing thousands of tons have slipped down into the hole. It seems to be more or less stable now. Fortunately, although this collapse happened whilst the quarry was operating, it happened during the night so no one was hurt.

> Whilst I was quietly standing here, I saw a fox (Fig. 3.7) below me – before he saw me. When he spotted me, he moved fast, showing me his prowess at crossing steep rocky ground. I could see his black-tipped ears and white-tipped brush for a minute or more before I finally lost him in the chaos of rock.

Figure 3.7: *'What me kill your chickens? Never!'*

The western quarry is quite different. There's a tunnel entrance to it from the north – which I have walked through. If you do this, be very careful. It's slightly scary and if you don't want to be scared, you can see everything from the quarry edge above anyway, so you won't miss anything. The tunnel brings you out on a sort of shelf high up on the inaccessible quarry side. In front is a scene of desolation, the only sound being trickling water and the wind. Dead ahead is a winding drum, the iron wheels displaced from their bearings and the remains of another incline that runs off below to the right. Great rock masses have slipped into the hole. This tunnel was only used when the quarry was much smaller, for dragging out the slate from the upper part, now completely mined away. Later, the slate was trammed out at the level just after Locality 5 which explains the large tips below that level, at the top of the two inclines. An iron pipe emerges from a vertical shaft just at the entrance. The shaft is mostly flooded but you can see masses of quartz veins cutting the slate here.

If you want, you can walk around the west rim of the western quarry, past a group of ruined cottages, complete with fireplaces and mantle shelves. Please beware here: the quarry edges are still very unsafe and you will be killed if you fall in for it's a long drop down into this huge hole. So stay well clear of the edge! In fact, there are huge caverns directly under the west side of the quarry that you can see very well if you walk round to the south side. Access to the quarry is very difficult – the cleavage surfaces are steep, smooth and slippery – and I do not recommend it at all. You can see all you need from walking around part of it.

The slate in the quarry was of good quality – the reason for its existence, of course – there being no dolerites or any other different rocks to mess up the cleavage. This also meant less waste though as you've seen from the tips, there was still plenty. The quarrymen removed the slate underground by using the pillar and stall technique (see Ramble 8), leaving as little as they dared as pillars to support the roof. Obviously in some of these operations, they were pushing their luck, as you have just seen in the eastern 'crater'. Anyway, if you were a quarryman, if a rock fall didn't get you, silicosis probably did.

To the east is Moel-yr-hydd. Beyond are the other quarries around the once-great slate centre of Blaenau Ffestiniog.

Due west of the quarries, about half a kilometre from here, is a set of rocky outcrops forming a little peak on the ridge running up to Moelwyn Mawr: Locality 7. Below it are numbers of quartz boulders. Walk over to this locality.

Cwm Croesor, dolerites again and a view: Locality 7 [6613 4536]

From this viewpoint you can see down to the Croesor Quarries. You can also see a very obvious glacial moraine impounding a tiny lake, and beyond it a wilderness of morainic humps and hollows and vast erratic boulders. All this fresh moraine stops abruptly, defining very clearly the limit of this last gasp of glaciation, the Younger Dryas ice advance that ended about 11,500 years ago.

The quarrymen were busy down below as well as the glaciers. You can see a number of small trial levels where they dug into the mountain side to test the quality of the slate. You see such trials all over Snowdonia, some for slates and others for minerals. All you can see of Croesor Quarry's workings are the enormous waste tips – so there must be some very large holes under this mountainside.

Back towards the pass (Bwlch y Rhosydd), you can see a clear tramway that snakes its way around various rocky outcrops at the head of Cwm Croesor, and then stops quite suddenly in the middle of a precipice. You can just make out a very steep incline that plunges down from this point to the valley below. (You visit this on Ramble 9.) Beyond that, you can see the lakes of Llynau Diffwys and Llyn Clogwyn-brith (nestling inside a dolerite intrusion), and the rather hidden valley which contains Llyn Cwm-y-foel, right under the slopes of Cnicht. A whole series of magnificent waterfalls has developed where the outlet of this lake runs over the hanging valley lip.

The grain of the country is very clear (Fig. 3.8). All the beds dip north or northwest, forming a whole series of small scarps and dips right the way up to Cnicht itself. Some of the crags of Cnicht are formed by dolerite sills that help give the mountain its distinctive pyramid-like form, best seen from over towards Porthmadog. The screes below Cnicht are quite something too, all formed in the last 13,000 years or so, since the ice melt. (No doubt screes formed after earlier glaciations which affected these mountains, but they would have been easily swept away by later glaciers, the last of which would have melted away at the end of the main glaciation, some 14,000 years ago).

Figure 3.8: *All the rock formations in this photo dip gently northwest. The dolerite sills are especially striking forming strong scarps. You'll cross this ground on Ramble 9.*

But what of the rocks beneath your feet here? They are fairly featureless blocky things rather like those you saw at Locality 5 and this is indeed another dolerite intrusion. Here, the veins aren't pretending to be beds ... they're quite irregular, filling cooling joints that probably formed parallel to the top and bottom of the sill. On some of the weathered surfaces, you can see quite clear feldspar crystals. The rock also has a distinctly red tinge characteristic of Snowdonia's dolerites.

Continue on to Moelwyn Mawr. To your right is a great scree of debris which has fallen off the slate crags that fringe the summit area. At the bottom of the scree is a large rusted wheel, part of the winding gear for a mine shaft or incline far below. I wonder how the miners got it there?

Moelwyn Mawr: Locality 8 [6583 4486]

This is your highest point and best view, especially to the west out to Llŷn and the great estuaries of Traeth Mawr and Traeth Bâch. Find a place to sit and hop into your imaginary Time Travel Machine. Set the dial for about 18,000 years ago and what do you see? You guessed it: ice, ice everywhere. Almost every familiar landmark has vanished. The cwm below you is filled with ice and the Croesor valley is invisible, buried under the ice. You can just make out the dark rocks of the very top of Cnicht black against the blinding glare. Farther away, you can see Snowdon and, with care, some of the other higher mountain peaks with their snowy precipices mostly buried by glaciers. To the east and southeast is almost unrelieved white ice sheet, forming a vast dome. This was the main reservoir for the Welsh ice that streamed out to all compass points as continuous thick sheets, probably over 1000 metres thick. (Today, it is an upland plateau of bogs and wilderness called Migneint.) The whole of the Vale of Ffestiniog is lost under this crushing ice flow from the Migneint, and the flow ramps up over the Moelwyn range and through Cwm Orthin, over Bwlch Rhosydd and down Cwm Croesor. We know from studies of today's glaciers that the ice at the base can move in quite different directions to that in the higher layers. Remember, ice – though hard – is plastic. It deforms and creeps, though too slowly for you or I to see. This is why, although many of Snowdonia's valleys run northeast-southwest, the thick ice sheets were able to move, overall, to the northwest.

Look now, in your imagination, towards the present Cardigan Bay. All you can see is a series of converging glaciers whose bases are grinding and cutting away at their rocky beds – now well below sea level. The ice is slowly excavating what would become the great estuaries. If you could fly from here out over the Irish Sea, eventually you'd come to the ice shelf edge about 100 kilometres southwest of Land's End! Here, the ice would begin to float as it got into deeper waters, just as it does in the Ross and Weddell Seas of Antarctica today. From time to time, huge icebergs, some many kilometres long, would break off the ice shelf and drift with the currents into the Atlantic.

> **Sealevels and locked-up water** ... Because of the global Ice Age, huge amounts of water were locked up as ice, mostly on land masses like North America and Northern Europe and Asia. (Sea ice has no effect on sea levels because it is floating.) But strip the ice out of Traeth Mawr and Traeth Bâch too and you'd see those as deep glaciated valleys whose rock floors were probably at least 100 metres below today's sea level. Because sea levels were so low, the ice could continue to erode much deeper than it can today in places like Alaska where glaciers run into the sea – and float.

If you now return slowly to the present day, you'd see all the ice sheets melt away as torrents of brown flood waters roiling down the valleys – to meet the gradually encroaching seas. As soon as a fast-moving river, loaded with boulders and debris, runs into an essentially still body of deeper water like a lake or the sea, it loses all its energy and simply drops everything it was carrying (p. 3). As time passes as you return, you see Traeth Mawr filling up, starting with a delta at the Aberglaslyn end that gradually built out to fill the entire flat area between Porthmadog and Penrhyndeudraeth. The process continues slowly today as the winter rains disgorge flood waters into the estuaries, but these waters aren't powerful enough to carry boulders this far down. The best they can manage is sand. So the estuaries are now capped with an icing of yellow sand which the sea currents spread around a bit to form the beautiful stretches of Black Rock Sands. So when you next build sand castles there, remember you have the Ice Age to thank for it.

The summit area of this mountain is, slightly oddly, entirely formed of slates – part of the thick Nant Ffrancon Group muds and silts. Why? Aren't slates usually soft, forming valleys rather than mountains? The northwest extension of the summit ridge offers some clues here and **if you wish, you can walk along to it (labelled 8A [6556 4496]); about 300 metres each way and about 40 metres of descent.** As you walk, you'll notice that some of the slates have distinct bedding but by the time you reach 8A, the rocks have become sandstones. The strike of these harder sandstones helps define the shape of the ridge here, dipping northwest at about 30°.

Did you notice any other rock type before you got here? This unnamed northwest summit is actually underlain by a thick dolerite sill, which crops out as it crosses the ridge. The existence of these hard rocks (as at Locality 7) within the softer slates helps explain why slates form the highest parts of the Moelwyn range. You'll see additional clues at Locality 9.

Return to the summit (if you went to 8A) and make your way down the grassy and increasingly steep slope to the southeast towards Craigysgafn, the middle part of the Moelwyn range. As the ridge narrows, you come to slates with quartz veins and at this point, a path becomes more obvious. The descent to the col, Locality 9, is quite steep but short. Below is Llyn Stwlan whose natural level has been much increased by the concrete dam and the pumped storage scheme. At the col, turn left by the pile of stones and walk a few paces to the east, this is Locality 9.

Locality 9: Rhyolites [6600 4458]

Look around you. Do you notice anything about the rocks? There's a dramatic change of rock type and you can actually stand on the junction between them. What you are standing on forms all the crags to the south (Craigysgafn) whilst the summit slates form everything above you. You can follow – with your eye – this contact for some distance along the steep northeast slope of Moelwyn Mawr, to Moel-yr-hydd. The rock whose top surface you can stand on (Fig. 3.9) is an intrusive rhyolite. In fact, this body of rock – a sill – continues on at this level, forming the crags of Moel-yr-hydd and finally stopping at the shores of Llyn Cwmorthin about 200 metres north of Locality 3.

Figure 3.9: *Looking back to the top surface of the rhyolite sill at Locality 8 (right centre). Above this are the Nant Ffrancon Group slates.*

A puzzle unravelled? When is a rhyolite not a rhyolite? When it's intrusive. How do we know this rhyolite is intrusive? Why can't it be a lava? The tops of lavas are usually highly irregular and very much broken up. The top of this body is smooth and planar. Also, on Moel-yr-hydd, the top of this rhyolite cuts through – transgresses – the overlying beds, something a lava flow could never do because there simply weren't any overlying beds when it flowed and froze solid. Anything on top of a lava must have come later. There are no exceptions to this rule. There's a third way to tell – though not here: intrusive rocks, because they are hot liquids, cook the rocks into which they force themselves, converting them to the sort of thing you saw at Locality 1. Again, lavas can only affect the surface underneath them and this they rarely do because they lose their heat to the atmosphere or sea within as little as a few hours. Intrusive rocks are well insulated both above and below and can take thousands of years to cool. This gives plenty of time for the cooking and in the case of the Tanygrisiau granite, as you've seen, the sediments are well and truly roasted (but low fat of course, and positively no cholesterol).

This thick and extensive rhyolite forms a sort of backbone for the northern Moelwyn range and undoubtedly is part of the reason for the actual summit being slate rocks. If there are both intrusive rhyolites and dolerites underneath, then the slates may also have been hardened somewhat by the slow cooking process. Dolerites are better cookers because they are hotter.

As you begin the short climb to Craigysgafn, you find yourself crossing flow folded and flow brecciated rhyolites. **At the top is Locality 10.**

Locality 10: Craigysgafn summit [6599 4434]

Underfoot here is the same rhyolite as at the last locality so it's quite thick.

Now take a ringside seat to look into the great natural amphitheatre of Cwm Stwlan. Notice how all the outcrops below are smooth and rounded. To the right of the lake, you can see some huge bedding surfaces (part of the MVF which you'll cross later). These have caused the moving ice to ramp up and scrape over them so they are, in a sense, 'natural' *roches moutonées*. This stepped topography continues right the way back down to the carpark. The ice may have moved up these mountain slopes as well as down. This was because of the enormously thick ice cap which existed at the depth of the ice ages, overlying the Migneint area, east of Ffestiniog. This was so powerful that it spilled right across the Vale of Ffestiniog and ploughed its way up and over almost the whole Moelwyn range.

After the main ice melt, a small glacier grew once again in Cwm Stwlan during the Younger Dryas cold period. So 12,000 years ago, there would have been ice right below you and – as yet – no lake. Thousands of years later, people came and left their imprints on this rocky cwm. You can see a number of old tracks and tramways, connecting various dead slate quarries or trial levels.

There's a steep but clear path down to Bwlch Stwlan. Just after you start your descent, you come to a mass of quartz veins over 2 metres thick. These cut right across the rhyolite. **Then there's a little steep scrambling, some loose scree and a small grassy col.** This is virtually the base of the rhyolite. Below this point, the rocks are different again, being brecciated. **Half way down to Bwlch Stwlan, the path emerges from scree onto green grass.** Underfoot, slates outcrop again and the breccia is now behind you, overlying the slate.

What is the breccia? It is, as you see, full of small angular holes – breccia fragments. There's no sorting so it's not any kind of ordinary sedimentary rock. It's also entirely made of pieces of lava but looks nothing like the rhyolite that overlies it. That gives us two possibilities: it could be a type of lava that has completely broken itself up as it cooled and yet continued to flow: a block lava. This would have almost certainly been under the sea because the sediments both below and above are all mud rocks which you would expect in deep water. There's no sign of – or need for – a sudden uplift. Perhaps more likely is that it is a pyroclastic (mass) flow, for this is roughly the same unit you saw back at Locality 3. What do you think?

At the col, you walk across onto a grassy tramway and some pale grey

ice-smoothed outcrops. Locality 11 is centred around a ruined building on the left about 30 metres along the embanked tramway.

Locality 11: Blobby rocks at Bwlch Stwlan [6614 4402]

The rock here is another, lower member of the Moelwyn Volcanic Formation. It's thick (at least 20 metres) and almost completely massive except in its topmost layers, nearest the col, where you can see fairly good bedding (Fig. 3.10). The blobs are rarely bigger than a tomato and most are thumbnail-sized lapilli.

These tuffs grade up into sandstones and, finally, siltstones and mudstones – those you crossed coming down to this locality.

Figure 3.10: *Bedding in the knobbly blobby rocks.*

Rock faces ... If you look up to the northwest precipice of Moelwyn Bach, you see a face with a prominent nose and rather receding chin.

From here, you can either head back to the carpark or continue on up a clear track that starts at Bwlch Stwlan – not the tramway which runs through this locality – to Moelwyn Bach and complete your examination of the Moelwyn range. This climbs up the scree slope to the east side of the unstable-looking slate and quartz-veined crags that form the north side of Moelwyn Bach. Near the top, a small pile of stones marks an abrupt right turn of the path which brings you to the summit area.

From here, you can look down at the Tanygrisiau Reservoir and Moel

Ystradau on its east side. This is the central area of the microgranite. You are looking at the very top – the roof – of this large intrusion (see Box earlier). If Snowdonia had been uplifted another thousand metres or so, the granite would probably form a substantial mountain range of its own instead of lying dog-like at the foot of the Moelwyn range. The rocks underfoot are again slates, the same beds that you crossed just before Bwlch Stwlan, and are being eroded pretty fast which is why the north face is so unstable with landslip blocks and active screes below. In time, as the slate is stripped off by erosion, the tuff you saw at Locality 11, will form all of Moelwyn Bach. At present, it only forms the southern part of it as you will see shortly at Locality 12, the final locality on this ramble.

From the north end, you can look back over all the ground you've crossed since Moelwyn Mawr and, usefully, see the sequence of rocks you've walked down in its entirety.

Have you noticed something else about this summit area? Perhaps you didn't believe me when I said that the ice sheets from the east had flowed right over this range (710 metres high here)? Well, here's the evidence, everywhere. Boulders of volcanic rocks are dotted about – on the slate. Can you think of any other way they might have arrived there?

Underlying the slates are the volcanic rocks that form the south part of the summit plateau, **so as you walk the 200 metres south to the final locality,** bear in mind that you're still walking down the rock sequence – walking back in Time.

Figure 3.11: *Beautifully bedded sandstones that form the top of the MVF here. Binoculars (centre left) give scale*

Locality 12: Perched blocks, giants, knobbles and a memorial [662 436 area]

As soon as you reach the pale, ice-smoothed volcanic rocks, you should have a feeling of *déja vu*. Why? Because you've just seen the same rocks back at Locality 11. The path up to Moelwyn Bach ran parallel to but slightly higher than the northwest-dipping volcanic rocks which form this large area of pale grey outcrops. And just to ram home the point, here is an array of perched blocks, dumped all over the place by melting ice. They look as though they were placed here last week ... but they've actually been there for about 15,000 years.

As you cross the contact between the slates and these underlying tuffs, you first find thin silvery-white sandstone beds which are rhyolitic and beautifully bedded (Fig. 3.11) with occasional indications of currents or waves in the form of ripples.

After them (underneath) come the underlying main tuffs **as you walk south and slightly up. Now you begin to wonder: are these blobs and knobbly things really lapilli? Or are they something else?**

> **More *déja vu*; this time in the Lake District.** If you have my book *Lakeland Rocky Rambles*, you may have done the Coniston ramble. On that, beside Goat Water, you will have seen rocks closely similar to these. I called them blobby, lumpy and swirly – geological custard – and suggested that they formed due to processes that took place in the rocks after they were laid down. This may be the case here. The 'lapilli' may be secondary growths around smaller 'seed' particles, similar in appearance to the nodules you find in some welded tuffs. The process is a common though often poorly understood phenomenon called diagenesis which can retexture some rocks quite dramatically after they have been laid down. You can find evidence for this here if you look carefully: clear beds (including current beds) simply disappear as you follow them. They've been overprinted. If you thought rocks were immutable after their deposition and burial, your illusions are now shattered! And when you realise this can happen, it does make understanding old rocks that much more difficult.

By the time you reach the south end of the summit plateau, the knobbly rocks have become quite coarse. Some lumps reach the size of a football (well, an angular football, Fig. 3.12) though most are smaller and some seem to be rounded, like cobbles. They all seem to be rhyolite.

What do you make of these coarse beds? Most likely they are debris flows, perhaps triggered by some not too distant eruption, so some of the material here may be directly derived from an underwater pyroclastic flow event. The more rounded cobbles must have been rolled about in shallow water (or even on a beach or in river beds) and then hooshed into deeper water. The major flow 'event' that produced this thick mixed rock unit, must have ended up in fairly deep water because – as you've just seen – it becomes finer upwards (as the 'event' waned in power) and passes up into deeper water muds and silts: the slates which form the highest part of Moelwyn Bach.

> **A memorial?** At the south end, set into the rocks and decorated with a ring of quartz lumps, is a small rectangular slate plaque with the inscription 'R. A J. 1982' and an arrow pointing left. I wonder what this signifies?

Figure 3.12: *Coarse tuffs with some large angular volcaniclasts (binoculars for scale at centre).*

Before you start your return, find a comfortable spot to sit with a view south to the Harlech Dome and beyond. In your mind Time Machine, zoom back to the mid-Ordovician about 460 million years ago, somewhat before the Moelwyn Volcanics you're sitting on formed. To your south is the early Harlech Dome, probably quite a large island surrounded by shallow seas with surf breaking on offshore shoal areas where curious ironstones and phosphate-rich sediments are forming. The east and west sides of the island are active fault lines, making it a horst. Further north, if you could move the sea out of the way, you'd see a deep basin in which muds and silts were slowly accumulating (Nant Ffrancon Group). Now one of the more extraordinary events to happen in Snowdonia begins as you watch, tweaking your Machine's time controls to speed up the millennia: the older Arenig age sediments, now solid rock ramped up on the steep submarine north flank of the Harlech Dome island, begin to break up into titanic rafts and slide slowly down into deeper water, lubricated by wet mud but driven by gravity. This process, caused by further uplift of the Harlech Dome, continued for a while and gradually you see that a jumble – melange – of massive chunks of the older rocks accumulates in the deeper sea areas to the north (around where Rhyd, 2 kilometres southwest, and Penrhyndeudraeth are today). One characteristic of this melange sequence is that the rocks now tell lies to us about their age. So now you can find bits of older formation within a much younger one, a perplexing issue for geologists. This story is perhaps the best answer we have to explain bizarre raft-like masses of Arenig age sediments (notably a distinctive formation called the Garth Grit) 'floating' within Caradoc age mudstones. Weird.

Return down the path to Locality 11. You can see now how the knobbly tuffs of Locality 12 do indeed run below the slates you're walking on, straight down to the previous locality, and on beyond it towards the lake. **From the col, you can easily make your way down directly to Llyn Stwlan. The grassy track passes ruined cottages built, rather crudely, of blocks of MVF and slate. Descend a grass-covered incline,** below rounded outcrops of coarse breccia, the equivalent of those at Locality 12. **Then follow the southern lakeshore towards the dam.** The slate that forms Moelwyn Bach's summit, has been quite extensively quarried in the past as you see above the southwest lakeshore. The tuffs themselves you can trace right down to the lake. Likewise the pyroclastic flow (between the rhyolite of Craigysgafn and the upper slate) continues on down to the northern lake shore whilst the rhyolite (Locality 9 and 10) forms the crags above.

Nature and timing. It's interesting to note that no plants have been able to colonise the area of shore covered and uncovered once every 24 hours as the pumped storage reservoir fills and empties. Ocean tides are, of course, double this frequency and many plants like algae have evolved to use that endless routine.

Walk east towards the spillway. You pass a couple more heavily ice-scoured massive volcanic units, the lower part of the MVF, which form the huge bedding surfaces you looked down on from Locality 10. These too are mixed debris flows with some large blocks 'floating' within them. Some of these are almost the size of a person.

There are several possible ways back from here. The road is easy, but lengthy and boring. The best is to follow the old quarrymen's inclines and tramways directly down. Walk around the spillway edge and so down beside the dam. At the bottom, don't cross the fence but follow it down to the top of the old tramway system.

Some of the inclines – especially the first – are quite steep so be careful if it is wet. At the top of each incline, two dry-stone piers, neatly made, held the cable drum. Just above head-level, each side has , a massive anchor stone with holes bored through and iron bolts connecting to a wood frame at the top that formed the axle support for the drum. The trucks could then pass underneath the drum and, firmly hooked and carefully braked, be allowed to run down to the base of the incline.

The second incline is less steep. It cuts through the pale, hardened siltstones like those you saw at Locality 1, for the heat of the microgranite penetrated well up into the rocks above. **At the bottom of the third incline is a bridge over a stream on the left. Cross this and head straight for the carpark. Below is the power station and you pass two heavily fenced structures on the left from which a ghostly whistling sound emanates. These are access points to the tunnels and pipes through which the water surges down to the generators. Beyond these fenced areas is a locked gate. Keep well to the right and cross a fence at the stile and so over a wooden footbridge. Join the road and return to the carpark.**

Rocky Ramble 4: Moel Hebog and Moel Yr Ogof

How to get to the start of the ramble

From Tremadog, take the A487 west. Turn right after about 1½ miles towards Brynkir Woollen Mill, but then turn right in ¾ mile to Cwm Ystradllyn (signposted). In 1½ miles, you see a remarkable cathedral-like shell of a building as you descend to cross the Afon Henwy (see Introduction). Shortly, you arrive at Tyddyn Mawr [5552 4424] where you can usually park well out of the way of farm vehicles. This is the start of the ramble. If you prefer, there is a carpark [557 441] by Llyn Cwmystradllyn. If you use this, it will add 500 metres to your total walking distance.

The nearest you can get by bus is the turn-off to Cwmystradllyn [533 420] near Golan Mill. This is the Ffestiniog-Porthmadog-Caernarfon Service 1. Call Express Motors on 01286 674570. You then have a walk of 3 kilometres on a quiet road to the start, passing Ynysypandy slate mill on the way. You don't have to return this way: you could head off northeast at Bwlch Meillionen (near Locality 7) down the path through Beddgelert Forest to the A4085 where you can catch a No. 95 bus (Snowdon Sherpa). Call KMP on 01286 870880 for times. This makes the overall walk, bus route to bus route, about 14½ kilometres.

The ramble: needs, distances and times

Unfortunately, this ramble straddles parts of OS Outdoor Leisure Maps 17 & 18. You have two choices: use the two OS maps, which offer no overlap at all, as best you can in conjunction with mine, or make a photocopy (colour is better but pricier) of the relevant part of each sheet and make up your own map by cutting them and carefully joining the two along the 45 gridline. The distance is 14 kilometres (8¾ miles) and you'll be climbing 720 metres (2360 feet), less if you skip Moel yr Ogof. This is a full day walk.

Introduction:
Ynysypandy Slate Mill

The 'cathedral' you passed ¾ mile back is Ynysypandy, Melin Llechy (Fig. 4.1); the abandoned remains of the water-powered slate mill which once sawed and planed slate slabs from Gorseddau and the Prince of Wales slate quarries. The enterprise, started in 1855 and once interconnected by a tramway system, failed in 1871. In its brief years of glory, it employed 200 men who produced 1,300 tons of slate per year. This was carried out on the tramway down to the port of Porthmadog. Much of this tramway which was used until the 1890s is now scarcely detectable though parts are used as a footpath.

This ramble starts by going through Gorseddau Quarry and returns via the tramway which runs for miles from the head of Cwm Pennant. You'll climb right through the Snowdon Volcanic Group in some of its most exciting exposures. If you've never seen cannonballs and pillows made from rock before, you certainly will today.

Figure 4.1: *The roofless shell of Ynysypandy slate mill, a 1-minute walk from the road and well worth a visit. It seems appropriate that an Eisteddfod was once held here (1888). You can make out the Gorseddau Quarries to the right and your ramble route passes along the middle skyline to reach the east side of Moel Hebog.*

Tyddyn Mawr to Gorseddau Quarry

At first the path meanders through many fields and over streams, passing through small gates. Most of the time, it is quite obvious and is in any case marked on the OS map.

Set off northeast from Tyddyn Mawr and go through the new left-hand gate (this is a public footpath) and then drop down onto the old, parallel, grassy track on the right which angles away towards Llyn Cwmystradllyn, with drystone walls on both sides at first, then only on your left. Turn left through an iron gate (footpath sign). Cross a stream and go through a gap in a wall almost at the lake shore. The rocks here are cleaved siltstones and sandstones with obvious bedding, dipping northwest. The outcrops are all heavily sculpted by glaciers. **Walk on round to the right approaching the lakeshore and an iron gate which you step over (it is padlocked). Continue with an iron fence on your right.**

In spring here, you'll hear wheatears (Fig. 4.2) singing their little twittery songs from the tops of convenient bushes or trees. You should hear larks, cuckoos and curlews too and see wagtails. There's a surprising variety of trees along here including hazel, hawthorn, oak, Scots pine, spruces and rowan. Beneath them, or in the walls, you may find violets and celandines.

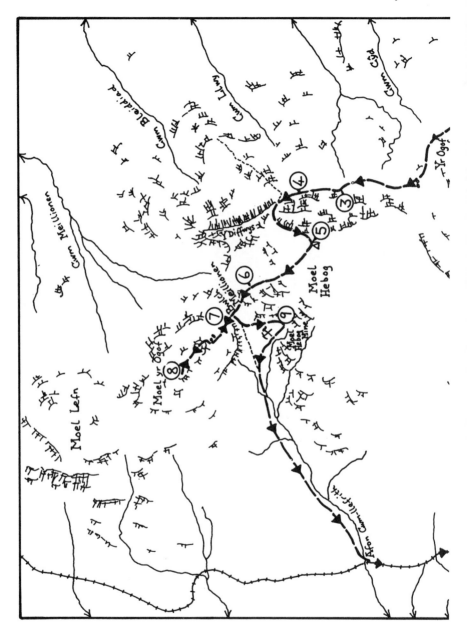

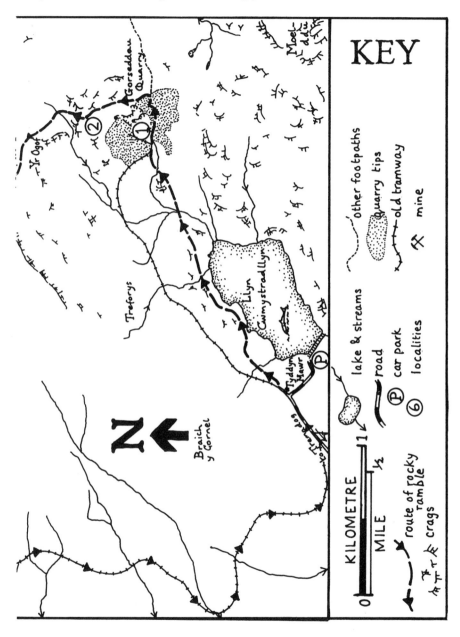

KEY

other footpaths
quarry tips
old tramway
⌘ mine

lake & streams
road
Ⓟ car park
⑥ localities

KILOMETRE
MILE
0 ½ 1

route of rocky ramble
crags

Whoatear

Figure 4.2: *Wheatear, summer visitors which breed everywhere in these mountains.*

The path goes through another gate in a wall and continues slightly higher up around the lake edge with a ruined wall on the right. Cross a stream on slate slabs and head on up through another gap in another wall. A fence is now on your left and the ruined wall on your right. Cross another stream just before some outcrops. Before yet another stream, you pass through a gap in the wall almost at the lake shore. Cross the stream, through another ruined wall and across a boggy bit. The path now heads via another iron gate towards the quarries. Now there's a fence on your right and a wall on your left and a huge glacial erratic boulder with an ivy bush. After this is another iron gate which you don't go through. Keep the main wall – which runs straight up to the slate quarries – on your left and push on over rough fields. There is a vague path with slab bridges over streams which avoids the wettest ground. When you see a ruined building at the base of the slate quarries, head for that.

Nests. In the wall here, I found both a wren's and a meadow pipit's nest, the latter with four speckled camouflaged eggs in it.

Around you now are either glacially-smoothed rock outcrops – *roches moutonées* - or boggy peaty hollows between them. The ice left very little material here.

Not far from the first quarry tips, you come to a wall with a green-painted iron gate which you cross to turn right onto the old Ynysypandy tramway. Follow this past the main incline from the upper levels. To its right is a boggy drainage level, now collapsed. Walk on above the level through a shallow valley between slate tips. At the top of this small valley, turn left onto a slate causeway which takes you directly into the lowest quarry, the first locality.

Gorseddau Quarry: Locality 1 [5722 4530]

This is an impressive and sombre place, now the haunt of wrens, choughs, ring ouzels and a few sheep. In the century since the quarry closed – the quality of the slate was not as good as the numerous other larger and more convenient quarries – nature has begun to reclaim her own. The inherently unstable walls have in many places collapsed so keep clear of the steep faces. Sphagnum mosses, sedges, soft rushes and a few sundews cover the flat wet quarry floor. The drier rock debris hosts mosses and parsley ferns.

The rock is a strongly cleaved mudstone, the oldest of the rock sequence you'll walk through today, for it pre-dates the vast eruptions which were to shatter the peace of this area which, at the time these mudstones formed, lay deep below the sea. This deep water, though the norm in the entire region during the Caradoc, began to shallow locally as you'll see as you cross towards Moel Hebog.

In places, the bedding is quite clear, dipping at variable angles to the southwest whilst the cleavage is near-vertical everywhere.

Return to the entrance and continue on up to the south of the actual quarries, skirting them as you climb, but working your way around to the upper east side. Every so often, you come out onto the top of one of the slate tips where the waste has been trammed out from different levels of the main quarry. Keep off the tips at all costs. They are most unpleasant to cross, so steer a course between the tips and the quarry. In places, there's a vague path for there is a route over the pass and down to Nantmor on the east side of the ridge between Moel Hebog and Moel-ddu. In several places, you come across small stone shelters. Slate is sharp and pieces flying through the air can be as lethal as shrapnel so the quarrymen would have retreated to these whilst blasting.

The route is not obvious but with care and a little scrambling, you'll find that you can get onto the highest level without having to climb any loose slate at all. The top level runs along a hillside so steep in the first section that the quarrymen had to build an embankment. When you reach the top level, turn left onto it and walk along its flat grassy top to another shelter, beyond which is the highest quarry. Ring ouzels nest here in spring and, though shy, usually make their presence known by their mournful bell-like calls, not at all like their lowland blackbird relatives.

Now you have a fine view way out to the Llŷn peninsula. Closer at hand is Moel-ddu. The geology is quite complex but it's a great story; worth waiting for!

From here, you climb steeply up the grassy slopes (Ffridd Uchaf) behind the quarrymen's cabin, staying well to the right of the top quarry, heading north towards the next locality. After the first bit of steep climbing, you can see almost to the top of the ridge to your right. This is obvious because a ruined wall runs northwest along its crest. Don't climb up to that because you'll only have to lose height again. Contour round, climbing slightly and heading towards Moel Hebog. There is no path here, but it's quite straight-forward. Shortly, you come to the wall I mentioned which runs straight down to the west. This is Locality 2.

Tranquillity belies a violent history: setting the scene at Locality 2 [5729 4568]

It doesn't matter where you meet this wall. The point of this locality is solely to look at the scenery and flesh it out with some ancient history. So take a seat ...

First, let's begin with the rocks underfoot which, as you will have noticed, continue to be the grey slates you saw at the quarry. As you will see as you walk over the col ahead, these gradually change to become sandstones. The beds all dip northwest which means that effectively, you will be walking up

Figure 4.3: Panorama of the south and east faces of Moel Hebog.
S – sandstone, PT – Pitt's Head Tuff, LR – Lower Rhyolitic Tuff Formation.

the sequence; up in Time. Why should sandstones begin to appear? These represent a steady shallowing of the once-deep sea due to uplift and infilling. The oldest sandstones (closest to you here) were laid down in the shallow sea in front of a river delta which was gradually building out (just like today's Mississippi). Then the beds tell us that shallowing continued with a clear sequence starting with offshore sandbars, then braided streams, then lagoons (now blocked to direct access from the sea) and finally alluvial fans, representing dry land. So the youngest sandstones you'll walk over as you approach Locality 3 were washed out by a river from mountains not far to the west.

Currents, sands and what they tell us. By careful measurement, we can even tell from which direction the sediments came. The currents which brought the sediments down from their sources came from the west. From the grain size, you can tell roughly how far away the land was too. Coarse gravels obviously don't move so far from their source as lighter fine sands. Likewise, mud rocks such as you've just seen at the quarry must have been laid down in deep water some distance from land. So the coarser a rock is, the closer it must be to its source. This applies to volcanic rocks too.

Then came catastrophe ... or so it would have been if there had been land plants or animals at the time to witness it. (Life then, except for possible primitive arthropods, was still restricted to the world's seas.) A mighty eruption of the most violent type began on this land which the sandstone

Localities 3 & 4 marked. Note that the Pitt's Head Tuff is broken by a fault.

has been telling us about. This produced a giant ignimbrite flow which seems to have coincided with a major collapse to form a caldera. These types of eruption have occurred many times in the Earth's long history but never in the few millennia that humans have been around to witness and record them. Let's hope this continues because they are the most violent processes on the planet, releasing the equivalent energy of dozens of nuclear explosions and devastating huge areas. The Pitt's Head eruptions were partly trapped: most of the welded tuff simply filled up the collapsing caldera which probably formed as it erupted. This is why no Pitt's Head Tuff exists to the southeast (at Moel-ddu for example as I mentioned earlier). But it did burst out of its confinement to the north and east, flowing as a fiery hurricane for several kilometres down the alluvial fan slopes (where Moel Hebog is now) into the sea. Undeterred by the waves, it continued right on under the sea as if nothing had happened for at least another 10 kilometres (Rocky Rambles 2, 5 & 10) before petering out. The tuff inside the caldera (intracaldera tuff, centred on Llwyd Mawr [503461]) is over 700 metres thick. This was the first and most southerly of several gigantic eruptions from a series of vents linked to fracture zones and more calderas between LLwyd Mawr and Snowdon. You'll be seeing the results of these eruptions – the Snowdon Volcanic Group – on most of these rambles for they are the foundation of the mountains of western Snowdonia.

From here you can see the grand sweep of the thick and distinctive Pitt's Head Tuff which you'll shortly be able to examine. The tuff is thick here because it was close to the eruption centre of Llwyd Mawr, and it forms the foundation for the whole of Moel Hebog (Fig. 4.3).

The next part of your route is across the col above Yr Ogof and round the base of the east face of Moel Hebog to the ridge which forms the skyline (Fig. 4.3). There you meet the well-used path from Beddgelert which you can see from here. Well to the left of that, almost vertically below the east end of the flat summit ridge but near the bottom of the east face is a massive overhanging crag: Locality 3 (Fig. 4.3). Continue to the col, contouring around two small stream valleys. In the second valley, there's a good deal of quartz vein and a small slate trial level.

Once on the col, you can look down to the old quarry tramway and also see a series of ruined cottages (Treforys) to the right of a group of trees. Thirty six semi-detached cottages, each with a quarter acre of land, were built in the mid-19 th century for the slate workers. By 1871, these were already derelict ... hardly surprising given the rough land from which these poor folk tried for a few years to scratch a living. Plas-llyn, to the left of the trees, was the quarry agent's house.

The lowest part of the col, a grassy hollow, marks a change. From here onwards, the rocks become sandstones. They are well-bedded and dip steeply northwest with a strong cleavage. In many places, the beds are parallel, representing sheets of sand laid down during floods, whereas other parts show trough cross-bedding (Fig. 5.3, p. 120) caused by repeated current scouring and redeposition by streams in the delta system.

Keep to the highest parts of the col, crossing whaleback sandstone outcrops produced by the glaciers which flowed west over here. **You pass two tiny lakes at the north end of the col before beginning to bear right and ascending towards Locality 3. The rock is still sandstone underfoot but shortly, you can see the overhanging lower Pitt's Head Tuff of the next locality (Fig. 4.4).**

Showers, balls and blown minds: Locality 3 [5685 4672]

This locality is easy to find because it has a tiny waterfall plunging down into a shallow cave formed by the overhang. You could cool off here if you get overheated by the exciting rocks.

The first thing you notice is that the rock is full of what look like cannonballs. You'll see many more of these as you continue and later, I'll discuss how they formed. In the meantime, see if you can come up with any ideas as to what they are. The questions to ask are: were they erupted as balls? – and if so, how? If you can't imagine any process which could make these as a direct result of an eruption, then could they have formed in the rock after it had been deposited? If so, how?

The rock with the balls is the Pitt's Head Tuff. Above, forming the lower east face of Moel Hebog, the tuff is up to 90 metres thick – the result of one colossal eruption which blasted out from the Llwyd Mawr volcano which was, at the time, several kilometres from the sea. The tuff you see here rests on what was dry land whilst further northeast, it rolled on into the sea.

Figure 4.4: *The Pitt's Head Tuff (PT); S – sandstone, LR – LRTF. All these formations dip quite steeply from right to left (northwest). The sandstone is covered by scree from the PT and LRTF around here, but you see it further on (Locality 4). I've marked Loc. 3 as well as the base and top of the PT.*

The tuff itself is highly characteristic; you can easily recognise it wherever it crops out (as far away as Y Garn, p. 131). You see it best as you **pick your way carefully across the blocky screes which are mostly fairly stable, contouring around and climbing gently towards Locality 4.** Not all the boulders and blocks are Pitt's Head; many come from higher up – the LRTF (which overlies) – with all kinds of tuffs and breccias.

As you negotiate your way along and up, you can see that you are really keeping to the same level in the tuff flow, for ahead and on your left, you see many more outcrops of the cannonballs which become ever more striking. Most of them are about the size of a large cabbage. Above and below the balls, the tuff is full of streaked out fiamme. **The next locality is where you see the best balls of all.**

This rock has balls: The Right Tuffs? ... The Pitt's Heads?: Locality 4 [5682 4704]

Yes, you too can think up your own punning title for these amazing rocks (which could almost be a rock group ... geddit? Sorry!). 'Cannonballs' seems a good way to describe the balls, but some of them have a macabre resemblance to human heads. But what are they really?

The evidence is clear enough if you examine them. The streaky fiamme of the welding foliation continue right on through the balls as if they weren't there at all. The only way you can explain this is that the balls formed after the tuff had accumulated and the welding process was already largely complete: the pumice lumps had already flattened into the disc-shapes (see Box).

Flames and discs: fiamme origins. The term fiamme means 'flame' (Italian). The fiamme you find in welded tuffs often look like candle flames. They started out as blocks or lumps of pumice which, being largely gas bubbles (which is why pumice usually floats although it is rock), is not particularly tough. Imagine what happens to a near- red-hot pumice lump if thousands of tons of overlying ash and pumice are pressing down on it. Like a lump of pastry yielding to your rolling pin, the pumice flattens into a disc like a pancake. The fiamme you can see are 2-dimensional slices through innumerable pumice discs.

Obviously no one can ever directly examine what goes on inside a thick ignimbrite sheet as it cools, if only because none has ever been produced by a volcano since people started to get interested in them. Geologists explain these balls (see Box below) – which at smaller sizes are quite common in welded tuff flows like this – as being due to the trapping of volatile fluids (like water vapour) below the relatively impermeable central strongly welded parts of the flow. These balls are only 3-4 metres above the base. They form, like concretions in sedimentary rocks, by crystallisation from silica-rich fluids around a central core, building up concentric layers of siliceous material. In some exposures here, you can see that the balls do have cores and crude outer shells though much of this fine detail has been messed up by later events (squashing whilst the flow was still hot enough to move slightly, silicification and metamorphism). The cannonballs are an extreme example of nodule growth in welded tuff.

Nodules, balls and crystallisation: geo-marbles. The Pitt's Head cannonballs are particularly large and formed shortly after the huge flow had come to rest. Not all nodules form like this. Some seem to develop at a much later stage due to silica-rich fluids not connected with the original flow. Much of the original material in ignimbrite flows is glassy but glass is unstable. It is non-crystalline but over time, tends to gradually develop crystal structures – it devitrifies (which is why many people are alarmed about vitrification of radioactive waste from nuclear reprocessing). In doing this, extra silica is released into the slowly circulating hydrothermal fluids. This builds up around focal points like crystals or even bedding planes to form nodules. You see similar things in sedimentary rocks (Box, p. 89).

At this locality, you can see (Fig. 4.5) the cannonball layer within the welded tuff and also the base of the tuff where it rests on sandstones of the earlier fan deposits.

Walk on to cross a small fresh-looking scree. This was the site of an aircraft crash many years ago and below on your right are several pieces of wreckage: bits of fuselage and undercarriage. **After the short scree, you come to a patch of juniper bushes.** Something odd has happened here. The rocks ahead where you'd expect to see the Pitt's Head, are now sandstones. Look up to your left above the juniper bushes towards the skyline. There again are the cannonballs, much higher than those behind you.

Figure 4.5: *Pitt's Head Tuff cannonballs forming an obvious band about 3 metres above the base. Above and below are welded tuffs, the lower ones showing columnar joints which formed by contraction as they cooled.*

Scramble up the gully above the juniper bushes to the cannonballs. This is steep but not at all difficult, being mostly grass. As you climb, you notice a large crack at the top of the gully separating the two different cannonball levels. This is, as you'll have quickly guessed, a small fault which has thrown down the rocks (about 20 metres) on your left (west) relative to those on your right.

Continue on to your right below the cannonballs, angling upwards along a grassy bench. You are again at the contact between the sandstones (on your right) and the Pitt's Head Tuff. **Follow this contact until you hit the obvious gravelly Beddgelert path. Turn left to continue the vigorous climb to Moel Hebog.** You cross more cannonballs before the path, some which are the size of pumpkins; some spherical and some oval and some ... (Fig. 4.6).

Starry saxifrages prosper in damp crevices here.

The Beddgelert path works its way through the cannonballs and on up through the main Pitt's Head Tuff, full of fiamme. At one place (on a left branch of the track), the tuff contains more balls, this time no larger than tennis balls, but due to the same process. You may spot another layer with marble-sized balls too. There were actually two Pitt's Head eruptive events, but the upper one (indistinguishable here) never got further north or east than Moel Hebog, presumably because it was impounded in the caldera.

Figure 4.6: *Are Creation 'Scientists' right after all? A human skull in the ancient Pitt's Head Tuff? Perhaps these ancient megacephalics ('big heads' – look at the size compared to Val) were all destroyed in this eruption, an early manifestation of the wrath of god?*

Soon, you notice a change. The Pitt's Head is pale grey-white near its top and then the rock becomes much more broken up and darker grey. This is the beginning of the LRTF. This contact represents quite a long time break for this part of the district remained above sealevel for a long period after the Pitt's Head eruptions. Further north and east, sufficient time passed for over 200 metres of muds, silts and sands to build up on top of the Pitt's Head Tuff, before the main LRTF began to be erupted, but here there's nothing at all; an unconformity. So hundreds of thousands of years or more may be 'missing' as you step from the older tuff to the younger.

As you scramble on up, you quickly realise that the LRTF doesn't look a bit like the Pitt's Head. It has a reddish grey colour and is full of variably sized volcanic chunks without a trace of the eutaxitic welding fabric which you saw throughout the Pitt's Head. In short, it's rather a messy rock.

Quite suddenly, the slope slackens off by two stone piles and you're on the northeast ridge of Moel Hebog. Continue zigzagging up through scree and broken outcrops. Many of the outcrops are well-bedded and have obviously been laid down in shallow water though they're entirely made up of volcanic debris. These are tuffites, deposited here at the edge of the undersea LRTF caldera (p. 99). **Finally make your way over the summit plateau to the trig point and next locality.**

Moel Hebog summit: Locality 5 [5648 4692]

On a clear day, you have a wonderful, all-round view encompassing most of Snowdonia and right out to the end of the Llŷn peninsula. Looking across to Moel-ddu, you can see what looks like a downfold in the rocks east of the anticline I pointed out earlier. This is rocky deceit. It's phoney! (For another example of this sort of geo-fibbing, see p. 230). Some of these structures are indeed traps for the unwary so seeing is deceiving. If you were a geologist, not knowing the structure of the landscape here, you might indeed assume that this 'syncline' was real, but you'd then go and check it – and quickly realise that you had been mistaken.

To the west is the great range of Mynydd Graig Goch, Garnedd-goch and Craig Cwm Silyn. These mountains are almost wholly formed of the Pitt's Head Tuff, for this was the central part of the Pitt's Head caldera. If you could travel back in time some 455 million years, you would be standing on and looking at the eastern flank of a large island. The central part of the island had collapsed due to the great eruptions of Pitt's Head ash flows leaving a steep-walled caldera. But you'd have to turn your gaze to the east to see the next piece of action which started up around Yr Arddu (p. 174). A huge caldera would form, mostly under the sea, almost 15 kilometres across with Moel Hebog at its southwest end and Llanberis Pass at its northeast end. This would become the new theatre for the next volcanic production of which the rock you're standing on was an early player with one of the principal roles.

The rock which forms the summit area here is all LRTF (which I won't say much about here because you'll see it much better on later rambles). The trig point is built on it and you can see outcrops of rhyolitic breccias just 30 metres south, beyond the right-angle bend in the wall. Here you can see lumps of tuff and probable flow folded rhyolite lavas all mixed up together.

To your north is Moel yr Ogof (Fig. 4.7) whose obviously different black rocks herald a new player in the volcanic cast: basalt. You'll see this to perfection at the next two localities. What is more, you can just about make out that these dark rocks are folded into a syncline. Those on the east side dip northwest whilst those in the central part are almost flat-lying and those to the west dip east. You can follow this fold structure via Clogwyn Du'r Arddu (p. 54) to beyond Cwm Idwal (p. 119).

Follow the wall northwest towards Moel yr Ogof. Locality 6 is not far above Bwlch Meillionen at the point where the wall changes direction from north-northwest to northwest.

Figure 4.7: *Moel yr Ogof, annotated to show you the basalt lava flows (B) within the Bedded Pyroclastic Formation. I've marked localities 7 and 8, the latter being a rather odd rhyolite (R). F-F are faults.*

A new basalt player on the stage: Locality 6 [5621 4740]

Here you meet the Bedded Pyroclastic Formation (BPF for short). You are at the contact between the underlying LRTF and the BPF, both dipping north-west. The LRTF is pale grey to white (being rhyolitic, rich in pale minerals) whereas the BPF is dark, being made of basalt lavas and water-lain basaltic tuffites. It tells us of a major phase of basic volcanic activity which followed the LRTF acid phase. Several vents within the great Snowdon caldera spewed out a mixed bag of lavas and tuffs, some of which were rapidly dispersed by waves and currents in the shallow seas. Here and there, small volcanic cones briefly built up above sealevel, before being knocked down or subsiding below the waves once again. Most of the exposures at this locality are tuffs formed of ash, lapilli and blocks which are not bedded (Fig. 4.8), so they haven't been sorted by water action and were probably genuine pyroclastics. They should be quite close to their source volcanic vent about which I'll say more shortly.

Figure 4.8: *Block tuff verging on pillow breccia. For more about pillow breccias, see below. I've outlined some of the larger blocks. Tape recorder for scale.*

> **Why the change?** The differences between the LRTF and the BPF are striking. Why the sudden change from one to the other? What does the change mean? Magma rises up through the Earth's crust, in this case along deep-seated fracture systems. It tends to collect in huge subsurface chambers formed by muscling the host rocks out of the way, doming them upwards or shoving them sideways. Imagine a magma chamber as being like a syringe filled half with oil and half with water. The oil – being lighter – will always separate from the water and float on top. So if you tip your syringe up vertically and gently push in the plunger, oil will 'erupt' from the needle until it's all used up. Then water will erupt. It's much more complicated than that in reality, but basic (basaltic) magma is much denser than acid and so the acid liquid sits on top and erupts first (LRTF). Only then can the basic magma (BPF) start to come out. Basalt is rich in heavy iron-magnesium silicates which give it its dark colour.

What happens when lava erupts below the sea? I can begin to answer this question at the next locality. Some very odd things form and you'll see some wonderful examples both here and on the Idwal ramble.

Drop down to the col of Bwlch Meillionen. About 20 metres before the col, you'll encounter a scrambly section down a large smooth ice-polished surface beside the wall. The surface is covered in fresh glacial striae, covered by soil unti erosion from walkers' boots and rain exposed it. Right below this rock is a large puddle, full of tadpoles in spring. **At the col, a ladder stile**

crosses the wall and this is the return path. You may wish to skip the next two localities though I hope you won't because they're both fascinating.

To continue, take the clear path northwest which zigzags up to a chasm in the rock face ahead. It's pleasanter to make your way up the grassy slope through an easier gully 30 metres to the right of the chasm to emerge onto another col occupied by several tiny lakes (not marked on the OS map). This area is Locality 7.

Pillows, tuffs and breccias: Locality 7 [5596 4760]

The rocks at the top of the gully before the lakes are fascinating. Now and again you spot distinct shapes like pillows and much of the remainder is like some vast irregular jigsaw puzzle with all the pieces slightly moved and not quite fitting together. This rock originated as a lava flow from a submarine volcanic vent but, on contact with the cold seawater, the red hot lava was quenched and then broken by continued lava movement below the insulating skin of the flow.

Pillow lavas only ever form under water – as hot basalt lava oozes out from the front of a moving flow. Because the lava cools very fast, it either chills to form glass which (not being Pyrex) can't stand the temperature stress and shatters into lumps and bits which geologists call hyaloclastite. If you heat up a glass bowl on a stove and then pour cold water into it, the glass will shatter ... so don't try it. The same happened with these lavas. The shattered debris formed a mantle over the slowly moving flows, protecting them to some extent from the chilling. Pressure from within the flow (and remember, these rocks were really hot as basalt lavas are the hottest lavas of all with temperatures of 1000-1250°C) caused lobes of molten rock to extrude like toothpaste out of a tube into the cold water and almost immediately solidify. These were the pillows which you can see hereabouts.

Remarkably, divers have actually been able to watch and film pillow lavas forming. This was in Hawaii where the pahoehoe (Hawaiian name for smooth, ropy lava) flow had entered the Pacific during the Mauna Ulu eruption between 1969 and 1974. The divers could see the flow front, apparently motionless. Suddenly, a rounded lobe of lava glowing red would pop out and chill. This blob would then bud another, and so on and on, each pillow sagging and deforming around its hardened predecessors. What is really extraordinary is that this could be seen at all. You'd expect violent explosions and indeed these can occur ... but not with pillow lavas. If you were to hitch a ride in one of the research submersibles with hulls capable of withstanding the immense pressures of the ocean depths, you'd be able to see that these same types of lavas are probably the commonest in the world. They form along all the active mid-ocean ridges where the seafloor is actually breaking apart and spreading as the continental plates slowly drift away from each other. Until recently, no one had ever seen – or even suspected – this.

When the other type of flow – aa (Hawaiian name for clinkery block lava) – advances into the sea, hyaloclastites tend to form as the whole flow front blasts itself to pieces. Rather than flowing placidly across the seafloor like the pahoehoe, aa tends to build up a sort of delta, creating new land in the process – a land of glass! But what water quenching doesn't smash up, ordinary weathering processes quickly do and the unstable glassy bits break down (devitrify).

As you walk up to the lakelets, the pillows cease and the entire unit is made up of lapilli and ash. At its top, you can begin to see bedding, so obviously the eruption which produced this thick unit had ceased and the sea currents and waves were getting to work rearranging – reworking – the top of the pillow lava, though eruptions nearby probably continued to pepper the surrounding seafloor with volcanic debris: scoria.

From the top of these outcrops, you have a good view back to the previous locality and the now-obvious contact between the LRTF and the BPF. You can trace it from above the forestry to the east and up, paralleling the middle sector of the wall. The BPF forms all the western slopes of Moel Hebog.

The lakelets were scooped by the ice sheets which ground their way right over all these mountains from east to west. A few frogs live here (I heard them croaking whilst I camped here one moonlit night) and many tiny water creatures.

The path from here at first runs close to the wall, but after a short ascent over grass, there's a branch to the right which zigzags its way up through small crags keeping roughly to the centre of the Moel yr Ogof ridge, aiming for the right hand of two gullies on the skyline. This seems to be blocked with large boulders but isn't; the path runs through it. The rocks here are basaltic block, lapilli and ash tuffs like those lower down, with bedding visible in places. At the top of the gully, the beds suddenly become rhyolitic again, but they are probably quite distant from their source unlike the basalts. **The path winds its way to the summit of Moel yr Ogof and Locality 8.**

Moel yr Ogof a volcano? Locality 8 [5569 4785]

Whatever became of Owain Glyndwr's cave (ogof=cave) I don't know. I imagine it was one of the great glacially-tilted blocks which had sufficient space beneath for a man to shelter. The glaciers have been over here as you can see from the various perched blocks not far from the summit.

But what of the rock at the summit? It's nothing like anything you've seen so far today. As you can see, it's made out of large almost white angular blocks (Fig. 4.9), some of which are the size of a TV set and most are larger than fist-size. If you were to look, you'd find that these form an almost circular outcrop about ¼ kilometre across, so it may have been the actual vent which first spewed out the thick basalt flows and tuffs below. We know that rhyolite magma punched up through the older rocks in the caldera during the BPF's formation. Many formed rhyolite domes; others intrusions. This one seems to have burst up through the older basalt volcanic vent.

If this story is true, this is the closest to actually standing at the business end of an old volcano that you're going to come on these rambles. I often find that people, knowing that the rocks of Wales or Lakeland include many that came from volcanoes, rightly ask where the volcano was. As you've already discovered, this is usually not an easy question to answer because, depending on the amount of folding and state of erosion, the volcano may have been 'up in the air' or be still buried under younger rocks.

Figure 4.9: *Rhyolite breccia plugging the vent of the Moel yr Ogof volcano. My tape recorder is in the centre.*

From the summit, you can see Moel Lefn to the north which is a rhyolite intrusion. The mountains which so decoratively adorn the north end of Cwm Pennant are mostly formed of upper Cambrian and lower Ordovician mudstones, siltstones and sandstones (Carnedd y Filiast Grit), strengthened by several intrusions of rhyolite. Behind them is the Mynydd Mawr microgranite (p. 46).

Retrace your steps to the ladder stile at Bwlch Meillionen and cross the wall. The final locality is Moel-hebog copper mine whose open stopes and dumps you can see to the south. If you want to visit it, contour around through a ruined wall towards the main workings.

Moel-hebog Mine: Locality 9 [5596 4716]

The main working of this mine is open but the floor is partly flooded and there's an open shaft. **Beware!** The vein, which trends northwest-southeast and dips steeply southwest, has been stoped out.

> **Taking the best and leaving the rest ...** This is what the miners' technique of stoping is all about. You only removed the vein containing the high grade ore and left everything else. Obviously if the vein was thinner than the width of a miner, he had to take a little more to be able to get into his own workings. Mostly stoping was 'overhand'. You cut an adit level along the vein and then prised, hacked or blasted at the vein in the roof, so that it fell down into the level and could be trucked out. The trick was to take as much as you could without the hanging wall collapsing onto the footwall of the stope. This would have been bad news for the mine and for the unfortunates who were crushed and indeed such collapses weren't uncommon. Usually small sections of vein would be left for support, or stout timber props jammed in. You can see the remains of some of these timbers in this mine where the vein has been stoped out to the surface a few metres above the entrance.

Inside the mine, you hear the sound of falling water because a stream runs in at some higher workings and cascades down the shaft in the floor. In the walls of this shaft and also in the right hand entrance wall, you can see beautiful green malachite, deposited by seepages from copper-rich vein material. The main copper ore was probably chalcopyrite and you can find traces of this on the dumps, along with masses of decaying pyrite. On the whole, the miners were parsimonious about their ore: they wasted none of it. Outside, they broke up the mined vein with hammers and separated out the copper-rich parts, placing it in baskets for transport, probably down to the tramway to the west (which you'll be joining shortly). You'll be unlikely to find any spectacular copper mineral samples here. Minerals you may find include quartz, chlorite, pyrite, sphalerite, galena and chalcopyrite.

Figure 4.10: *Moel yr Ogof and the Moel Hebog syncline. I've sketched on the hinge axis, marked with Xs, and the main beds which pick out the shape of the fold structure. B – basalt lava, R – rhyolite vent (Locality 8).*

The rock which contains the veins is the BPF: lapilli tuffs and lavas, the latter commonly with gas cavities. These gas cavities – vesicles – developed as the lava erupted and released gases which had been dissolved in it. This happens when you open a bottle of fizzy drink. Unlike the drink, some of the bubbles of gas 'froze' in the cooling lava.

From here, you can look north to Moel yr Ogof and the hinge of the Moel Hebog syncline (Fig. 4.10) which I mentioned earlier.

At the bottom of the main tip is a slot-like entrance from which a stream flows. Unlikely though it may seem, you can find starry saxifrages here and violets are common in late spring. **Drop down the tips to follow the stream to a curious rectangular tower structure on one bank.** What this was is anybody's guess. Any ideas? **Cross the stream and broken down wall to rejoin the main walkers' path from Bwlch Meillionen. The path descends to a ladder stile over another wall. Climb over this and continue on down – there's no obvious path for much of this – a little to the north of the Afon Cwm-llefrith to avoid the boggy patches. This is a permissive footpath which is closed once a year on February 1st. A wire fence runs to your left for part of the way. After about 1 kilometre, you pass well to your left a blasted-looking clump of conifers by the stream. A fence runs north from this and there's a gate (sometimes open) and ladder stile (which was not in use when I last passed by in late 1995). Keep on down towards Cwrt Isaf farm. Three hundred metres ahead is a cluster of deciduous trees which marks the old bridge – now unfortunately dismantled – where the tramway crosses the small river gorge. About 30 metres before this, cross the wire fence on your left. A length of barbed wire has been removed so that stepping over is easy. Then you have to hop, skip or jump across the stream. There are three large boulders which make this quite easy though beware of slipping if they're wet.**

After the crossing, join the easy, grassy and level tramway and follow it all the way back to the road near the start of the walk at Tyddyn Mawr.

As you've noticed, most of this large area of shallower hillslope is largely devoid of rock outcrop. It's entirely covered in a variably thick layer of glacial till. The Afon Cwm-llefrith has cut into this somewhat, leaving the largest boulders which it can't move even in the biggest floods. Featureless areas like this, often marshy with patches of soft rushes, are almost always an indication of till deposits. Because they are ill draining, farmers often dig drainage ditches. These seem to have little effect but to open up the land to deep gullying erosion as you'll see as you walk.

The left side of the tramway is also a ditch in some places, to prevent flooding of the track. In spring, this ditch becomes a seething mass of tadpoles.

When you come to a fence with a ladder stile, about 100 metres to the right of the track ahead is a fine *roche moutonée* which was, back in prehistory, used by people as a house platform. You can see why. The rock is the only dry spot is a vast area of bog. **The track curves around to cross a stream by a footbridge (Ceunant y Ddôl) and another ladder stile.** Keep your ears cocked for the bubbling cry of curlews which like these quiet boggy slopes as do larks.

BRY LYNAS 5/1996

Figure 4.11: *Curlew whose lovely plaintive bubbling cry is far less frequently heard than it used to be. It, like the peewit, seems to be suffering from loss of its wetland habitats.*

The tramway loops around a grassy hillside on the left with hawthorn trees (the ruin of Cae bâch is out of sight on its south side). You can theoretically cut off this bend on a path marked in green on the OS map. Don't even try! The path doesn't exist and there's no access with high walls and barbed wire. The tramway is longer but very easy.

The grassy lobe the tramway loops around is probably an old moraine. Many of the boulders dotted about on it are the familiar Pitt's Head Tuff, dragged down from further up the valley by the ice sheets. **A footpath goes off to the right over a ladder stile but you keep on the old tramway as it bends round to the east, becoming rather lost in the rushes in places.**

The OS map marks a 'settlement' and 'hut circle', both of which you can see from the track, though neither is particularly obvious. It does remind us that this area has been inhabited by humankind for many millennia. They probably favoured these slopes which were drier and easier to clear of forest than the lower ground. Also the climate was warmer and drier (Sub-Boreal; see Timescale) 4000 years ago when these peoples moved into this area.

After more stiles and an awkward iron gate above Braich-y-big, be sure to keep straight on (don't follow the track down to the right) on the old tramway. Cross another ladder stile, past a new plantation and a final stile to the road onto which you turn left to walk the short remaining distance to Tyddyn Mawr or the Llyn Cwmystradllyn carpark.

And so ends a long walk with an outstanding sequence of both sedimentary and volcanic rocks. You'll be seeing more of all these players on several later rambles. During the final part of this walk, you were crossing back down through the same sequence, but all of it is buried under the glacial till dumped there by the huge glacier which once ploughed its way southwest from broad Cwm Pennant. But I expect you were rather glad there weren't any more rocks to see. You can have too much of a good thing ... even rocks!

Rocky Ramble 5: Cwm Idwal, Y Garn and Glyder Fawr

How to get to the start of the ramble

You'll find carparks just off the A5 at Ogwen Cottage, near the Youth Hostel [649 604]. Bus No. 65 (Bangor-Bethesda-Llanrwst) stops at Ogwen Cottage. Call D & G for information: 01248 600787.

The ramble: needs, distances and times

The distance is over 12 kilometres, much of which is quite steep climbing. Total climbing is about 1050 metres (3260 feet), nobody's idea of a picnic. The descent of Y Gribin can be tricky if you're scared of heights or downright dangerous in bad weather, but you can shorten your route by coming down the Devil's Kitchen path. You could then complete the second part of the walk (Glyder Fawr; 600 metres of climbing) the following day. OS Outdoor Leisure Map 17.

Introduction

This ramble takes you over some of the most exciting scenery in Snowdonia. Cwm Idwal is justly famous, not only for its beauty but also for its rocks and natural history. You'll see rocks ranging from vast upended beds of tuffs – the Idwal slabs – to jumbled pillow lavas at the top of the Devil's Kitchen (Twll du). The relics of the great Ice Ages are amongst the most well known in Wales, visited on countless field trips by schools. The summits you cross give superb views over to the Snowdon range followed by an exciting descent along Gribin ridge.

Several famous scientists have set foot here, but it was the indomitable Charles Darwin who realised before anyone else that the scenery around him was entirely the work of glaciers. He would have known better than other geologists of his day, most of whom had never seen a glacier. He'd just returned from his epic *'Beagle'* voyage and had seen real glaciers at work in Patagonia. 'It is, I think,' he noted, 'impossible to stand on these mounds and for an instant to doubt that they are ancient moraines ... The three or four linear ridges evidently mark the principal stages in the retreat of the glacier.' He was right, of course, as is now blindingly obvious to us. At that time, this was near heresy and it took another 20 years for British geologists to accept that ice sheets had once covered much of Britain.

The footpath leaves the car parks behind the snack bar and public toilets. At the start is a useful display explaining something of the geology and landscape of the area.

> 300,000 people visit this area every year so please try to ensure that your visit leaves
> as little impact as possible. This is hard to achieve when scrambling up or down steep
> mountain tracks where you inevitably leave your erosional mark. Even so, I think it's
> more important that we should do what little damage our walking causes and so be
> able to see for ourselves these great wonders wrought by nature and time. That way,
> through understanding, we come to care and feel for our wonderful planet and its
> landscapes.

**Almost immediately after you've set off, you come to a pair of ladder
stiles from which, already, you have a wonderful view of Tryfan and Cwm
Idwal.** In the foreground, you'll notice a great jumble of huge boulders and
ice-scraped surfaces, just as if the glaciers melted a few years ago (which, of
course, they did in terms of the vastness of geological time). **Cross the stream
and begin to ascend the broad and well-made cobbled track. To your left
after about 150 metres, you'll notice a series of steep, slabby outcrops of
rock some 30 paces from the track. Head for the top of these – Locality 1.**

Glaciers and ancient sandy deltas: Locality 1 [6515 6021]

The hillocks here are fine examples of *roches moutonées*, planed off on their
east sides by the giant glacier which once ripped and gouged its way down
the Ogwen valley and Nant Ffrancon towards the Irish Sea. The down-mov-
ing ice 'plucked' the west sides of these *roches moutonées* leaving them steep
and rough.

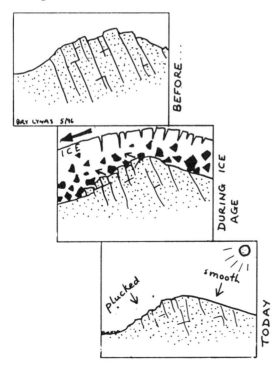

Figure 5.1: *How roches
moutonées form: before,
during and after. A hard
'rib' of rock with steep
joints or bed surfaces is
literally plucked by the ice
as it flows up, over and
down. The upside is
protected by the rock to
the left until that, too, is
plucked. So the rib of
hard rock becomes eroded
both downwards and to
the right. Note how the ice
is full of (black) lumps of
rock which help scour
and groove the rock
underneath. Note too how
crevasses open as the top
of the glacier stretches
and flexes due to the rock
bar underneath. You can
see this in any modern
glacier.*

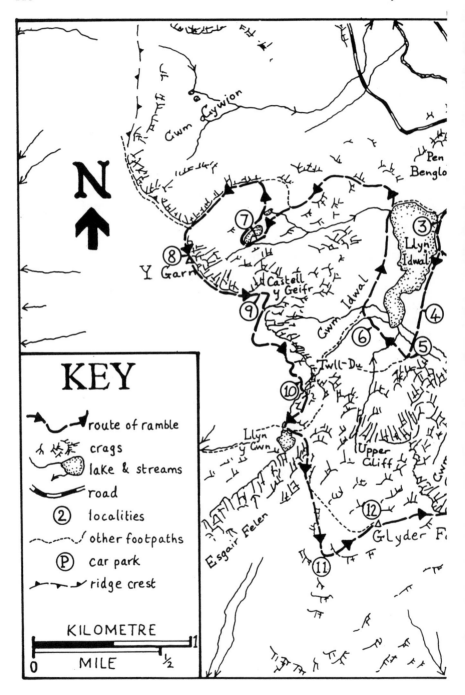

Cwm Cywion

Pen
Benglo

7

3

Llyn
Idwal

8

Y Garn

Castell
y Geifr

Cwm Idwal

9

6

4

5

Twll-Du

10

KEY

route of ramble
crags
lake & streams
road
2   localities
other footpaths
P   car park
ridge crest

Llyn
y Cwn

Upper
Cliff

Cwm

12

Glyder F.

11

Esgair Felen

KILOMETRE

MILE

0   ½   1

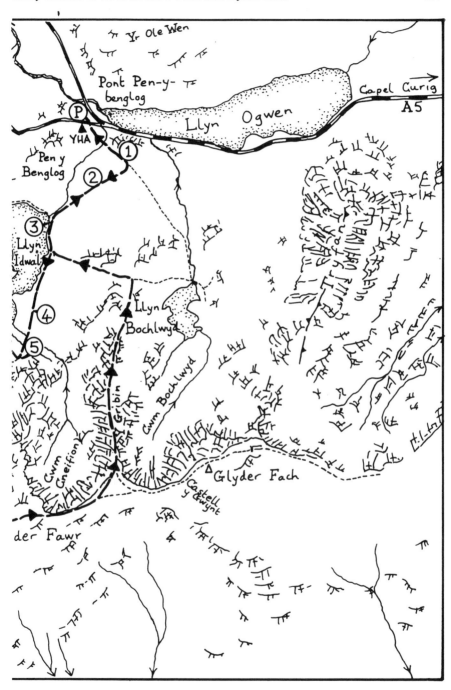

And when this powerful glacier finally decayed, it dropped its load of rocky rubbish everywhere. Naturally, all the finer muds and sand particles have long ago been washed away, but the boulders – left as perched blocks – are all around you.

What do you make of the rock itself? It's dark grey and obviously bedded. The beds have fairly steep dips to the west. The rock is a sandstone and in parts, you can find actual channels where later erosion has cut down into the underlying sands. The channels then filled up with more sand. This, in turn, tells us something about the environment at the time these rocks formed. It was almost certainly a river delta, probably exposed at low tide, cut across by wandering streams, winding their way towards the nearby sea. In younger rocks, you might reasonably expect to find fossils like bits of tree and even footprints of dinosaurs, but these old rocks formed before there had been any serious attempt by life to colonise the land.

Some of the small beds show load casts, where the heavier sediment beds have 'loaded' down into the sloppy wet sand below. You regularly find load casts in sediments that were laid down under water, usually on a small scale like this but sometimes on a much larger scale.

Geologists working near Llynnau Mymbyr (near Capel Curig) found gigantic 'load casts' a few years back. In this instance, a thick and hot ash flow had erupted and flowed into what was then the sea. Against all expectations, this flow simply continued on – almost as if the sea wasn't there, flowing out into deeper water, and still remaining so hot inside that it became a fully welded tuff after it had settled. But this extraordinary deposit had another trick up its sleeve: because it was so much heavier than the wet sediments underneath it, huge masses of it – some tens of metres thick – began to sink down into the stuff below, like great drops of molten wax. Some of these hot blobs of rock sank so far that they separated completely from the parent ash flow above, ending up as separate giant balls of welded tuff within the sediment. And – if you know where to look – you can see these today. One effect of this amazing discovery was to turn one of geology's basic principles on its head. We normally think of the present as being the key to the past. Observing things happening today helps us to understand how rocks formed hundreds of millions of years ago. But until these members of the Capel Curig Volcanic Formation had been exposed for what they were – very odd welded tuffs that had been laid down under the sea – no one believed that ash flows could weld anywhere except on the land. This dogma meant that whenever you found a welded tuff – and there are dozens in Snowdonia – then it had to have formed on land. Now we know that's not true. In fact these tuffs are even odder, for bits of the flow seem to have sputtered away from other parts (a bit like dropping water onto a hotplate) ending up as completely isolated pods of tuff which survey work has turned up in the Nant Ffrancon Group sediments well south of Capel Curig.

From this locality, you can see the great Idwal slabs (Locality 5) below the upper cliff of Glyder Fawr. As you'll see, these are all bed surfaces dipping steeply northwest (about 60°). If you have binoculars (so useful for this sort of thing), you can follow this sequence of slabby beds right into the black chasm of the Devil's Kitchen below the pass of Cneifion Duon. But then what happens to the right of the chasm? Suddenly you realise that the same beds are all dipping at about 50° the other way – to the southeast. What you can see from here is one of the finest examples of a huge downfold – the Idwal syncline (Fig. 5.2) – that you'll see anywhere in the country and you can follow it for many kilometres from Carnedd Dafydd through Clogwyn Du'r Arddu (Ramble 2) to as far south as Moel Hebog (Ramble 4).

Figure 5.2: *The Idwal Syncline, taken in winter. The snow picks out the details rather well. The Idwal slabs form the left edge. Everything is LRTF except the core (incorporating the chasm of Twll Du).*

Also from here, you have a good view down Nant Ffrancon to the north. You can see classic examples of truncated spurs coming off the mountains bordering it on the west side. The glacier ploughing its way down the valley simply ripped off the lower part of the ridges coming down from Foel Goch, Mynydd Perfedd and Carnedd y Filiast. It did so much damage in Nant Ffrancon because the underlying rocks are relatively soft; most are siltstones laid down before the first of the massive outbursts of volcanicity (the Llewelyn Volcanic Group) which form the steep rise up from Nant Ffrancon to Ogwen Cottage.

Finally, if you look at the spur from Carnedd y Filiast, you can see that this is made of some pale rock. If you could see it closer (binoculars again), you'd notice that it was – like the Idwal slabs – made up of huge, steeply dipping beds. And if you could see even closer, you'd see that these beds are covered in a whole series of enormous ripples. This is the older and very distinctive sandstone, the Carnedd y Filiast Grit you saw on Ramble 2.

Return to the main cobbled track. As it begins to curve round, you walk

through very stony ground – moraine – and a couple of paces off the track, half way around the curve, is a beautiful erratic boulder.

Figure 5.3: *Trough cross-bedding in sandstone. The glaciers have inconveniently left this boulder upside down. Binoculars for scale.*

Have a quick look at this wonderful example of current bedding, telling its own story of shallow water, currents and trough fills. One interesting point – had you noticed? – this boulder is upside down. How do I know that? Turn the book (and the figure) upside down and you'll see what I mean. Now you can see how shallow troughs have become filled with sands – and then had their upper parts stripped away by more currents – until the next trough became filled. Logical, isn't it? And useful too to geologists because such common sedimentary structures provide us with way-up criteria. If you find these in beds of sediment, you can tell if the rocks have been turned upside down. And there are plenty of places in Wales where the rocks have been folded so strongly that they *are* upside down. Way-up criteria help us sort out the details of such complex fold structures.

Continue along the track, crossing a stream. In front, you can see the terminal moraine ridge of the glacier which scoured out the hollow occupied by Llyn Idwal. The *roches moutonées* to the right of the path are again covered in perched blocks. You'll see a particularly fine block perched on the right just as you cross a tiny stream. This is Locality 2.

First tuffs: Locality 2 [6496 6004]

Perched blocks perch on the tuffs, parts of which contain tiny broken bits of glassy bubble called shards. The tuff here is full of feldspar chips and there's no sign of bedding – quite a change from Locality 1 sandstones. For here we're into the Lower Rhyolitic Tuff Formation (LRTF) which you've met before. An earlier episode of volcanic eruptions gave rise to the Llewelyn Volcanic Group (including the Capel Curig Volcanics), but this erupted from centres well to the northeast and now forms much of the Carneddau.

Walk on up to the ladder stile. There before you is one of the finest sights in Wales: Cwm Idwal and its lake, surrounded on three sides by mountains. The Countryside Council for Wales has placed a little notice here, politely welcoming you to Cwm Idwal Nature Reserve. **There's one particularly large erratic boulder some 30 metres to the left from the stile which is a fine place to sit and think about the grandeur and how what you see now came to be as it is. This is the next locality.**

Cwm Idwal: Locality 3 [6469 5978]

Why is this cwm here? Almost every schoolkid knows that places like these have been created by glaciers, for Cwm Idwal is a perfect example of a large glacial cirque. It was created by the rotational movement of the ice as it continually built up right under Glyder Fawr and Y Garn. The sheer weight of the build up forced it to flow over – and gouge and grind – the rocks below, dragging with it any rocks that had fallen onto the ice or been pulled into it. It was these 'chunks' of rock (one of which is the whopper right behind you) which did the grinding; not the ice.

Hop into your Time Machine and set the dials for about 15,000 years ago. Pull the levers and watch out! Suddenly, right in front of you – instead of Cwm Idwal (which hadn't quite finished being made and certainly hadn't been named, for there were no humans around here then) – there's a huge glacier. You can see the blue of the ice in the crevasses and caves that penetrate it, and its surface is laden with boulders and rock of all shapes and sizes. It's a warm day in summer and the ice is melting fast. Piles of ice and rock slurry teeter and then fall, sliding down the steep ice snout to pile up as part of the moraine you're sitting on. Grey-coloured water, laden with rock flour, surges from an ice cave right in front of you. The surging of the waters is overwhelmed suddenly by a roar: a great slice of ice above the cave collapses, thundering down into the river and smashing up into big blocks of ice as it does so. After a minute or so, all is relatively quiet again though the river bobs and surges with masses of floating ice. Further away, another roar warns of the start of an ice avalanche from the higher slopes of Glyder Fawr. Blocks of ice peel off from the slopes high above the hidden Idwal slabs, to smash themselves to icy smithereens far below. A great fog of smashed ice particles gradually drifts away in the gentle breeze. Can you imagine this? For that is more or less how it was as the climate warmed and the glaciers beat an almost-final retreat.

Almost final? The icy grip wasn't quite done ... and for all we know, still isn't. Advance your time machine a couple of thousand years. This is the warm period glaciologists call the Allerød (see Timescale). The ice is gone completely and the mountains are more or less as you see them now. Move forward to about 12,500 years ago. Look! The snow and ice are back. Another glacier is forming in Cwm Idwal. Advance another thousand years and the ice is melting fast, leaving the beautiful fresh moraines you'll walk through in a few minutes (Locality 4), and giving Llyn Idwal its 'throat'.

Now back to the present. Remember that what you have just visualised has happened many times here. We've just looked at the last of the glaciers, but the Ice Ages of the Pleistocene came and went for at least 2 million years. And the world had started to cool millions of years before that. That's why I said earlier that we really don't know if the ice ages are finished, or if another one will start in 10, 50 or 500 years. What we *do* know is that relapse into cold periods could happen astonishingly fast – in a matter of a decade or so. Perhaps even more alarming is that we know that the reverse can happen too. Earth's climate seems not to do anything gradually. It prefers to flip from one state to another due to changing patterns of ocean currents – and right now, we know they are changing. The great tropical current in the East Pacific, known as El Niño (or ENSO, El Niño Southern Oscillation), is behaving very oddly and this giant upwelling current ordains the weather in the tropics throughout the world. Now we know that there are similar currents in the Indian and Atlantic oceans. At present, we just don't know what these changes mean, but they certainly do mean that the world's climate is altering. And any alteration is likely to be bad for humans ...

The terminal moraine that you saw forming during your imagined time travel forms a dam which is the reason Llyn Idwal exists. Not all lakes formed by glaciers are impounded by moraines; Llyn Ogwen is held by the rock step at Pont Pen y Benglog that the glaciers couldn't shift. **Walk on round the lake on its east side.** As you walk, look up towards its south end and the great hummocks of the last terminal moraine formed during the Younger Dryas cold snap (which only lasted a millennium). Dead ahead you can see the Idwal slabs and higher above is the Nameless Cwm, Cwm Cneifion.

In 1957, patches of ground were fenced off just to see what would happen if the nibbling of sheep ceased. You can see that the tussock grass is much longer and a few clumps of heather have grown. Probably, trees like rowan will appear in the years to come.

Shortly, the path runs through the Younger Dryas moraine hummocks.

The Great Cold Snap: Locality 4 [6464 5925]

As you stand amongst these wonderfully fresh moraine hummocks, free your imagination again (as Charles Darwin did over 150 years ago), this time to see before you a much smaller glacier about 12,000 years ago. Now just the upper part of Cwm Idwal is ice-bound, including Cwm Cneifion and the Idwal slabs. If you come here in the winter or early spring, whilst there's snow about, it's much easier to imagine. Quite large cornices of snow remain at Cneifion Duon, south of Castell y Geifr, and high above the Idwal slabs. These build up because of back eddies and turbulence from the prevailing westerlies which whisk snow off the exposed western slopes of the mountains and re-deposit it in the heads of the northeast-facing cwms. This is part of the reason most of the cwms in Snowdonia do face northeast. The other reason is simply that this is the direction which receives the least sunshine, so the snow remains in shadow for almost the whole day during the shorter days of winter.

Back to the small glacier snout. This build-up of ice lasted only about a thousand years and ended as abruptly as it started some 11,500 years ago. The ice that had been adding a final polish to the Idwal slabs beneath it, finally melted fast, leaving its terminal moraines which represents the furthest it extended out into Cwm Idwal.

It's quite interesting to try and visualise how an ice sheet moves, both advancing and retreating simultaneously. This apparent contradiction first dawned on me when I visited the Franz Josef Glacier (Fig. 5.4) in southwest New Zealand some years ago. As we all know, a glacier isn't static; it's moving continuously downhill driven, like many geological processes, by gravity. If that was all there was to it, then all the world's glaciers would reach the sea. Some do, of course, in Greenland and the Antarctic where they promptly float and break off into icebergs. But the Franz Josef Glacier doesn't, although it's not far from the sea. Why should this be? The reason – obvious, you say – is simply that as the ice tongue gets lower down the mountain, the air temperature increases. The converse is, of course, true and important for all of us who climb mountains and is the reason for the warnings about taking warm clothing when intending to spend time high up. Air temperature decreases by around 0.65°C for every 100 metres you ascend. So by the time the glacier has descended 1500 metres or so, the temperature has soared by around 10°C. So the ice melts ... What you see is an apparently static snout of ice, gushing water from its subglacial streams. What's happening, too slowly for our eyes to register, is that the ice is in a state of dynamic equilibrium: as fast as it moves down the valley, it melts. When this sort of apparent stasis occurs, the glacier dumps big piles of moraine, its terminal moraine. This is what happened here during the Younger Dryas cold snap.

You can see the other part of this fresh moraine on the opposite shore of the lake and, later, you'll walk through it. As the ice continued to melt, retreating ever higher up the mountain slopes, vast quantities of water became unlocked and began the job of washing away much of the glacial rubbish. Some was too heavy to move far – look at the size of the boulders around here – so the gushing torrents built up alluvial cones. Unlike the glaciers, the processes that build these cones are still operating as flood waters sluice away moraine and scree from higher up the mountain. There's a fine example dead ahead, built by the streams draining from Twll Du. This cone is slowly filling the south end of the lake.

Look up to the Devil's Kitchen and you'll see a dramatic rock fall. The main walking path up to Llyn y Cŵn wends its way through this. The fall, certainly after the glaciers, is probably thousands of years old.

Continue on to the Idwal slabs, crossing a couple of streams as you do. Climb the rocky track towards the slabs. Head for the lowest part of these enormous slabby outcrops.

Figure 5.4: *Franz Josef Glacier, New Zealand Alps. I took this photo in 1975. The glacier has since advanced. Note the meltwater gushing out from the subglacial tunnel at the glacier snout. The material to the right and left is moraine-covered decaying stagnant ice.*

The famous Idwal slabs: Locality 5 [645 590]

These are tilted bedding planes, and although normally partly obscured by climbers – for this is one of Snowdonia's most famous easier climbs – you can take a look at them along the bottom. No climbing skills needed! These thick beds are all ash flow tuffs of the LRTF. They are pale grey with many feldspar crystals. They have a slight foliation and you can see a few large cavities up to the size of an orange that must have been bigger but softer lumps, now weathered away by erosion. In places, quartz veins run parallel to the beds; in others, they intersect in complex networks.

If you walk up the slope (towards Twll Du) for about 50 metres, you find that the rocks are much better bedded: volcaniclastic sandstones with large oval holes in them. Some of these holes reach the size of a TV set, though most are rugby- or tennis-ball-sized. You don't have to climb up to look at them for there are plenty of fallen blocks below which contain them. They're made of a sort of dark brown soft stuff that you can dig out with a knife blade. Probably they once contained calcite which rapidly and readily dissolves out leaving a brown insoluble residue. What they were originally is more uncertain. They seem to take little account of the bedding and so probably formed as concretions after the beds had been laid down. This is not uncommon though it can be confusing.

Between the massive tuffs of the main Idwal slabs and the upper bedded part is a prominent bed of broken up material that has been picked out by erosion, forming a notch which runs right up to the skyline, and over which the bedded tuffs hang. The notch is a mudstone interlude between the primary LRTF below – the direct result of the eruption – and the overlying sandstones (which are tuffites, being made mostly of volcanic debris). These sandstones were eroded by wave action from the top of the older tuffs and redeposited – reworked. Studies of these beds tell us that they built up here as mass flows and turbidites in water at least 100 metres deep. They must have been eroded from the shallower north caldera rim (about where Llanberis Pass is today). The primary LRTF here was a part of the eruption which burst out to the north and east of the great Snowdon caldera: they are outflow tuffs.

Now you have a choice of routes. The ramble continues on around Llyn Idwal but you can, if you wish, miss out the Y Garn sector and head straight up to Locality 10 above the Devil's Kitchen, Twll Du. Just follow the track up into the head of the cwm where it meets another and makes its scrambly way up to Llyn y Cŵn. Otherwise, continue slightly down towards Castell y Geifr, across the lower part of the active alluvial cone you saw from Locality 4. You can tell that the cone is active because parts of it are not covered in vegetation yet. Once a cone, or a scree, ceases to build up, plants quickly colonise the new land. Most of Snowdonia's screes are now so covered so that you scarcely notice them.

Because the alluvial cone material is quite fresh, the cobbles and boulders within it are clean and unaffected by weathering. This makes it a very good place to look and see what sort of rocks there are higher up in the headwaters

– and mostly inaccessible. I've found various sorts of sandstones, muddy sediments and, of course, tuffs which vary from dark grey to white in colour, and from coarse to fine in clast size. Some are so fine that they're like flint. Others are definite welded tuffs. Some are well bedded and others are not. So there's quite a mix here.

As you start to cross over the broad green alluvial cone of the main stream that descends from high above, you should notice something happening to the rocks on your left as you walk: At first, they're dipping steeply northwest, but once you're two thirds of the way across the cone, they're dipping in the opposite direction. You have just crossed the axis of the Idwal Syncline.

The Idwal Syncline and some holey rocks: Locality 6 [6424 5914]

By the time you reach the outcrops just after the cone finishes completely

– four little crags on your left (just before another stream) – then the rocks dip southeast. If you look up to Twll Du, you can see the same change has occurred up there too. It's worth climbing up around the edge of these small crags which are most odd-looking rocks indeed. They have rows of elliptical holes along parts of the bedding, for these – if you examine them closely – are tuffites and the holes (like those you just saw back at Locality 5) must have been calcite that has now dissolved away completely. As before, these nodules (concretions) could have formed in one of two ways: when the particles of volcanic ash were settling out on the sea bed or later.

Figure 5.5: *Curious holey rocks at Locality 6.*

> **Diagenesis** is the name geologists use to indicate chemical changes which occur as soft, watery sediments become rock. Calcium carbonate, the compound from which calcite is made, is highly mobile. It can be both dissolved by or deposited from water moving through rocks or sediments, depending on how acid the water is at the time. (If you doubt that calcite dissolves easily in weak acid, try putting some vinegar on bits of limestone or chalk ... see how they fizz!). Nodules commonly form in certain sediments *after* they've been laid down, when calcite precipitates around some kind of a nucleus. The nucleus can be almost anything, though in younger rocks it's often a fossil shell.

In these same outcrops, you can see a fairly strong cleavage (also in Fig. 5.5 where it is almost perpendicular to the bedding planes, dipping from upper left to lower right). And there's more! ... If you look carefully around, you'll find that some of the beds have been cut out by eroding currents, and then covered over with younger beds, filling troughs cut into the older beds.

From the top of this locality, you have a fine view to the wonderfully fresh Younger Dryas moraines back at Locality 4 and along the west side of the lake, with the main walking track (which you'll shortly join) running along the base of a great dyke-like mass of glacial debris, forming a lateral moraine. **Now cross the stream and turn right onto the main walking track to continue on north, along the west side of Llyn Idwal.** I once saw what I think was a red-breasted merganser, a fish-eating diving duck, swimming on the lake near here.

Shortly, you leave the fresh moraines behind, dropping down to the lake shore and crossing the stream that descends from Llyn Clyd. This stream has cut itself a small ravine since the glaciers melted. **Now Y Garn begins to come into view again, towering high above the cwm of Llyn Clyd (Locality 7).** Watch out for wheatears for they love this sort of rocky grassland. Ahead you can see the low wall of the older moraine (which we considered at Locality 3) that impounds Llyn Idwal itself. **After the bridge, the track runs along a pebbly beach, but you bear off left towards another fenced enclosure on the skyline to join the track up to Llyn Clyd. From the low col that you shortly reach – at the point where you go through a dry stone wall – is a good viewpoint before starting the stiff climb.**

Looking northeast down Nant Ffrancon, you can see the boggy floor of the valley – once occupied by a lake – and the great screes from Braich Ty Du (Carnedd Dafydd) and truncated spurs from Foel-goch, Mynydd Perfedd and Carnedd y Filiast. Beyond are the purple slate tips from the huge Penrhyn Quarries at Bethesda. Pen yr Ole Wen is now very clearly made up of steeply dipping beds (sandstones) in a thick sequence all dipping southeast. Further round to the right is Llyn Ogwen, Tryfan, Y Gribin and Glyder Fawr ridge.

After a long slogging climb, suddenly you find yourself in the entrance to Cwm Clyd, Locality 7. If you feel pushed for time, you might want to skip this.

Cwm Clyd, the secret cwm: Locality 7 [635 597]

This is a delightful little cwm, not visible from anywhere lower down, guarding its two small lakes from casual gaze. Here, as you'd expect, you'll find some fresh terminal moraines from the Younger Dryas cold period. Above, Y Garn's formidable precipices loom, reminding you that you've a good deal of climbing yet. At the northeast end of the cwm, there's quite a bit of sphagnum bog. In April, the small pools here are filled with masses of frog spawn.

You can easily walk all the way around these two lakes and this locality is centred on the group of outcrops which form the southeast rim of the larger (southern) lake. The rocks here are strongly cleaved tuffs, in which the beds are fairly thick with distinct bands of lentil-sized volcanic fragments (clasts).

Fossils to find for the adventurous ... or foolhardy? You can head due west, straight up the scree and gullies which bring you out just north of Y Garn summit. I did this once. It wasn't at all easy and I can't recommend it except to say that you may find fossil shells (brachiopods of orthid type) if you keep your eyes peeled. I found several about the size of my thumb nail, rusty red in colour. These occur in the sandstone beds (part of the Cwm Eigiau Formation), some of which form the rib-like outcrops above the scree, and are the exact equivalents of the sandstones you saw at Locality 6, Ramble 1 and between localities 2 and 3, Ramble 4. The presence of these shells indicates shallow sea, probably offshore sandbars.

In all the outcrops visible in this cwm, the beds dip consistently at around 50° southeast so they should get older the further northwest you go (they do!). But as you now know, the beds on the other side of the Idwal Syncline become older to the southeast (*they* dip northwest, remember).

An odd feature of the lake here is that at the head of the cwm, the main stream from the back of the cwm doesn't even run into the lake; the lake outlet joins it instead.

Continuing on around the lake, you'll notice that the west edge – above which the bergschrund crevasse would have been – still goes deep very quickly; you can't see the bottom after a few metres. You could dive quite safely off some of the rocks along the shore here. Want to try it?

The next part of the climb is quite stiff again but because you're climbing the spine of the ridge, you have fantastic views all the time. You can angle up to the left slightly to meet the track again – you don't have to walk back to where you started into Cwm Clyd. This ridge is an arête – a knife-edge ridge – typical of more vigorously glaciated mountains. Cwm Cywion on the north side has a few small lakelets too. The ridge steepens towards the top with the strongly cleaved mudstones smashed up by the relentless freezing and thawing of these exposed slopes.

Night on a bare mountain with spectres: If you come up here in spring, you'll see that Y Garn always collects itself some quite impressive snow cornices which remind you poignantly of how things used to be here just 11 millennia or so ago. The flat top of one of these provided me with a convenient sheltered campsite one night when I was researching this ramble. The snow also meant I had a water supply. My reward for putting up with the inevitable vicissitudes of this icy eyrie was to have the sun rising to the left of Tryfan followed by a series of the best Brocken spectres I've seen in Wales as the sun cast my rainbow-girt shadow onto the shreds of cloud which kept forming below the west side of the summit in the stiff (bloody freezing!- my tent was coated in ice) easterly wind.

Finally, you reach the summit area and the next locality (Fig. 5.6).

Figure 5.6: *Campsite on Y Garn summit, April 1995. I have been a great deal colder camping in the Andes ... at 4,500 metres!*

Y Garn summit; views, marbles and structures: Locality 8 [631 596]

The summit offers you views in all directions but particularly striking is your first view of the Snowdon range and lower Llanberis Pass.

Apart from the spectacular nature of the grand mountains all around, you can see several striking structures from here. The northeastern face of the Snowdon range has, as you'd expect, been severely damaged by destructive glaciers, Cwm Glas being a perfect example of a Younger Dryas cwm. Further to the right (Fig. 5.7), you can see the continuation of the Idwal Syncline where it runs through Llechog ridge above Cwm Glas Bach, continuing on into Clogwyn Du'r Arddu behind. Further to the right (you may care to walk a little to the southwest down the summit dome to view this more completely), you can see the steep craggy sides of lower Llanberis Pass (Fig. 5.8).

Figure 5.7: *Early morning view of Snowdon (Yr Wyddfa just visible) with Cwm Glas a particularly prominent 'bite' out of Garnedd Ugain. In the right middle distance, you can see the continuation of the great Idwal Syncline downfold (see text). BP – Bedded Pyroclastic Formation, LR – LRTF, R – rhyolite intrusions (often complicated mix-up with LRTF), M – moraines.*

Further still is the continuation of the same fold at Clogwyn Du'r Arddu (Ramble 2) which has a tiny central core of BPF. To the right of the series of slate quarries is a great sandstone bed (the Graianog Sandstone, lowest of the Ordovician formations in this part of Snowdonia) which runs straight up the side of the pass and, almost unbelievably, flips over at the top to form a tight upright anticline (an isocline, from the Greek *isos* meaning 'equal', because it has parallel limbs, quite unlike the broad and open Idwal Syncline; p. 119). You can see more bits of the actual hinge (or core or closure) of this fold just after the bend in the Afon Nant Peris.. Further to the right, you'll notice thick beds of Bronllwyd Grit (of the older Cambrian) forming Clogwyn Mawr. This looks like – and is – another anticline. But where's the syncline which there must be between the two? The answer seems to be that several large faults cut through the sequence between the Graianog Sandstone and the much older Bronllwyd Grit. Because these faults run parallel to the strike of the beds (so that geologists often call them 'strike faults'), they are very difficult to detect, but here there can be no doubt they exist because a goodly chunk of the sequence of formations has disappeared in this Llanberis Pass sector. You see nothing of this on Ramble 2 though the rocks involved are actually underfoot.

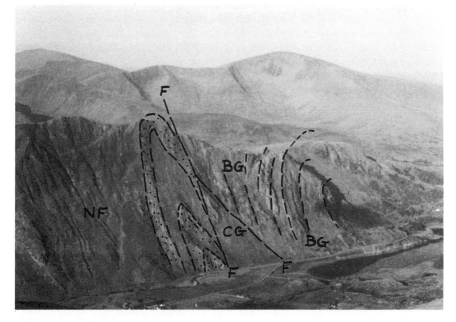

Figure 5.8: *Lower Llanberis Pass and Llyn Peris. You can make out the near-vertical sandstones of the Cambrian and Lower Ordovician, complicated by a 'tight' anticline (isocline) with parts of the fold limbs removed – sheared-out – by large faults (F-F); dotted beds – Graianog Sandstone; CG – Carnedd y Filiast Grit, BG – Bronllwyd Grit, NF – Nant Ffrancon Group*

If you have binoculars, look at Carnedd y Filiast, the farthest of the three mountains running northwest from Y Garn. A wall runs up from the west side to the flat summit. Where this stops, you can see a great grey expanse of rock covered in ripples (which incline gently from right to left) on an enormous bedding surface: the one I mentioned back at Locality 1. These are about the best display of fossil ripples anywhere.

Between Mynydd Perfedd and Elidir Fawr lies a large upland (cwm glacier) lake: Marchlyn Mawr. This now functions as the upper storage reservoir for the Dinorwig pumped storage hydroelectric station at Llanberis. Llyn Peris acts as the lower reservoir and so the Afon Nant Peris which used to flow into it from Nant Peris is now diverted through a tunnel to run out directly into Llyn Padarn.

Do you recognise the streaky and knobbly rocks forming the summit of Y Garn? It's the Pitt's Head Tuff again (p. 52 and 101), but here quite thin because it is some distance from its source. It is almost white and certainly rhyolitic. Parts have strong banding whilst others are nodular (p. 102). About 20 metres from the summit on its southeast side, the Pitt's Head is quite striking, looking like a pile of rather badly-made jumbo marbles.

Below to the southeast is the prominent rocky ridge of Castell y Geifr. This is the next locality. The Pitt's Head Tuff is overlain just east of Y Garn summit by the same sandstone that you saw at Locality 1. Slabs of this litter the slope. You could (if you were a raven) follow these rock units, including the Pitt's Head Tuff from the summit area of Y Garn as they run right down to the *roches moutonées* at the outlet of Llyn Ogwen. Then they climb again to form the 'nose' of the Pen yr Ole Wen ridge through which the Idwal Syncline axis runs, before dying out in the complex volcanic sequence over Carnedd Dafydd.

Look down to the broad flat marshy area at the top of the Devil's Kitchen (Cneifion Duon). This is very clearly a valley where glaciers have crossed, perhaps repeatedly, from the Ogwen to the Llanberis side – or vice versa. Glaciologists believe the ice moved from the south. What do you think? This is an example of glacial diffluence. The lower outcrops are all ice-smoothed whaleback features, whereas higher up the mountainsides are much steeper.

Descend now towards the Castell y Geifr ridge and walk out a little way along it (or skip it and continue on to Locality 10). It's worth the slight extra walk because you can contour round to rejoin the main track.

Castell y Geifr: Locality 9 [6350 5938]

The outcrops here have been ravaged by periglacial weathering. The freezing and thawing of water has opened out the cleavage planes like the pages of a book whose 'pages' litter the ground. Some of the ground itself seems to have landslipped into Cwm Clyd. All the loose rock has formed great screes. The beds are all LRTF tuffs with feldspar crystals, ash-sized particles and a few lapilli up to the size of a walnut. You'll probably notice quite a few matchbox-sized mudstone lumps scattered about. If you go right to the end, you have a wonderful view into the head of Cwm Idwal (Fig. 5.9) and the system of terminal moraines that you walked through earlier. You can also see clearly the lateral moraine on this side of the lake and three on the other side, representing short-lived static periods between bouts of rapid melting of the Younger Dryas glacier.

Now contour on round towards Locality 10. Cross the remains of a wall and rejoin the main walking track to cross a fence at a ladder stile. But don't continue on this track which goes directly to Llyn y Cŵn. Turn left and make your way through all the whaleback features towards Twll Du (literally Black Hole). The syncline axis must run through about there. Furthermore, the rocks change dramatically. And is if that wasn't enough, this is a good place to listen to the trilling songs of both meadow pipits and larks on a fine spring or summer's day.

Figure 5.9: *Younger Dryas ('Darwin's') moraines in upper Cwm Idwal. I've dotted the ridge crests or edges to emphasise them and marked Localities 4 and 6 and the alluvial cone at the lake head.*

Twll Du, Cneifion Duon and undersea eruptions: Locality 10 [638 588]

Whilst this fascinating area of outcrops has its centre at the head of Twll Du (the great black chasm), I suggest you to wander about here and see what you can find. The rocks are fabulous and repay a little time spent on them.

Remember that you're still walking up the sequence – up in Time – because the beds are, for the moment, all dipping southeast. The first rocks you see are dark-coloured tuffs with a red tinge reminiscent of many dolerites. This hints at their basic character because, like dolerites, they come from chemically similar magmas.

Closer to Twll Du, the rocks become a jumbled chaos. What do you make of this? You should find more bedded tuffs within this chaos, but mostly there's no sign of any order at all.

If you look around, you should find plenty of fresh rock surfaces not covered in lichen which show what it's like inside. The matrix is an even, fine grained grey material with loads of plagioclase crystals which, being slightly more resistant, stick out proud of the surface. Some of these crystals are well shaped and others are less so. Some may be gas cavity fills – secondary minerals that crystallise from circulating fluids as the rocks cooled. Many of the exposures show vaguely rounded pillow-like structures; others are just a smashed up mess which is now rock. Here and there, bits of order appear again – tuff beds – which show that whatever volcanic process was producing these rocks involved some ash eruptions where the ash was laid down in water and was sorted to form the bedding you can see. These beds give us the odd clue we need as to our whereabouts in the Idwal Syncline. As you'll discover, the actual hinge of the fold must be around about Twll Du itself for once you go further southeast, you begin to find beds dipping northwest again.

As for the rock, look at those on the southeast side of the stream just before it cascades down into the black chasm. Here are fantastic outcrops of crude blobby pillow shapes, for these rocks are genuine pillow lavas (Fig. 5.10). At the top of the gully, you'll find outcrops of a superb coarse lapilli tuff, surrounded by the pillowed lavas (p. 108). This area is dramatic. Don't miss it!

There's a small path which runs out along the southeast side of Twll Du chasm, bringing you to a wonderful viewpoint overlooking the whole of Cwm Idwal.

Now make your way back to the main paths at Llyn y Cŵn, walking up close to the stream which runs down into Twll Du. About halfway, you become aware of a very straight grassy embankment forming the skyline to the southwest along which runs the track you left after the ladder stile. This is another moraine. **Shortly you emerge at Llyn y Cŵn and turn left onto the track from Cwm Idwal.** The lake has, at its back, a beautiful alluvial cone which is gradually filling it in.

Now you have the option of returning down to Cwm Idwal or of continuing on up the steep gully to Glyder Fawr. I should warn you at this point that the descent along Y Gribin is not for the nervous. Nor should you venture on this next sector if the weather is threatening or it's late in the day. Route-finding can be difficult in cloud. Y Gribin is steep and you'll need to be quite careful, especially if the rocks are wet. It is, however, a popular and well-used route and my experience is that people rarely come to grief on such ground because they know perfectly well that they have to take extra care. Most accidents seem to occur when people are not taking care, on the final part of a walk when the difficulties are over. That's when you trip and fall flat and break a rib (and feel damned stupid in doing so. I speak from experience!).

If you choose to return to Cwm Idwal, the path is quite exciting. The steeper parts have been built into slabby steps (lethal in icy weather!). At first, you walk down large bedding planes and you should see good ripple marks: oscillation ripples due to the rocking motion of passing waves over the sandy shallow seabed. Great crags of the BPF loom to your left as you approach the bottom of Twll Du chasm – which you can walk up into: very impressive. **Then you make your way down through the rock avalanche which fell off from the BPF cliffs and take either the right or left track, depending on which side of Llyn Idwal you prefer.** Some of the landslip boulders rolled almost to the lake.

Figure 5.10: *Twll Du chasm, pillow lavas and Cwm Idwal below.*

To continue the ramble, you turn right just after Llyn Cŵn and begin an obvious ascent towards a gully. Remember that you've now crossed the syncline and so the beds are all dipping northwest which means that as you walk up Glyder Fawr, you're walking down in time, into progressively older rocks. At the bottom of the gully, the rock changes from the dark coloured basic lavas which you saw so clearly around Locality 10, back to the paler acid tuffs of the LRTF. You can see that all these beds are dipping quite steeply northwest as you enter the gully. **After a short climb, the gully forks. Follow the track up the right fork.** Just before the fork is a large boulder which is well worth looking at: it appears to be tuff cut across by pipes of fragmented material produced by superheated steam blasting its way up through the hot tuffs which, like the later basalt lavas, were erupted below the sea. Such pipes (really tiny eruptive vents) and the pulverised material they contain are not uncommon in volcanic rocks where heat and water were involved. You can see other similar examples in the outcrops to the left of the gully.

On now up the scree-filled gully. At the top, as the slope slackens somewhat, there's a noticeable change to white-weathering rhyolites. The gully is roughly parallel to the dip so that the rocks you started with at the bottom are more or less the same at the top. This is a good place to take a breather and look back down to the BPF around Locality 10. Now you have a near-aerial view and you can indeed make out the general sequence of dipping beds. The beds on the southeast side of the syncline – whose hinge line runs southwest from Twll Du – look subtly different to those on the other side (northwest). This is because those on the near side have scarp features facing you whereas those on the northwest side show only their dip slopes. This gives an apparent difference in colour which makes it quite clear where the fold runs. The hinge axis continues on (hidden by glacial deposits) down Cwm Cneifio.

If the white-weathering rocks underfoot here look familiar, they should! These are the same rocks as those which form the western side of Y Garn and Castell y Geifr – the other limb of the great downfold you've now crossed over.

There is no law which says you must stick to the main walking track, worn by the passage of thousands of booted feet. If the weather is fair and you have time, you can branch off to the right somewhat to head more or less due south onto the western shoulder of Glyder Fawr summit ridge. (Otherwise, continue on the track to the summit and Locality 12.) As you walk, the view across to Snowdon becomes better and better. Increasingly now underfoot, you see a white-weathering pale grey rock which weathers into small pinnacles and columnar chunks all broken up by frost action (for this area is over 900 metres above sealevel). It's often full of vesicles and so was obviously a rhyolite lava or intrusion and parts show complex flow folds. Survey shows that it is an intrusive rhyolite. **Once you arrive on the crest of the ridge, you're at Locality 11.**

Glyder Fawr west and lapilli tuffs: Locality 11 [6392 5778]

At this locality, you should find some large but rather broken outcrops of a block lapilli tuff. The lumps of rhyolite in this are angular and clearly the whole mass must be close to its source. It may be an avalanche deposit where a lava has simply broken up and cascaded down a slope, or it may be the result of an actual violently explosive eruption. I wouldn't like to have been around when all this stuff was falling.

You are now as close to Snowdon as you can be at this level (unless you happen to be carrying a hang glider) and it's worth scanning the scene with binoculars to see what you can make of the beds opposite in Cwm Glas and Cwm Uchaf. The rocks are the same as you've see here today: Bedded Pyroclastics overlying the LRTF, and forming much of Garnedd Ugain, Crib y Ddysgl and Crib Goch but they are made more complex by several small fold structures. You might be able to make out some of this by following the beds where you can see them.

Figure 5.11: *Menhir-like outcrops forming the northwest summit of Glyder Fawr. This tuff is cut by a strong set of vertical cleavage joints which cause it to split into slabs from which you could build many Stonehenges (if you were feeling strong).*

If you turn and look up towards the summit of Glyder Fawr (not visible from here), you can see a striking colour change in the broken up rock which forms the ridge. The foreground is all pale rhyolitic material, banded or brecciated, which suddenly stops and is replaced by strongly cleaved grey slabby rock which forms the actual ridge crest. You'll see this shortly.

As for the plants, there are some which survive in this inhospitable place – there are always plants almost everywhere on the planet's surface, even in the Antarctic. Lichens – here orange and green – are the hardiest of all though they are not strictly speaking plants, being an association of fungus and alga. But here there are also spiky mountain grasses, clubmosses and crowberries.

Make your way (northeast) up towards Glyder Fawr summit, crossing the junction between the pale and dark rocks I mentioned. Before you reach the dark rocks, you cross a small track (marked with cairns) which, if you turn left onto it, will take you directly to the summit if you don't wish to linger here. Otherwise, take a quick look at this rock which is an ash flow tuff (Fig. 5.11) though probably not welded.

This rock continues to the summit itself – Locality 12.

Glyder Fawr summit: Locality 12 [6427 5796]

Poor Glyder Fawr! Just one more metre and it would have made the thousand, but even at 999 metres, it is still one of the highest of Snowdonia's peaks, and has a view to match. As for the rocks, the slabby block tuff has become quite coarse so that it's hard to tell what's rock and what is fragment. The clasts are a pretty mixed bag from vesicular rhyolites to fairly basic feldspar-bearing rocks.

If you look along towards Tryfan and Glyder Fach, the broad summit ridge has several pinnacular tor-like outcrops, all affected by the strong vertical cleavage, but mostly all you see is periglacial blockfield: rocks which have been churned up and smashed by freezing and thawing during the intense cold of the ice ages. Because the blockfield hasn't moved much, it is a reliable guide to what's underneath and you can again see striking colour changes from the white rhyolites (welded tuff with fiamme) to the darker grey tuffs, though the whole lot is part of the LRTF of the Snowdon volcanic centres. In fact, the geology is quite complicated hereabouts for some of the rhyolites are intrusive and – yes, there's more – there are some outcrops of basic vesicular lavas too. But that's as far as I'm going to take it because this has been a long day and it's probably time to head down.

Continue along the summit ridge towards Glyder Fach and aptly-named Castell y Gwynt (Castle of the Wind) skirting Cwm Cneifion on your left side. The track is rather vague as it crosses the blockfield though there are cairns. Soon it becomes clear again as you approach Y Gribin. You can see the bedded rocks which form the upper Idwal slabs very well from up here.

As you approach Glyder Fach, keep to the left to get onto Y Gribin – the broad flat ridge nearer to you and dead ahead. You do not go on to Glyder Fach. As you walk along to Y Gribin, look back to the crags on the west side of Cwm Cneifion. Now you can see why it's difficult to make much sense of what's going on on the ridge itself: there's a whole series of northwest-dipping units here and you just see bits of these on the ridge, hinting at the internal complexity of the LRTF in this area. **Now below on the right are the precipices at the head of Cwm Bochlwyd. Y Gribin soon becomes a real knife-edge ridge.** Tryfan, you can now see, is also formed of thick beds of

Figure 5.12: *Nant Ffrancon.*

volcanics. The whole of the northwest side dips steeply towards the Idwal Syncline (which you can see to your left again), though Tryfan's rocks are older than those underfoot being part of the Capel Curig Volcanic Formation. The top of Y Gribin is grey well bedded sandstone, again mangled up by freeze-thaw action, but looking just like that at Locality 1 – which, in fact, it is. **At the point where the ridge suddenly starts to drop steeply down – and you begin to wonder why the hell you ignored my warning back at Llyn y Cŵn – is the last locality.**

Y Gribin, a scary descent and an old friend: Locality 13 (unlucky for some!) [6508 5831]

From here, you can see to perfection the classic view of Nant Ffrancon – the 'U'-shaped glaciated valley with the truncated spurs I mentioned earlier (Fig. 5.12). The rock outcrops which form the whole of this steep descent ahead are a familiar rock indeed. They are all welded tuffs with beautiful fiamme: the Pitt's Head Tuff again. The fiamme are dark green, standing out in contrast to the white feldspar-rich matrix which encloses them in the many fresh and clear examples you'll see as you begin the scramble down. You'll probably see some quite large clasts

The path, well used but which splits up into several routes, is initially on the Cwm Idwal side of Y Gribin, but don't be tempted to go too far over in that direction. You need to keep more or less on the spine of the ridge. Beware of loose blocks (and other people) and take care. Where the steep slope stops, so does the Pitt's Head Tuff. It overlies a mudstone unit which accounts for the contrast in steepness of slope here.

Whilst you're (literally) getting to grips with the ignimbrite, you might spot the odd cluster of starry saxifrages which grow here.

After another steep descent and some shallower ones, you come to a ruined wall. There's an obvious path to the right (to Cwm Bochlwyd) and a less obvious one to the left. Take the left path which leads you down to Llyn Idwal avoiding the Gribin Facet and at first ascends slightly, so don't be discouraged. Then it drops down steeply through some magnificent breccias with large lava clasts (some up to half a metre) and a whole mishmash of other volcanic rocks, jumbled together to form what must have been a debris flow.

Eventually, this long descent ends and you rejoin the strollers' track at Llyn Idwal, turn right and head for the ladder stiles and home. I think you'll agree that it's been a spectacular day and you've seen some of the best volcanic geology in Snowdonia, Darwin's moraines and one of the most famous fold structures.

Rocky Ramble 6: Cwm Cau and Cadair Idris

How to get to the start of the ramble

At Minffordd, the junction of the A487 and B4405, you'll find a large free carpark (with toilets) [731 116] provided by the Snowdonia National Park Authority, close to the Minffordd Hotel. The Crosville bus No. 94A (Aberystwyth-Dolgellau) passes the Minffordd junction. Call 01492 596969 or 01248 370295 for information about times.

The ramble: needs, distances and times

The distance is about 11½ kilometres (about 7¼ miles) with around 970 metres (3180 feet) of climbing. The track is easy but a bit slippery on the short steep part of the descent from Mynydd Moel. This is definitely a good weather ramble only. Cadair Idris, being the highest range for miles and close to the sea, tends to generate its own cloud in damp westerlies. The views for most of the walk are superb so try to do it on a good day. You need OS Outdoor Leisure Map 23.

Introduction

Cadair Idris at 893 metres is not one of Snowdonia's great peaks. Yet it has a special nobility all of its own for two reasons: it rises almost directly out of the Mawddach estuary and it is remote from the higher mountains of central Snowdonia. Strictly, it isn't really 'Snowdonia' at all though it comes within the boundary of the National Park. It's nearest rival is Aran Fawddwy which is just 8 metres higher. Both ranges are built of the same rock types which, as you may have guessed, are mostly volcanic. This accounts for the rugged scenery which ceases further to the south where younger Silurian rocks form the more subdued hills and mountains down into central Wales.

This is a fine ramble which shows you not only the rocks and glacial remains but – with fair weather – gives you unusual views north to Snowdonia proper with the incomparable Mawddach estuary not far below. Cadair Idris is the last outpost of the Ordovician volcanic rocks which ring the Harlech Dome. The highest of its volcanic rocks are the same age as those forming Aran Fawddwy and the Arenig mountains away to the northeast (and possible the Moelwyn Volcanics, Ramble 3), but they are older than the rocks of central Snowdonia like the Snowdon Volcanic Group (see Timescale).

The ramble is, I think, the most attractive round-trip you can make in the Cadair Idris range.

The Minffordd Path beginning

Set off along the clearly-marked Minffordd Path, through a wooden gate at the back of the carpark. You cross a water leat and turn right onto a small causeway, flanked by horse chestnut trees, which crosses the Afon Faw. A hundred metres after the river, the path bears left through more open parkland with unusual trees like wellingtonias and various types of

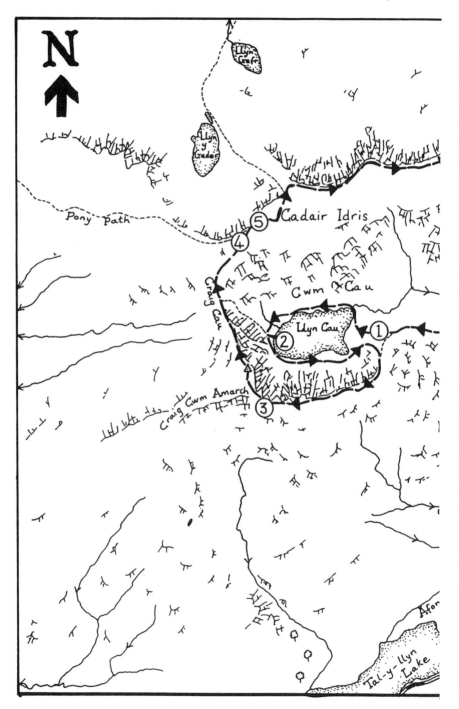

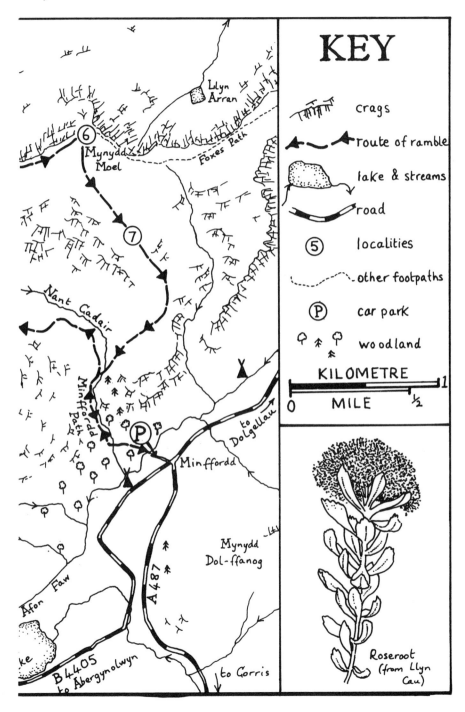

KEY

crags

route of ramble

lake & streams

road

⑤ localities

other footpaths

Ⓟ car park

woodland

KILOMETRE

0   MILE   ½

Roseroot
(from Llyn
Cau)

cypress and pesky rhododendrons. **Shortly, there's another gate with a kissing gate on its right side in front of a small house (Ystradlyn, Country- side Council for Wales). Turn left in front of the house to continue 'to Cadair Idris' as the sign says here.**

Now you can hear the rushing Nant Cadair which you roughly follow all the way to Llyn Cau. Being a powerful stream when in flood, it has built out an alluvial cone, so forcing the Afon Faw further to the east in its flood plain. Ystradlyn is built on the better drained alluvial cone, well above flood waters.

Just before you cross Nant Cadair, there's a notice welcoming you to Cadair Idris Nature Reserve together with a small map giving you a few basic details of what you might see. (I'll try and improve on that!)

Go through a small gate after the bridge and begin the climb. The woodland is mostly native oak and rowans with a few exotics like beech, limes and horse chestnuts. **The stepped path climbs through the moss-covered boulders and trees. The climb is stiff but beautiful with waterfalls just to your right, many of which you can quite easily see.** On the opposite side of the stream, conifers hold sway: larches, spruces and pines. **After a short while, you reach a drystone wall with an iron gate which you go through to leave the woodland behind.** From here, you have your first views across the Tal-y-llyn valley to Mynydd Dol-ffanog (opposite) whose lower slopes, particularly in the wooded areas, become a sea of bluebells in spring (May). The smooth slopes of the hills on the southeast side of the valley tell us that they are made of very different rock – soft sediments – to that underfoot which is volcanic: craggy outcrops, screes, large boulders.

The path works its way round to the north and then northwest, wending its way up towards Llyn Cau. Ahead you see large patches of scree; bits of rock which have broken off the crags on Mynydd Moel. **You can also see the return path which drops down its south flank steeply to rejoin this path back near the woodland you've just left behind. The path becomes almost flat for a while before turning more to the west.** Around you now are a series of large grassy humps, the eroded remnants of the moraines from the Cwm Cau glacier as it retreated up the cwm. These moraines date back to the end of the Devensian glaciation about 15,000 years ago. You can also see a great train of boulders dropped by the decaying ice sheet but overall, there doesn't seem to be much glacial debris left in this valley. You can, for example, see large rocky masses cropping out on the right side of the Nant Cadair. The plants you see around you are wiry mountain grasses, tormentils and white milkworts (Fig. 6.1). Undoubtedly you'd see more variety if it weren't for the constant nibbling by the Welsh Mountain sheep. **As the track bends away from the stream and flattens out, to the right** you see a small fenced portion in which the natural vegetation can grow as it will without interference from sheep. Here, heather and bilberry plants are regenerating. You'll also spot another larger fenced boggy area.

Just before this fenced patch, 3-4 metres to the right of the track is a big flat glacially-polished surface which is covered in quite deep striae, cut into the rock by the chisel-like boulders held fast in the base of the ice sheet.

From here, you have your first view up to the rock barrier which impounds Llyn Cau, with a cataract of waterfalls tumbling down it. Some of the glacial erratics around here are enormous, some the size of a small house. Many large boulders seem to have tumbled later from the precipices high to your right. Most of these boulders are rather nondescript lavas or intrusive rocks, but one tabular block close to the track is a fine example of a well bedded tuff.

BRY LYNAS 5/96

Figure 6.1: *Milkwort (A) and tormentil (B).*

Wheatears, which migrate from Africa each spring, love this sort of rough country for breeding. In spring and summer, you can't fail to see and hear them. The male has a striking black eye stripe and a pale grey back. Both sexes have distinctive white patches at the base of their tails as they flit away from you making their 'wheet, chack, chack' alarm call (rather like stonechats).

Then there are the ubiquitous meadow pipits. Their nests are brilliantly concealed and the only way you ever see them is if the parent bird is present as you walk too close. Then she will bolt in panic from her nest enabling you, if you're sharp-eyed, to take a peek at her eggs or her fledglings. With difficulty, I found a nest with three fledglings high on the slopes of Mynydd Moel. Even though I could see the tiny birds moving inside, the camouflage was so effective that if they ceased to move, I couldn't see them any more.

Gradually the path edges its way ever closer to the rock outcrops on the south valley side. You come to a large pile of stones marking the point where the Minffordd Path turns off to the left. You'll rejoin this path higher up, later. Continue on up towards Llyn Cau.

Let's breed again, like we did last summer... Scared parents and selfish genes:
Most animal parents have a strong urge to protect their children so as to ensure that
their genes continue the line for another generation. (We might, more kindly, say
because they love them. But what is the emotion we call 'love' for? To ensure the
effective nurturing of other individuals involved in your genetic heritage is probably
the simplest, rather unwholesome, answer!) So why does the pipit flee her nest when
someone comes too close, almost certainly betraying her chicks to a potential
predator in the process? It's a hard fact that if you think you're about to be crushed,
along with your babies, by the foot of a giant, your choice is either to stay and risk
destruction of all your genes or to scarper fast, leaving your babies to likely death
whilst yourself living to breed again. Richard Dawkins might cite this as an example
of the behaviour you'd expect if 'selfish' genes were to be maintained. (For the latest
on this fascinating idea, read Dawkins' book *River out of Eden,* Weidenfeld &
Nicholson, 1995.)

Whaleback and Llyn Cau: Locality 1 [7196 1236]

This wonderful whaleback is so obviously carved and moulded by the
repeated passage of ice sheets that I hardly like to insult your intelligence
and say it! The reason it's quite so impressive is serendipity: the strike of the
massive volcanic breccia bed which forms it was exactly parallel to the ice
movement direction. The breccia was probably a water-saturated debris flow
and contains lumps of volcanic material up to fist-size and occasional blocks
of ripped-up sediments up to the length of your forearm. The particularly
massive bed dips at about 45° south, forming the vast smooth rock surface
just to the right of the path. The other side of the whaleback – the scarp side
– is quite steep. The glaciers left several separate lines of evidence of their
handiwork here. How many can you spot?

The first is in the form of perched blocks. But much more spectacular is
the deep groove over 1 metre wide honed neatly out of the spine of the
whaleback. As if that wasn't sufficient, you can also find myriads of fresh
striae on the smooth rock surface right beside the path (Fig. 6.2).

It's an ill wind that blows nobody any good ... and Time perspectives again. The
reason you can see these striae so well is because they've been protected by soil
cover until very recently. Now the path is so much tramped over that erosion is picking
away some of this soil, exposing these fresh features for the first time since the ice
age for you and me to see and marvel at. Nobody wants path erosion but here's some
good from it. The absence of striae on the weathered parts of this whaleback give us
a perspective on the sheer slowness of weathering – in human terms. The striae here
were probably made about 15,000 years ago. They are rarely more than a few
millimetres deep and the fact that you don't easily find them on weathered outcrops
tells you that over this time period (a mere nothing in geological time, of course), just
a few millimetres at most of this rock have weathered away due to rain, freeze-thaw,
acids and oxidation. Not much, is it?

Figure 6.2: *Me with my Peruvian hat – much despised by my children but useful in the freezing Andean nights – pointing out the fresh striae above the path. I've enhanced a few of these.*

Llyn Cau is impounded by the obvious and splendid terminal moraine, littered everywhere with large erratic boulders. The moraine dam is no more than a few metres high and almost certainly underlain by a rock step. Llyn Cau, a classic corrie lake, was gouged out by various successions of glaciers, the latest of which was the Younger Dryas glacial advance about 12,500 years ago. Higher up on the north side of the valley, you can see the remains of older lateral moraines, degraded now by downslope movement of debris due to rains and scree formation. Earlier, more powerful versions of the Cwm Cau glacier must have extended over the rock step, dropping steeply down as an icefall towards the moraines you saw before the fenced enclosures. Earlier still, of course (say 18,000 years ago), everything in the entire district – probably including the summit of Cadair Idris – was submerged in ice hundreds of metres thick. This ice moved west towards what is now the Irish Sea from the reservoir area north of Bala which glaciologists call the Merioneth Ice Cap or MIC.

A path runs right around Llyn Cau, passing Locality 2 *en route*. You can skip this if you want to get on. Otherwise, make your way around the north side, first crossing the moraines and then following a somewhat up-and-down path which skirts the shore and various outcrops of slates.

If you hear a mournful 'weet, weet' birdsong from nowhere in particular, you can be sure that it will be a ring ouzel, the mountain blackbird. They're easier to hear than to see. Like wheatears, these members of the thrush family just come for the summer – to breed. There's much to be said for this.

Llyn Cau precipices: Locality 2 [7119 1236]

A path descends from the pass high above at Craig Cau and joins your circum-lake path as you cross the stream's alluvial cone to head towards a cluster of quartz boulders. The locality begins about here, so look at the outcrops as you scramble on round to the south.

The rocks here crop out rather spectacularly to form the precipices which loom over Llyn Cau. These are the Craig Cau Formation, the topmost part of a great collection of volcanic rocks which crop out around the east and south of the Harlech Dome: the Aran Volcanic Group. The Craig Cau eruptions must have occurred at about the same time as those which produced the Moelwyn Volcanic Formation (p. 68) in early Caradoc times.

The streams have built up an alluvial cone, mostly from the softer mudstones which form part of this sequence.You can see that this cone is still forming for the rushes are periodically buried by fresh flushes of slate debris, hooshed down in floods. The mudstone – the Ty'r Gawen Mudstone – represents what was a continuous background 'rain' of mud in the fairly deep seas of the early Caradoc Epoch. It formed the theatrical backdrop into which the volcanic 'players' of the time erupted. I've just mentioned the Craig Cau Formation and at Localities 4 & 5 you'll meet another slightly older one: the Pen y gadair Volcanic Formation of earliest Caradoc age.

As recently as 12,000 years ago, this cwm was filled with ice. The debris which now forms the cone would have fallen onto the glacier or down into the bergschrund. This is the origin of the 'glacial sandpaper' (p. 33) which so effectively eroded the bedrock below the moving ice.

The broad stream gully you crossed is all underlain by dark cleaved mudstones without any trace of bedding. This crops out as you approach the precipices of volcanic rock which overlie the mudstone. **Follow along the base of the outcrop, leaving the path a little below you to do so. Cross more slate and many quartz veins after traversing a small scree cone, now stabilised by mosses, bilberry, parsley fern and grass. Follow the outcrops as they angle upwards steeply** to an obvious junction at the point where a larger and still-active scree disgorges from the next gully. About 10 metres above and to your right from this, you can see the beautifully exposed continuation of this massive sandstone overlying the slate. But before this event occurred, smaller beds were being laid down along with muds and silts, indicating signs of activity to come. These beds show up in the mudstones below the obvious contact. The ancient seafloor environment was changing. The sudden influx of the sandstone tells us of a major change of conditions – a shallowing perhaps, or some nearby volcanic event. But this was nothing compared to what was to follow: the thick and massive sequence of volcanic rocks which form the precipices overshadowing Llyn Cau from here on.

As you cross the active scree cone, look at the rocks underfoot as you pick your way. They have fallen from high above and because the cone is active, its constituents are mostly fresh, giving you a good idea of the rock types: slates, much feldspar-rich tuffite and tuffs (Fig. 6.3). Although it's not immediately obvious, the volcanic sequence is bedded and so must be extrusive. To the right of the scree, you can see this bedding quite clearly. Because you can see *that*, you can begin to make sense of the general dipping sequence of rocks here. When you see bedding in this area, it almost always dips at a moderate angle to the south.

Figure 6.3: *Well bedded tuffites above Locality 2. The bed in the centre of the photo is particularly striking with its flat top, though internally it shows no bedding at all: a good example of what geologists mean by 'massive'. This thick bed was almost certainly formed by one single event like a major earthquake which triggered a mass flow of coarse volcanic debris.*

The plants around here are quite varied as befits a nature reserve. There aren't too many sheep, presumably deliberately to allow the rarer plants a chance to regenerate. You'll see parsley and other polypody ferns, heather, grasses, foxgloves and even a few bluebells. The crags south of the scree cone are a treasure trove of unusual species: alpine strawberries (*Fragaria vesca*, yum!) and lady's mantles (*Alchemilla* species*)*, wood anemone (*Anemone nemorosa*), wood sorrel (*Oxalis acetosella*), a white-flowered bittercress (*Cardamine*), bitter vetch (*Lathyrus montanus*), members of the Stonecrop family like roseroot (*Rhodiola rosea*, see Ramble Map), English stonecrop (*Sedum anglicum*), and starry saxifrages (*Saxifraga stellaris*; Fig. 6.4). You may find even more flowering species than this if you look about. As I said – a treasure trove. One or two tiny rowan trees cling to the precipice higher up.

Figure 6.4: *Starry saxifrage*

Return to the path and continue round the lake. From the path, look back up to Locality 2. Now that you know what to look for, you can see perfectly clearly that all these rocks are bedded. You can also see occasional signs of bedding in the precipice right above you too. From fallen blocks, you can see that the precipice tuffs are dark grey with well formed feldspar crystals.

Along the south side of Llyn Cau, you have to go up and over some outcrops of whitish volcanic rock. Take care if the rocks are wet – they're slippery. Ahead on the near skyline are two perched blocks. Behind these is the Minffordd Path. You can head to the right of these up a rough grassy hollow filled with moraines and boulders to rejoin the main path.

When you reach the top of this short but stiff climb after joining the badly eroded Minffordd Path, you have your first good views to the south. As you see, there's not much rock outcrop because almost the entire sequence above – that is overlying – the Cadair Idris volcanics, is mudstone and siltstone of the upper Ordovician and Silurian. Further afield, you can see the slate quarries at Corris which exploit some of these cleaved sediments. Away to the southeast, you can see at least 24 wind turbines on one of the long ridges east of Machynlleth.

CATalyst for change? The Centre for Alternative Technology (CAT) thrives in an old slate quarry near Corris. Here you can see wind and water turbines, insulated houses, solar energy devices and organic gardens. This is a stimulating place to visit and you get a 50% discount if you arrive by bike. Call 01654 702400 for information.

Turn right to continue on west up the ridge. You'll notice many perched blocks about and here, you're at almost 600 metres. So the ice certainly buried this ridge for a time. You also notice (as at Llyn Cau) a good many healthy-looking bilberry bushes. They're a pain to pick but bilberry pie is mouth-watering ... Sorry, shouldn't be discussing food when you're puffing your way up a mountain.

The rocks are all dipping south and are all pale grey-pink-white rubbly-looking coarse rhyolitic tuffs: the Craig Cau Formation. This represents part of a collosal undersea ignimbrite eruption whose remains now form the highest parts of the Aran ranges and north to Arenig Fawr, Arenig Fach and Llyn Conwy – at least 40 kilometres distant. Oddly, there's no definite trace of this event in central Snowdonia. Nor is there any sign of a caldera structure like that which developed during the Snowdon Volcanic Group eruptions later in the Caradoc. This suggests that the actual source lay further east and so is still buried under younger rocks. At Cadair Idris, the tuff from this mighty eruption reaches almost 200 metres in thickness though when you include the lower part of the formation which you saw at Locality 2, it comes closer to 600 metres.

The stony path actually runs up one bedding plane for a while, the beds forming big flat tilted slabs, often with bits of quartz vein stuck on them like icing. **The next locality is where the ridge flattens out before the steep climb to the 791-metre cairn above Craig Cwm Amarch.**

Views and contacts: Locality 3 [7120 1192]

From here, looking out along the ridge of Craig Cwm Amarch, you can see the dramatic change in the landforms where the ash flow tuff stops and the enormously thick mudstone sequence which overlies it – the Ceiswyn Formation – begins. The slopes of the Craig itself are littered with blocks of tuffs. The outcrops at the top of the screes form clear sheets dipping at about 30° south. Much of the tuff has been broken up by freezing and thawing action so the higher slope is covered in blockfield. The tuff often contains elliptical hollows – probably weathered-out pumice lumps – and is mostly fine grained.

The slates which follow dip gently right the way down the west side of Cwm Amarch with grey screes below the dark lines of outcrops. A tiny lake on the ridge top (which is also followed by a fence) marks the core of a gentle downfold – syncline – in these beds, with the dip changing to northwesterly for a short distance.

The mere fact that mudrocks were forming both before and after these ignimbrite eruptions, tells us that the whole 'event' took place in deep water. You'll see some striking evidence of other, earlier, eruptions under water at the next locality.

As you continue on up the path, you can see some of Tal-y-llyn Lake and down the valley towards Abergynolwyn. Presently, you get to peer down the chasm you looked up at from Locality 2.

At the summit of the Craig Cwm Amarch ridge, you cross a stile over a recently refurbished fence. Just before the fence, to the left of the track, you can find outcrops of nodular tuffs. These nodules, some up to fist-size, probably formed like the cannonballs you've seen on Ramble 4. From this summit, you can now see right out to the Llŷn peninsula as well as across to the older Cambrian mountains at the south end of the Harlech Dome. **And quite close now is Cadair Idris summit, but unfortunately, you have to drop down to the col at Craig Cau to get there. About halfway down towards Craig Cau col,** you start to notice bands of slate underfoot. You can see right back down to Locality 2 from here which, you'll remember, was slate followed by sandstones, tuffites and finally the thick ash flow tuff formation you've just walked up. Now you're crossing back down through the same sequence of mudstone, volcanic breccias and tuffs. We now know that much of the lower part of this Craig Cau Formation is built up of slumped and slipped rafts and blocks of rock units which stacked up to make it thicker than it originally was. This was because of instability and doming of the seafloor, probably because of shallow intrusions at the time. There certainly were some large intrusions as you will shortly see.

But now, you're walking back in time. The rocks which form Cadair Idris underlie what you've seen so far and so are older. As you will see, they too dip southeast, but are a very different set of rocks indeed. And all the evidence continues to tell us that everything that happened in this district back in Ordovician times did so under the sea. There's no evidence at all of dry land nearby. The background sediment was always mud and silt into which the volcanics flowed as important 'events'.

At the col, you're back in the Ty'r Gawen mudstones (Locality 2) which explains the presence of this col: they were the weakest and most easily eroded link in the chain between Craig Cwm Amarch and Cadair Idris. From the smoothed state of some of the outcrops along this ridge, you can tell that the ice has ramped right up and over here too – over 700 metres above sealevel.

The final ascent starts after you are joined by the rough path from Llyn Cau. At first, you cross more cleaved mudstone. The skyline ahead is now dominated by castle-like outcrops. After you've climbed for a while, the rock underfoot changes though you can't actually see any outcrops. You can tell there's a change because what was slaty debris underfoot now becomes whitish-grey tuffs.

You might want to stop for a breather and consider the valley you can now see right down to Tywyn. If the tide is high, you should see Broad Water through which the Afon Dysynni runs on its rather tortuous course to the sea. It helps if you look at the OS map for this ... if the wind isn't too strong. The valley I've just described isn't strictly the same valley as that which contains Tal-y-llyn Lake. That valley is remarkably straight, but suddenly at Abergynolwyn, the river kinks to the west, breaching what has been a strong ridge to join the Afon Cadair in the adjacent valley to the north. Why should this be? And why is the Tal-y-llyn valley so straight?

The answer is extremely simple: a huge landslip from its southeast side [6710 0640] completely blocked the Tal-y-llyn valley, forcing the River Dysynni to flow through a smaller tributary valley, once part of a system of northwesterly drainage which was largely destroyed by the glaciers.

The Tal-y-llyn valley is straight because it follows the line of weakness created by one of Wales' largest faults: the Bala Fault. This fault has had a long history of movement, dating right back to the late Precambrian and continuing, intermittently, until the Carboniferous Period (about about 350 million years ago). At least some of its movement was sideways – strike-slip – rather than up one side and down the other. The infamous San Andreas Fault of California is a good modern example.

One final note. On the south side of Dyffryn Dysynni, you can see Birds' Rock – Craig yr Aderyn (the continuation of the Craig Cau Formation, folded into an anticline). Can you see how its slopes plunge straight down into the flat green fields at the base, just as if the grass was water? That analogy is closer to the truth than you might guess, for this valley – like most others at their seaward end in Snowdonia (p. 83) – was greatly overdeepened by the outflowing glaciers. After they melted and sealevels rose, the sea flooded right up this valley at least as far as Craig yr Aderyn. Sealevels were, for a time, higher than today's, for the land was rising too, though more slowly. So this great estuary was initially flooded and then filled up completely by debris brought down first by colossal floods from melting glaciers and later by normal seasonal floods. Sealevels have been relatively static for several thousand years but the whole of Wales has continued to rise by between 3 and 6 metres in the last 6,500 years. Geologists call this 'isostatic rebound'. It happens because the land is still springing up, released so relatively recently from the dead weight of ice which once overloaded it.

Continue on up the path. At about the point where the path begins to ascend more steeply, you start passing through the first exciting outcrops of Locality 4, not much more than 100 metres from the summit.

Pillows and more pillows: Locality 4 [7102 1295]

I suggest you turn to the left up a shallow grassy valley which connects across to the Pony Path. Here, you'll find many superb and spectacular piles of pillow lavas. Some are small, some large, but they all fit together and mould into each other. (For a description of how these form, see p. 108). These pillows weather to a pale grey but inside, they are dark and obviously basaltic. In places, you see a vague columnar jointing which developed as the hot rocks cooled and shrank. The pillows form part of the Pen y gadair Formation.

The youngest parts of this basalt eruption – the first outcrops you encountered as you climbed, for they are all dipping south still – are well bedded tuffs. The pillows form all the middle part (Figs 6.5 & 6.6).

Figure 6.5: *This fantastic jumble of pillow lavas has for me a rather ghoulish resemblance to piles of bodies, reminiscent of those unfortunates who were caught by the AD79 eruption of Vesuvius at Pompeii, now on display in Pompeii museum.*

Figure 6.6: *This is a particularly big pillow (my penknife for scale) whose surface is covered in shrinkage cracks. Well, you'd shrink and crack too if one minute you were at 1,000°C and the next 30°C!*

Many of the pillows contain vesicles as gases, dissolved in the magma, began to bubble out due to the sudden release of pressure. The bubbles (see Box) became 'frozen' for ever in the cooling lava. Near the summit, periglacial blockfields have formed in which many of the pillows have been weathered out completely and now lie about looking a little like the ghastly remains of some prehistoric massacre.

Bubbles in time. As you might guess, theoretically these gas bubbles should contain tiny samples of the original gases that this ancient eruption spewed out into the sea. Unfortunately, all rocks are 'leaky' over time, and the gas will have leaked away or been exchanged for something else during the millions of years of metamorphism which affected all Wales' Lower Palaeozoic rocks. But precisely the same idea has been used by geologists to take a peek at the fluids which form mineral deposits. The fluids are rich in dissolved minerals which gradually build up crystals. Crystals are rarely perfect and minute bubbles trapping portions of the original fluid commonly develop within the crystal lattice. Millions of years later, geologists can examine and sample these. These tiny 'fluid inclusions' not only tell you about the composition of the fluids but also their temperature at the time their crystal 'homes' formed. Amazing, isn't it?

When you emerge onto the Pony Path, you have your first view down to Llyn y Gadair. By now you'll recognise this instantly for what it is: a glacial cirque with a splendid series of terminal moraines left by the last retreating Younger Dryas ice.

You can now see right down the Mawddach estuary to Barmouth. Like Dyffryn Dysynni, this beautiful estuary has been glacially overdeepened, flooded by the sea and filled by sandy sediment. Unlike it, this estuary's sand contains gold!

> **Thar's gold in them thar 'ills!** It's true! A mining company even wanted to dredge up the sediment and separate the gold. The gold comes from the famous gold-bearing quartz veins in the Clogau Shales of the Harlech Dome, washed down into the estuary just like any other sediment. Traditionally, gold for royal wedding rings is from this area. Quite large amounts of gold were once mined, Gwynfynydd Mine being the best known of the 'Dolgelley Gold Belt'. The mine once employed 500 men and yielded 40,000 ounces of gold. This is now working again and you can visit it as it has become a tourist attraction. You can even commission your own Gwynfynydd gold bauble. (Call 01341 423332 for information.) Another once-famous mine was Clogau which yielded 15,000 ounces in 1865.

Just before the summit on the Pony Path, you may see, rather oddly, a bit of wall with a fireplace, complete with iron grate. This must have been an earlier shelter, now replaced by the blockhouse a few metres north of the summit.

The basic lavas, mostly with pillows, occupy all the ground up to the summit, Locality 5.

Penygadair, summit of Cadair Idris: Locality 5 [711 130]

Because this is the highest mountain for miles around, your views should be wonderful. Unfortunately, because it is both high and near the sea, Cadair Idris tends to form its own cloud muffler ... which muffles your view. On a good day, you can see right out to Llŷn and the whole of Snowdonia proper.

> **Idris, the giant.** 'Cadair Idris' is, in Welsh folklore, the 'chair' of Idris, a giant who was something of a polymath, being equally at home with astronomy (which he studied from his 'chair' – the deep cwm which contains Llyn y Gadair), poetry and philosophy. Legend claims that anyone who spent a night in this 'chair' would become either a poet or a madman.

The summit consists of massive blocky lavas, much broken up along the joints – without pillows, though if you hunt around amongst outcrops nearby, you'll find more pillows and pillow breccias. You can follow these basalts for a short distance to the west but they soon die out. The vents from which these lavas flowed must have been fairly nearby because further to the east (Cross Foxes), the basalt dies out. There's no evidence that any of these basalt volcanoes emerged above the waves so, although some of the eruptions were explosive, no islands ever formed.

If you look northeast to Rhobell Fawr, you're looking at another example of a thick sequence of basalt lavas. That volcano, whose eroded remnants form Rhobell, is much older (lowest Ordovician, Tremadoc Epoch) than the Aran Volcanic Group and was the first important burst of volcanic activity in this district.

If you walk past the shelter house and look into the cwm of Llyn y

Gadair, you can see that the entire sequence is bedded, dipping to the south as before. Looking towards Cyfrwy (Fig. 6.7), you can see what are obviously bedded sediments beneath a dolerite sill. Under these sediments is a thick formation of some kind of rock. You'll see this later. For the moment, notice that the only obvious structure it contains is columnar jointing, so it must once have been hot.

Figure 6.7: *Pony Path ridge with Cyfrwy (in cloud) on the right. J – columnar jointed igneous rock; D – dolerite intrusion. I've enhanced the contacts between the different rock types. The sedimentary rock in between the dolerite and the as-yet unexamined igneous rock is mudstone like that at Llyn Cau.*

The blockhouse shelter is built on and partly of a very different rock from the summit. You may recognise it as a welded tuff a bit like the Pitt's Head Tuff. It doesn't stick up much because it has broken up into enormous great rhomboidal blocks. The rock itself is full of feldspar crystals and its streaky eutaxitic texture is clear. This tuff is overlain by the lavas which you've already seen beautifully displayed between here and Locality 4.

You can follow this tuff unit down to the east. The walking path crosses the rock a few tens of metres from the summit, but the tuff continues down to the east, represented by piles of large blocks but no actual outcrop. Within 200 metres, you'll notice a change. The slope shallows to a grassy plateau and all the outcrops cease. To the right, you'll recognise more castle-like outcrops of pillow lavas which overlook Llyn Cau. If you look at the tuff at the eastern end [7127 1309] just before the plateau, you should notice that there's been a change in the rock. Here, although most of it is still quite massive, parts are distinctly well bedded. But what has happened to the tuff to the east? It certainly doesn't continue. Instead, you find pillow lavas. So we can suppose that there must have been later fault movement which has displaced the tuff to somewhere else. A fault line also explains the obvious break-in-slope here. But there is another possible explanation which we can't test, but can think about. In active volcanic areas, whether above or below the sea (this was below as the pillow lavas and mudstones have been telling us all day), the ground surface is rarely flat; quite the reverse. So it's possible that there was some kind of pre-existing 'high' (like a submarine cliff formed during some earlier eruption). If you pour porridge into a bowl, the bowl edges prevent it flowing out onto your table cloth (unless you keep pouring). It floods out over the bottom of the bowl and stops at the sides. Likewise, the ignimbrite eruption perhaps filled up the lower areas but stopped at the 'high' which could have existed here. Take your pick.

> **Cadair camp:** This flat area to the east of the fault is a good place to camp, well sheltered from westerlies. If you carefully cut a cylinder in the squelchy peaty ground here, clean water will collect in sufficient amounts to supply you with what you need for tea and dinner-making. Before leaving, carefully reinsert your cylinder of turf and no one will ever know you've been there.

Make your way slightly north of east in the general direction of Mynydd Moel, keeping close to the north edge of the ridge for splendid views of the precipices which form the mighty bulwarks of this mountain when you view it from the north. A path runs the whole way. Shortly, you can see down to Llyn Gafr.

The rock which forms the precipice (Fig. 6.8) crops out underfoot as you walk along. It's pink to white and so certainly not dolerite or any other basic rock (basic rocks are almost always dark because of the high content of dark-coloured iron-magnesium silicate minerals they contain). It was clearly once molten and is actually a very large intrusive sill. The minerals which make it are equal-sized and have solidified as intergrowths of well-formed feldspars and probable quartz with a few clumps of darker iron-magnesium minerals. The pale colour and probable quartz tell us that this rock is acid – silica-rich. The texture – neither fine (like rhyolite) nor coarse (like granite) shows that it was intruded at a fairly high level in the crust, thus cooling quite fast. Perhaps it was connected with the Craig Cau ash flow eruptions; Localities 2 & 3 (see Box below). This rock is a microgranite, really just a slightly coarser version of rhyolite. Had this magma made it to the surface, it would have erupted as an ignimbrite. This sill runs for around 5 kilometres, always at the same level and reaches over 600 metres in thickness. Another similar sill (the Crogenen sill) forms the lower ramparts of Cadair Idris, centred on Llynnau Cregennen [66 14]. That sill runs for about 8 kilometres.

Figure 6.8: *This enormous columnar-jointed microgranite sill forms most of the north-facing precipices of the entire Cadair Idris ridge.*

Proof v. Speculation: Trace element geochemistry. Anyone can speculate, whether it be in the Stock Exchange or when considering related rock types like the ash flow tuff and the sill here. Speculation is easy ... and often disastrous. It is really theorising without much evidence. Proof is hard and means you have to collect evidence systematically. One way of linking rock types which seem to be related is to analyse samples of them for trace elements. This is expensive, slow and time-consuming but does offer strong support – or no support at all (in which case your speculation goes out with the garbage). Major elements like sodium, potassium, magnesium, silicon, calcium, iron and aluminium (which, with oxygen, form most of all igneous rocks) are fairly mobile. During cooling and later metamorphic events, circulating hot watery fluids can and often do dissolve some minerals (and their constituent elements) and replace them with something else. Sometimes this mobility is very subtle and difficult to detect. With new and highly accurate methods of analysis, we can now analyse the minutest traces of rarer elements which studies show to be much less mobile. So by looking at the trace elements, you can often establish whether one igneous rock is of the same blood, or parentage, as another. This may not seem to you to be very important. But it is just such analyses which have enabled geologists to discover the plate tectonic setting (theatre) for volcanic episodes far in the past. It means that we can present the complete story of the driving forces behind volcanoes and their products. The type of volcanoes which are active in the Galapagos Islands, for example, are very different from those in the Andes. The trace elements from just a few pieces of either of these allow geochemists to tell which is which.

Figure 6.9: *Blockfield on the ridge to Mynydd Moel. Penygadair behind. The rock is the pale microgranite.*

Below you can see fresh screes, some of which have gullies with levées (like modern lava flows) where water-saturated debris flows have slurried down the mountainside during heavy rains. At the base of the scree, you can see a well-formed protalus rampart [717 135] which built up whilst a large snow patch survived here for a few decades. Beyond that is a waste of moraines, less ordered than those back at Llyn y Gadair, but large parts of them have yet to be colonised by plants.

Walk on towards Mynydd Moel. The main path, marked by piles of stones, is a little way to the south. This is boring and you miss the excitement of the other path which runs close – but not too close – to the edge. This is a fine and easy ridge walk. Parts of the plateau have been churned up into blockfields by periglacial freeze-thaw action which has really smashed up Mynydd Moel itself: it's largely covered in a mantle of broken rocks: either screes or blockfields (Fig. 6.9).

As you approach the summit of Mynydd Moel, you cross a ladder stile over a fence (not marked on the OS map). About 50 metres past this, in line with the summit outcrops, you'll notice some strange pink rocks which, if you examine them, you'll find are a variety of microgranite. These are much more broken up by intense jointing, which has allowed iron-rich fluids to percolate through the rock, staining them this colour.

Mynydd Moel: Locality 6 [727 136]

Here the microgranite continues, though to the northwest, much of it has broken up into scree. But the jointing is now much more close-spaced (as you saw at the pink outcrops), making the rock weaker and more easily torn apart by erosion. The rock underfoot is much altered, with feldspars intergrown with what were once iron-magnesium minerals but are now a secondary mineral: chlorite.

Looking back to Cadair Idris (Penygadair) summit, you can now make some sense of the rock units you've walked over, and the sequence in which they occur. The microgranite is, in the foreground, broken up into what geomorphologists call 'patterned ground'. This is caused by periglacial freezing and thawing. The constant churning of the broken material in an 'active layer' results in a characteristic sorting by size. On steeper slopes, this ends up as stripes of stones; on flatter ground such as here, polygons and rough circles often form. (For a detailed account and figures of these processes, see *The Periglaciation of Great Britain* by C K Ballantyne and C Harris, Cambridge University Press, 1994, pages 88 onwards).

Brocken spectres and glories ... I was here with Val in April 1996, checking this ramble. The cloud maddeningly stayed put for all the higher parts, but we did get some short-lived but fantastic rainbow-ringed Brocken spectres – glories – as the sun cast our shadows onto the clouds swirling below in the Llyn Arran cwm. Curiously, you can't see other people's glories – only your own.

To the southeast, you can see Craig y Llam overshadowing Cwm Rhwyddfor (Tal-y-llyn pass). You can imagine how the glaciers, forcing their way through this valley (whose existence is ultimately due to the great Bala Fault), ripped out much of the rock sequence (dipping southeast) to leave the crags of Craig y Llam. Since the glaciers melted, the crags have gradually broken down into screes. Eventually, the crags will disappear altogether, the scree will cease to be active and the whole slope will become covered in vegetation. These crags occupy roughly the same structural position as those of Craig Cwm Amarch (Locality 3) in that they represent the top of the ash flow tuff and the start of the overlying mud and silt rock sequence, the Ceiswyn Formation.

To the northeast of the summit is the almost square Llyn Arran with screes and a distinct protalus rampart forming its southern shore. The lake is the result of an active glacier in this cwm and is now being filled in by alluvial debris from the stream which has built up a little alluvial cone on the west side. Thick glacial till covers much of the area to the northeast and the stream is now cutting down into this. It's all quite featureless – a sure sign of later periglacial action which tends to flatten out any older moraine humps. The moraine close by the lake tells us that there was a small glacier in this cwm – little more than a large snowpatch – during the Younger Dryas cold snap.

To the northeast, you'll notice a change. The precipices end and the mountain slope is much more rounded and broken up. The reason is that just past Mynydd Moel, the microgranite sill has forced its way upwards through the rocks – to the south. It has pushed right up into the Craig Cau ash flow. You'll walk over this shortly. It is this transgression – cutting upwards into progressively higher units in the Cadair Idris rock sequence – that gives the final game away about the microgranite. A lava obviously cannot do this because, quite simply, any later (overlying) units didn't exist when the lava formed. Lava is, therefore, older than rocks which overlie it. An intrusion is, by definition, younger than the rocks it has pushed into. It couldn't push into something that wasn't there. So we know for certain that the microgranite is intrusive and younger than the rocks which enclose it – including the ash flow tuff. So my theory about them being related is, at best, suspect.

The escarpment which continues towards Cross Foxes is formed of the pillow lavas and dolerite which you saw at Locality 5. Much further northeast, you can see Llyn Tegid, Bala Lake. The valley containing this is the continuation of the Bala Fault system.

Head south towards the fence you crossed earlier and follow it down to the southeast. Although not marked on the OS map, there's a well-used track beside the fence with occasional stiles for crossing.

As you descend, you have fine views into Cwm Cau and the sequence you saw at the first three localities (Fig. 6.10).

As the slope steepens, you find both outcrops and screes to your left with a distinct line of springs at the bottom. The rock is the familiar microgranite to the east of the fence. To the west, basic lavas crop out for around here is the junction with the intrusive microgranite lobe I mentioned. **Here a prominent path from Penygadair joins from the right. This is marked on the OS map.**

Figure 6.10: *Cwm Cau and its rocks. P – pillow lava (Locality 4 is just to the right of the photo), M – Ty'r Gawen Mudstone, S – sandstones and tuffites of Localities 1 and 2 (both marked), C – Craig Cau Formation ash flow tuff (including Locality 3).*

Now you have a view of the entire lake of Tal-y-llyn. You can see how alluvium from the entering streams is gradually encroaching upon the lake.

Just before the steepest part of the descent, you'll find a wonderful viewpoint – Locality 7 – 15 metres to the west side of the fence. There's a simple stile where you can cross.

Squiggly rocks and a view: Locality 7 [7300 1298]

From here you can see the whole of Cwm Cau and the fine U-shaped Tal-y-llyn valley, dead straight because of the fault which underlies it. The rock underfoot and around here is a variant of the microgranite with feldspars up to half a centimetre long. Just below the viewpoint, you can see other indicators that this rock was once liquid: nodules (which though only marble-sized have the same origin as the cannonballs at Moel Hebog; p. 102) and flow banding and folding (Fig. 6.11). This, as you have seen, has not occurred before in this rock. It indicates rapid cooling. The chilling made the acid magma stiffer and didn't allow the usual intergrowths of feldspar and quartz to develop. In its higher parts, it is a true rhyolite – almost indistinguishable from some of the welded tuff it intrudes! This sort of continuum causes geologists some problems and logically, you'd expect the microgranite to be the likely source of the Cwm Cau ash flow. Unfortunately for this neat theory, the source of the ash flow seems to have been some distance to the east. Win some ... lose some!

Figure 6.11: *Flow folding in the microgranite intrusion. I've emphasised the folds for clarity.*

Your descent continues in earnest from this locality on a small path to a ladder stile. Far below, you can see how this path rejoins the Minffordd Path just above the woodland. Cross back to the east side of the fence at the stile, for the main path is on that side, zigzagging down through scree patches. Erosion has, sadly, taken a toll of the soils, peat and screes here. The fence joins a ruined wall and continues down. As the slope shallows, cross another ladder stile and you continue down to rejoin the Minffordd Path, passing a pair of large grassy whaleback features – apparently moraine – on your left. You soon arrive back at the woodland edge and cross the stream to join the main path back to the carpark.

Rocky Ramble 7: Llyn Dinas and Moel y Dyniewyd

How to get to the start of the ramble

At Nant Gwynant, you'll find a large free carpark (with toilets), marked on the OS map with a 'P'. The Snowdon Sherpa bus (Service 95; Llandudno/Porthmadog – Llanberis) passes the start of this walk. Call KMP at 01286 878880 for times which vary considerably.

The ramble: needs, distances and times

This is a relatively short ramble and need take no more than half a day but if you want to visit Sygun Mine, better to make it a leisurely full day. The highest point, Moel y Dyniewyd, is only 382 metres. Some of this ramble requires a little navigating because there's no path for a short sector. At no time do you have to climb walls (you go through gaps) or jump fences (there are always ladder stiles). Total distance is around 11 kilometres (under 7 miles) with 410 metres (about 1350 feet) of climbing. You'll need OS Outdoor Leisure Map 17.

Introduction

This ramble is *through* mountains rather than over them. One advantage of lower walks is that you can appreciate the grandeur of the scenery around you from a different perspective. From the summit of Snowdon, all the lower mountains look less impressive – puny even. From Moel y Dyniewyd, an infrequently visited 'puny' mountain, you have grand open views of the greater peaks in all directions – and yet you feel part of the mountains too. The last locality, Bryn Castell, is seldom visited but is a lovely spot to sit and contemplate.

Some of the rocks, too, are rather odd. Furthermore, you have a glimpse of an old copper mine, Sygun mine. You can even go in it if you want, as it has become a sort of living museum. You can walk with a guide through the bottom level and come out at a turnstile higher up the hillside – right beside the path to continue the ramble.

To Llyndy Isaf and the first locality

First walk south along the main road for 300 metres. It has a broad grassy verge and the view ahead is of the low but rugged country of this ramble. Turn onto the single track road, the first on the left, which heads up and over to the Nanmor valley. Cross the Afon Glaslyn. One hundred metres past the bridge, the road abruptly swings left and there's a track (a public footpath, though nothing tells you this) off to the right that you take to Llyndy Isaf. Stop here for a pleasing view up to Snowdon's summit and Y Lliwedd. Ahead you can see Moel Hebog.

Why is Afon Glaslyn valley here? At least in part because erosion has picked away at weaknesses in the rocks left by an array of faults – the

Beddgelert Fracture Zone (BFZ). Some of the faults run along the axis of the near-parallel Nanmor valley to the southeast.

Glaciers are not mindful of former topographies and, if they can straighten out crooked valleys, they generally will. The great valley that contains Llyn Gwynant and Llyn Dinas was such a one. The glaciers thundered slowly through, overdeepening parts of the rock valley floor which later flooded to become two of Wales' most beautiful lakes. Much of the valley floor is now smooth and flat because of the vast quantities of debris brought down from the east Snowdon range by glacial meltwaters. As they lost their velocity and power with lessening slope, they dumped their debris loads on this great valley floor. To this day, floods bring down rocks and debris from the mountains and so the lake slowly fills in as the Afon Glaslyn and its tributary streams build their debris deltas out into it. A few thousand years ago, it was much bigger, extending back to well beyond where you are here.

The road climbs a small hill, passing a barn with a tiny door, built out of rock blocks. You begin to see these rocks cropping out along the edge of the road. They are all part of the Lower Rhyolitic Tuffs and, as you'd expect, are all carved into *roches moutonées*.

After walking round a bend to the left, in front of you on the skyline you see a strange conical hill covered in Scots pines. This is Bryn Castell and is the last locality on this ramble.

Pass the farm of Llyndy Isaf, cross a stream, pass a barn on the left and keep straight on over a stile beside a gate beneath a graceful larch. The footpath is clearly indicated by signs. The wall on your right shortly does an abrupt right-angled turn to head towards the lake. You do this also, branching right off the rough farm track, to cross a ladder stile. The path is perfectly clear with a boggy area on your right and ice-smoothed rock outcrops on the left.

Shortly, the path is forced around the edge of quite a steep and high *roche moutonée.* **Bear left up this to its west end before entering the birch trees. This is Locality 1.**

Rock with a classic view: Locality 1 [6238 4968]

The rock you're on is strongly affected by a nearly vertical cleavage. It's a tuff, part of the LRTF and full of small feldspar chips. If you look carefully, you'll see that parts contain irregular volcaniclast, some rounded and some angular. These aren't easy to spot and are partly a question of 'getting your eye in', but they're there all right.

Down the valley is the lake with oak woods behind backed by LRTF crags on the other side, steepened up by the passage of the vast glacier that once ground its way down to Beddgelert and beyond to what is now the Irish Sea. Remember that had you been unfortunate enough to have been here around 18,000 years ago, you would have been squashed flat under hundreds of metres of ice. As always where ice sheets have existed, you can see not only the ice-smoothed rocks but also many erratics, scattered about around this area.

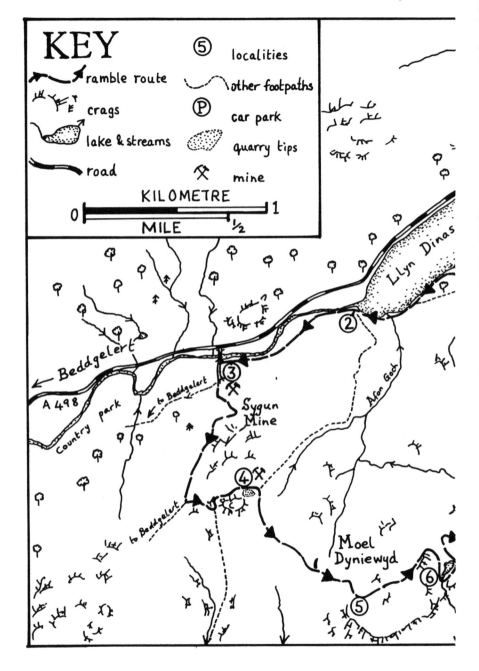

KEY

ramble route

crags

lake & streams

road

⑤ localities

other footpaths

Ⓟ car park

quarry tips

⚒ mine

KILOMETRE

0   1

MILE

½

Llyn Dinas

Beddgelert

A 498

Country park

to Beddgelert

③ ⚒

Sygun
Mine

Afon Goch

to Beddgelert

④ ⚒

Moel
Dyniewyd

⑤

②

⑥

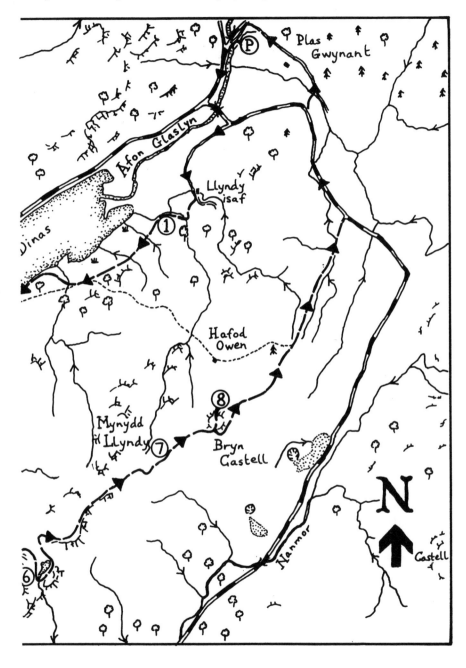

Note how the Afon Glaslyn is building out a small delta of gravels and sands. Other parts are simply silting up slowly. Right in front is a large flat area of bog with rushes, sedge and sphagnum mosses which are slowly building up to form peat. This was once part of the lake that would have come right to the base of this locality.

Away to the left, you can see Cnicht looking quite different from the handsome pyramid form which you see from the Porthmadog area.

Your route continues over this flat area, crossing a stile at the base of Locality 1 first and then skirting the former lake edge. The boggier parts of this are good places to find sundews. The peat is probably quite thick and in it will be preserved a record of the climatic events which have affected Snowdonia over the last few thousand years.

Peat and pollen: Peat, because of its extreme acidity, stops most normal decay processes. It starts to form because of waterlogging which increases the acidity. The bacteria and fungi which normally get to work simply can't function. So fibrous plants only decay partially. In particular, tough objects that fall into peat are preserved – mummified – almost perfectly. Such objects can be pollen grains, insects (whose hard body parts are made from a particularly resistant protein called chitin) and, occasionally, even people. If you were to sample the peat by boring a hole down through it and taking bits at regular intervals, you'd find (with a microscope) loads of pollen grains and probably bits of insect too. Insects are distinctive. You can easily tell a fly from a beetle for example. So, too, are pollen grains ... if you are skilled at palynology. So what? you might ask. Many plants (from which the pollen comes) and insect species are choosy about where they live – rather like people. You don't find cactuses in Wales because they don't like cold wet places. So the pollen grains or insects you find tell you a good deal about past climates. Because the peat is mostly carbon, we can date it fairly accurately using radiocarbon dating techniques (see Appendix) so you can tell *when* different pollen types were dominant. From this, you know what trees formed the local forests and, from that, what the climate was like.

The blanket peat which forms on mountains seems to have started because trees disappeared. The trees previously kept the ground aerated and sucked out the water for their own needs. Radiocarbon dates of the earliest peats show that they began to form around 5000 years ago. This just happens to coincide with a great decline in elms and although the climate changed from Atlantic to Sub-Boreal (see Timescale) at about that time, this did not mean more rainfall. So we must suspect human influences at work; people were cutting down or burning trees to make pasture for their animals. It can hardly be coincidence that the elm decline corresponds also with the earliest dates for the Lake District Langdale axes (see *Lakeland Rocky Rambles*, page 101 and 271).

After a short distance, you cross another stile at the edge of a rocky area on the left. Soon you can see an old ruin surrounded by a wall up in the wood to the left. Another stile crosses the fence on your left, doubling back up to Hafod Owen and marked with a sign. You continue on around the lakeshore, ignoring another path which bears off to the left. You'll notice bog myrtle bushes growing in the marsh to the right of the path. Rhododendrons are beginning to take over this area and once established, are almost impossible to remove. As you'll see, vigorous cutting campaigns are trying to keep them under control.

After you cross a new ladder stile, you find yourself forced quite close to the lake by a small scree slope and crags on the left. From here, you can see the outlet of the lake through a small gorge. The rocks on your left are LRTF and in this area are mostly strongly welded. **The other track rejoins from the left as you come to a wall with a ladder stile over an old iron gate. Continue on to the lake outlet.**

Keep your eyes peeled for water birds. I've seen more than one type of duck here and small shore waders like sandpipers (Fig. 7.1) and grey wagtails (which are mostly yellow). Stonechats nest in the rocky areas as do wrens.

Figure 7.1: *Common sandpiper.*

On bird song and human noise ... This is a beautiful walk. All you hear are the tiny song of wrens, the chack-chack of stonechats or the sweet cadences of willow warblers in the woods, with the odd krronk of ravens high above. It should all be perfect, but you are continually aware of the sound of cars travelling along the busy road on the other lakeshore. In summer, this procession never ceases and reminds us of the continuous noise and poisonous smell we inflict on each other due to traffic in every part of Britain. What is in some ways worse is that on still days or nights, far away in the mountains, you can still hear traffic noise – and if not road traffic, there's always RAF fighters and helicopters to keep up the barrage of people-generated noise. Is there no solution?

At the end of the lake is another stile. If you wish to miss out the old mine, you can take the southern zigzag path up to Locality 4 (the top of the mine). Locality 2 is just after the ladder stile.

Locality 2: Smashed rocks and sticky toffee [6120 4922]

A couple of metres to the left of the track, you find glacially smoothed and polished outcrops which show you some rather surprising structures if you poke about a bit (Fig. 7.2).

In these outcrops, you'll find the stump of an iron post. Just beside this is a very irregular contact between breccia and more homogenous-looking rock. You can follow this for 3 metres. Also near the post you can see several small concertina-like folds in the rock. Elsewhere, it's hard to see anything ... until suddenly you realise (e.g. 3 metres from the footpath signpost at the bridge) you're looking at a really smashed up rock – breccia (Fig. 7.2).

Figure 7.2: Breccia.

What does all this tell us? Some of these rocks look like flow rocks – lavas. They may have been intrusive; we can't tell from these outcrops. They may have been welded portions of the LRTF which began to flow slowly and thickly, like sticky toffee when still hot. Other parts are obviously smashed up. This could be primary – the result of explosive activity during eruptions meaning that these breccia lumps are volcaniclasts. Or they could have formed due to secondary explosions when the hot ignimbrite interacted with seawater, for we know that most of these eruptions were actually under the sea. Or do you have any other ideas? Whatever it was, there were hot, steamy and violent goings-on here once.

The track is now something of a gravelled highway. Keep on along the southeast side of the river. The lower mountain slopes left of the track are in parts almost completely smothered in rhododendrons. **After ¾ kilometre, you come to a road bridge and you'll notice a couple of iron waterwheels advertising Sygun Copper Mine. Turn left onto the road and so, passing a car park on the left, to the old mine: Locality 3.**

Sygun Mine: Locality 3 [605 487]

At the mine, there's a small museum and you can have a mine tour for £4 (adult), emerging higher up the hillside at Victoria level. Here there is a working water wheel (Fig. 7.3), though it is not powering anything any more.

There are a few trucks on the original rail tracks and a small picnic site (you'll find plenty of more peaceful spots than this later on the ramble).

There's even a display depicting the hillside above with a geological description of the ash flow tuffs and the faults sketched on for you, so it's worth looking at. You'll find an interesting array of ore minerals in glass cases (the only time you can't touch the exhibits in all of these rocky rambles) near the mine entrance waiting area.

For information about the mine and mine tours, call 01766890 595. It's open every day from 10 am.

Ingrid Bergmann woz 'ere ... Sygun Mine, formerly derelict, briefly became a Chinese village for the filming of *The Inn of the Sixth Happiness* in 1958.

The rocks here are mostly the LRTF though there are outcrops of the Bedded Pyroclastic Formation near the mine entrance. There are even sandstones from the rocks below the LRTF. This is odd because the LRTF is thick and the BPF should overlie it whilst the sandstones should underlie it. This tells us something of the amount of fault movement which took place here, mixing these different rocks up. These faults formed the plumbing system through which mineral-bearing hot fluids passed. Copper, lead and zinc minerals precipitated out from these fluids to form the ores. You'll see one such fault at the next locality.

Figure 7.3: *Waterwheel at Sygun Mine. This is powered by the water which drains from the deep adit level.*

The footpath turns off right before the fenced mine area and begins to zigzag its way up the mountainside. (A broad track to Beddgelert forks off almost immediately to the right.) Pass through a double gate and walk on up. At the second zigzag, there's a viewpoint across to Yr Aran and Y Lliwedd. Behind is the Victoria level which is where you come out after the mine tour. The area around is a little desolate, firstly because of the old mine dumps and secondly because of the continuing battle against rhododendron invasion. The air has the distinctive acrid sulphury smell which I associate with oxidising pyrite and the rhododendrons have taken over almost everywhere, covering the entire slope with their waxy dark green luxuriance.

The path continues on up the hillside through the rhododendrons. It's a steady slog along an old miners' track to the higher levels of the mine. Eventually, the bushes decline as you approach the ridge and, after a sharp left turn, find a signpost (Sygun-Beddgelert). The path from Beddgelert joins here. Keep straight on – head east – to the pass of Bwlch y Sygyn.

If you glance over to the opposite side of the valley, you see the vigorous stream Nant-y-cwm plunging down a series of waterfalls caused by the glaciers which oversteepened the valley sides to make a small hanging valley. When the stream reaches the flat valley floor over which the mature Afon Glaslyn meanders peacefully, it dumps any coarse debris it has carried to build out an alluvial cone. Craflwyn Hall is built at the west edge of this cone.

At the pass is a ruined wall. To the right is an old collapsed level with a dump on which you can find pieces of quartz but little else. You can see the vertical quartz veins the miners were trying out at the top of the collapse. The grassy path flattens out with ice-smoothed outcrops all around, heading towards a prominent rocky dome about 200 metres dead ahead. Shortly, you come out into a shallow valley with the craggy mass looming up in front of you. Here, the track divides. The right hand branch runs down to Nanmor. You take the left branch (to head north and then east) which begins to climb, swinging round the head of this little valley to pass just to the north of the rocky dome. By now, you can see much farther afield – down to Porthmadog and Traeth Mawr. When the track ceases to ascend, you reach a new wire fence and bear left, following the fence down to a ladder stile. Cross this and head for the top mine workings which you can see ahead on the northwest side of a shallow valley. This is Locality 4 and where you rejoin the ramble if taking the short cut from Locality 2.

Locality 4: Open stopes and former industry [6057 4830]

Here you can examine the highest workings of the Sygun Mine and search for minerals on the dumps. The first level you find is almost collpased but the small opening that remains exhausts a clammy cold draught with the characteristic mouldy sulphurous smell of old mines. The existence of a draught indicates connection through to other workings elsewhere lower down the mountainside. Directly above are orange-stained dumps and

stopes where the vein was mined out. You can examine these quite easily –
rather too easily – but be warned! You may not come out again. They are
very steep and the rocks inside are worn smooth and slippery. By all means,
peep cautiously in but ***don't go in.***

The dip of the former veins is steep – 45-60°. They trend almost north-
south, cutting through the strongly cleaved LRTF. You can imagine the effort
involved in getting the ore minerals out here. The hanging wall forms the
roof and the footwall the floor and the veins must have been up to 2 metres
thick. You can see a few traces of the minerals from this vein on the dump
directly below the stope: brassy yellow chalcopyrite and a few tiny silvery
cubes of galena.

Echoes ... Old stopes are scary mournful places alive with spirits of the imagination.
If you're on your own, this effect is magnified. Deep down in this echoing chamber
you can hear drips and plops of water. And you wonder ... how deep? ... where does
it go? ... does anything live down there? And you think of trolls lurking in the dark and
... well, I'll leave it to your imagination.

If you want, it's only a few metres of scrambling to the top of this heavily
glaciated small mountain (318 metres high). A little further northeast from
the stopes is a large slab which you might expect to be bedding but is actually
a joint partly covered in quartz and, from the rusty iron stains, probably
there was once a good deal of pyrite too. You can see how the miners have
picked away at the cross-cutting quartz veins here to see if they contained
worthwhile copper minerals.

There's one other run-in level here plus remains of buildings and ore
dressing floors. The tips below the levels are made of discarded lumps of
iron-stained tuff with quartz and decaying pyrite and a little fine grained
chalcopyrite.

**There's a little more to see if you want better mineral specimens. When
you come to the footpath signpost, turn left along a little track which takes
you to more workings about 50 metres away around the edge of the hill.**
Here you can find large lumps of granular decaying pyrite (silvery white)
mixed with chalcopyrite (brassy yellow). This seems to have been a dressing
floor where the ore was broken up and separated and, in one place, crushed.
Where all this came from becomes clear if you just climb a little above these
dumps. Here is an open shaft with water at the bottom, safely closed off with
steel bars.

**The next stage of the walk is a path which is clear enough on the ground
but not marked on the OS map. It heads southeast to Moel y Dyniewyd, the
highest point on the ramble (382 metres). Back at the signpost, take the
path to 'Aberglaslyn', heading south. After about 150 metres, there's a fence
on the right and a ladder stile and the main track goes down to Aberglaslyn.
But you keep on the less prominent path, more or less following the new
fence up towards Moel y Dyniewyd. (This fence replaces an old one, the
iron posts of which you see occasionally and which corresponds roughly
to the green boundary of National Trust land shown on the OS map.) The
path meanders about, always near the fence on your right and shortly you**

pass a large glacial perched block. Cross a valley with a small tarn (marked on the OS map). Here, ice must have passed laterally across this low col, and meltwaters may have gushed from one side to the other too. **Now the path climbs more steeply up the rocky slopes to Moel y Dyniewyd summit. The fence-builders have provided occasional ladder stiles for you where the pre-existing track crosses the line of the new fence . At the top of a steep scrambly bit, the path – which seems uncertain which side of the fence it really wants to be – continues clearly on the south side, and there's a stile. You stay on the south side from here on. Soon you reach the summit: Locality 5.**

Locality 5: Moel y Dyniewyd summit, tuffs and a view [6121 4769]

You have a wonderful all-round view from this minor summit. Snowdon, of course, dominates with Llyn Dinas below. To the south is Yr Arddu, on the opposite side of the Nanmor valley. Here you can see definite evidence of bedding in the shape of long parallel terraces picked out by heather and screes, with a rather more massive formation at the top (Fig. 7.4). This top unit is a rhyolite intrusion which, as in many other places, forced its way into the still-hot pile of ash flow tuffs. These intrusions were simply pods of magma which never quite made it to the Big Time: 'failed ignimbrites' which never got to erupt and have their spectacular, once-only debut on this volcanic stage; they just quietly oozed their way in.

Figure 7.4: *Yr Arddu with its obvious, almost flat-lying bedding features and rhyolite sill (R) on top. Behind is Cnicht, partly formed by dolerite and rhyolite sills.*

The Yr Arddu tuffs are almost the same as those upon which you're standing (or sitting) here: the LRTF, but Yr Arddu was itself a minor eruption centre on the other side of a great system of active faults, the BFZ, which today underlie the Nanmor and Gwynant valleys. These faults, and many other similar ones, moved either up or down in response to the various stresses set up by the injection of magma not far below in the crust. At certain critical times, the magma burst out at the surface, often guided by the faults which acted as conduits. Eruptions were mostly under the sea and spewed out unimaginable quantities (p. 231) of ignimbrites such as the LRTF.

A curious feature of the BFZ was that, with the passage of time, the focus of volcanic activity moved northeast along it. The earliest eruptions on this line were the Pitt's Head Tuff ignimbrites (pp. 98-99). Later came the Yr Arddu Tuff and later still the main LRTF eruption centred somewhere near Y Lliwedd (p. 246). Then followed numerous rhyolite intrusions. Much further northeast, the Crafnant centre (Ramble 8) burst into life followed finally by the Dolgarrog Volcanic Formation, the most youthful of all Snowdonia's volcanic events.

Humps or hollows? We usually associate volcanoes with huge symmetrical peaks like Mount Fujiyama, towering above the surrounding land – or sea. Snowdonia, 455 million years ago, was almost always covered by the sea. So most of the volcanoes erupted beneath the waves. This created some problems for earlier geologists because for many years people thought that if you found welded tuffs, which many of these rocks are, they just had to be erupted on land (see Box, p. 118). So everyone thought in terms of traditional volcanoes. After much work, the evidence became too strong to ignore: you could get welding below the sea and it followed that many of the Snowdonia eruptions were submarine – as other lines of evidence were strongly suggesting. As it turned out, the eruptions came from and mostly stayed in grabens – controlled by active faults and the eruptions themselves. As magma vomited out, calderas collapsed in on themselves (Box, p. 50), often triggering more eruptions ... and more subsidence. Some of the really huge eruptions like the LRTF were almost entirely confined to these northeast-trending grabens. This is why they're enormously thick in the Snowdon area but you find almost no trace of them further away. Had the eruptions been from a volcano sticking high up into the atmosphere as many do, then highly mobile events like ignimbrite eruptions would have meant a huge area of surrounding land covered by ash flows with accompanying ash falls up to hundreds of kilometres away (as at Mount Katmai; see page 231). Yet if you look at rocks which were laid down at the same time not far away in North Wales, you find almost no traces of these catastrophic events. This makes sense when you realise that the eruptions were under the sea, for the sea would quench any eruption column almost totally.

Later earth movements compressed the rocks into folds (as at Clogwyn Du'r Arddu, p. 54). Yr Arddu is the core of one such major syncline. An upfold, anticline, runs parallel to this along the Nanmor valley where it is also cut by the big faults I mentioned. Then there's another rather complex syncline just west of Llyn Dinas, and another anticline in the Cwm Llan valley (Ramble 10).

Due east is the great glacial cwm of Llyn Llagi with its craggy backwall, all formed by dolerite sills (Ramble 9). Moel Siabod, further away to the northeast, is also largely built of a great dolerite sill. The rocks which form this mountain top locality are almost white. If you examine them, you'll see that they are all tuff breccias with angular lumps up to fist-sized. About 200 metres southeast of this locality, the tuffs form steep crags overlooking the valley. The crags mark a dramatic change from the softer, older rocks below, which underlie the LRTF (Cwm Eigiau Formation). This noticeable change continues northeast for several kilometres and explains why you'll see several old slate quarries below on the valley sides.

Keep to the rather vague path on the right of the fence down to the col about ½ kilometre to the northeast and then make an optional detour to a tiny nameless lake and the next locality: 6. Skirt the lake and cross its outlet (south end) where someone has placed crude stepping stones and head for a great mass of white boulders on the southeast shore.

Locality 6: White rocks and weird water [6170 4781]

What do you make of these pure white rocks? They are, of course, quartz; solid masses of it. It doesn't seem to be a vein but more of a plug of quartz, metres thick, almost as if it was an intrusion. Just on the other side of the rocky bluff, 100 metres to the southeast, the tuffs are in contact with the underlying slate formation. Could this be something to do with hydrothermal activity? When the hot ash flow whooshed out over the mud seafloor, vast amounts of water would have been trapped in the sludgy muds below the flow. Much of this water must have flashed to superheated steam and blasted its way up through the flow. Superheated seawater fluids are pretty corrosive and able to dissolve many normally insoluble minerals like quartz. So maybe this quartz plug is the blocked and completely silicified remnant of a steam vent. This could explain the plug-like mass because, as you've seen elsewhere, quartz normally occurs in sheetlike veins along faults or joints.

What about the lake. Why is it here in a sort of niche half way up a steep, craggy slope? The answer, you'll have guessed, is something to do with the glaciers.

This is not like ordinary glacial cwms. How could it have formed? Here are some ideas: 1). A tongue of ice could have forced its way over the col (from which you descended just now), bursting out of the Gwynant valley glacier (which was large). The rock around this locality proved tougher than usual – perhaps because of the cementing effect of the quartz – and so the tongue split into two, carving this horn-shape you see now; 2). again because of the resistance of what is now the southeast side of today's lake, the glacier moving down from the higher ground to the east gouged out the slightly softer rock where the lake now exists; 3). as these huge ice masses began to melt, a torrent of rock-charged (and therefore very powerfully erosive) meltwater briefly ran off the glacier and cut its way into the bedrock at the edge. This would have been an ice-margin meltwater channel. All three processes may have been in action here. Glacial meltwaters have extraordinary potency when it comes to rapidly cutting channels during their brief lives. Much of northern Britain is littered with examples of such channels, some miles long, though the longer ones are generally associated with large temporary lakes whose normal outlets had been blocked by ice sheets.

This is a wonderful place on a warm summer's day for heather flowers and bumble bees. You can find three species of heather here: ling (*Calluna vulgaris*), cross-leaved heath (*Erica tetralix*) and bell heather (*Erica cinerea*).

Return to the col. Even here, one or two rhododendrons are beginning to take a hold. Pull them out if you see them. They are uninvited guests. **Keep to the right (southeast) side of the fence up to the next summit (343 metres). From the top, you see the remainder of the ramble, now without a path at all, but easy enough because you head for the prominent landmark of Bryn Castell with its Scots pines, the final locality.** You can also see clearly into the upper part of the Nanmor valley with its slate quarries, reminding you that you are never very far above the base of the LRTF as you walk northeast.

The fence goes on over to Mynydd Llyndy. Follow the fence down for a short way and fork off to the right – don't continue on to Mynydd Llyndy – and head for Bryn Castell (northeast). There's some fairly boggy ground ahead, so keep well to the right of it, close to the top of the rather diminished scarp you've been following since Moel y Dyniewyd. The walking is easy enough with glacier-smoothed rocky knolls, heather patches and short turf as well as the boggy bits. (If the cloud is low, you could get lost here though it's unlikely you'd come to any harm because the steep crags are mostly behind you.) Once you get down to the lower ground, you temporarily lose sight of Bryn Castell, but keep heading in that direction, staying well to the right just above the crags. There are several sheep tracks and there's no one way which is better than another. The next locality is almost due east of Mynydd Llyndy, just a few metres (as the crow flies) from an old dry stone wall which runs along the base of the same scarp you've been following since Moel y Dyniewyd, now reduced to a series of little crags. You should pick up a bit of a path here as you head towards a prominent wall which, trending northeast, goes up and over the scarp ahead. The next locality is 5 metres left of the path, about 30 metres before you reach the highest part of this wall.

Locality 6: Find it if you can! Something different ... [6236 4845]

This is by way of a change from the LRTF you've been seeing all day. Here you have strongly cleaved sedimentary rocks with a 'pod' of rhyolite pebbles or cobbles (Fig. 7.5). The beds dip southeast quite clearly, in marked contrast to the generally featureless tuffs which overlie them. These beds must be close to the contact between the LRTF and the underlying sediments which are mostly sandstones in this immediate area. Further down towards Nanmor, the rocks are entirely mudstones and siltstones (Cwm Eigiau Formation).

There are several small faults near here which shift the rocks around a bit, but further to the north, things are about to change abruptly as you will shortly see.

Figure 7.5: *Pebble bed. Notice how the once rounded or oval pebbles and cobbles have been squeezed by the cleavage forces into spindle shapes*

Walk along the path towards the wall and Bryn Castell. You'll see a few more outcrops of the pebble bed by the path. **You cross the wall at a large gap and beyond is the final locality: Bryn Castell.**

Head for Bryn Castell and another gap in a different wall so that you need not climb any. These walls no longer serve any purpose though that's no reason to knock them down. Make your way around to the south end of Bryn Castell where you find a small path which takes you up to its summit. This is Locality 8.

Bryn Castell; a contemplative spot: Locality 8 [626 486]

Castle Hill, the English translation, doesn't sound half so good, does it? This is a charming place to sit – plenty of comfortable grassy spots – and soak up the quiet grandeur. You can see the whole southeastern sector of the Snowdon range from Yr Aran to Gallt y Wenallt (above the invisible Llyn Gwynant), the eastern Glyderau (including – just – Castell y Gwynt), Moel Siabod and the great dolerite precipices of Craig Llyn-llagi. Above this is another lake – Llyn yr Adar (Ramble 9). Just 1½ kilometres away to the southeast is another prominent castle rock: Castell. This is a plug of intrusive rhyolite which may have been a feeder for some of the Yr Arddu tuffs, now eroded away completely but which once would have overlain Castell. Castell lies on the axis of the Yr Arddu Syncline which I mentioned back at Moel y Dyniewyd summit.

Bryn Castell itself owes its origin to one of those many accidents of glacial scouring. Its component rock – which we shall examine presently – must have been just that little bit harder than the surrounding rock, so it is preserved as this rather striking *roche moutonée*, now attractively decorated with Scots pines and a few larches (Fig. 7.6 A & B). A few small spruces (alias Christmas trees) have been planted here too. Parts of the top have been fenced to keep the sheep out and see what regeneration occurs. Tiny pines and larches seem to be appearing as you might expect.

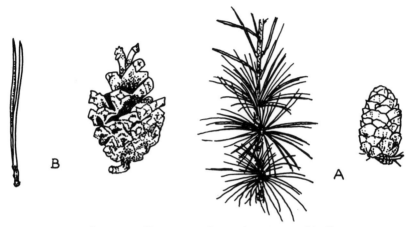

Figure 7.6: *A – Larch cone and leaves, B – Scots pine cone and leaf.*

Below, the dark ranks of the rhododendron forest march onwards, now almost surrounding Hafod Owen, and spreading over to Nanmor. They seem to have no enemies and evidently thrive in the poor acid soils here.

Return along the little path to the bottom of the rock. Walk around the east side to the small crags and fallen blocks near the ladder stile which crosses the wall here. The fallen blocks are the easiest to examine. In the largest block just 3 metres from the stile, you can see a clear slump fold in the tuffite. The rock is mostly a fairly massive tuffite with beds of lapilli. Everything suggests that it was once wet and although it superficially looks like the LRTF, it cannot be because of this watery origin. You never see slumps – and rarely see beds – in the main body of the ash flows. This rock must have a different origin and is regarded by geologists as a different formation – a volcanic megabreccia – though closely linked to the violent events of the LRTF eruptions. The megabreccia, as its name tells you, is simply a breccia with some very large chunks in it.

It's only possible to determine how big the chunks are from careful mapping out of the bedding structures inside them. Bryn Castell may itself be entirely part of one chunk for some reach the size of a football pitch! Unlike the tuffs, these breccias slid and slumped into place, almost certainly due to earthquakes and general instability caused by fault movements along the BFZ, eruptions and caldera margin collapse before the really huge LRTF eruption got into its stride.

Wood sorrel grows in and near Bryn Castell as do quite a few bluebells in spring. An old ivy clings to the east face above the fallen blocks.

Cross the stile and head on northeast along a fairly distinct path. This eventually become a proper track. A few 'false' cypresses (*Chamaecyparis* which despite their name are members of the Cypress Family) grow in this area, presumably planted years ago because they are not a native species. Today, you're more likely to find cultivars of these (the ubiquitous *leylandii*) growing as 'instant' hedges in British suburbs. Away to the left, you can just make out the white painted cottage Hafod Owen not quite lost in the rhododendron forest. It's a lovely gentle descent through this wild 'park land' with its Scots pines, larches and rowans and glacier-smoothed or broken outcrops, glacial boulders and green grassy hollows. From here, Bryn Castell is particularly dome-like (Fig. 7.7).

Figure 7.7: *Bryn Castell dome from northeast. The foreground is ice-smoothed megabreccia decorated by various conifers.*

About 150 metres before a wall with a gate and larch spinney to the left, you should spot a prominent perched boulder on top of the ice-smoothed outcrops to your left. Walk up to this (Rhododendrons may swamp this view in years to come) and look towards the spinney. About 30 metres in front of you, across a shallow depression, is an exciting outcrop facing back to Bryn Castell (Fig. 7.8). In it you can see a big raft of bedded sediment 'floating' in a former slurry of tuffite which has slumped and slid down a submarine slope. Now you get an idea of what the term 'megabreccia' refers to; the breccia lumps are big, many much bigger than this.

Figure 7.8: *Megabreccia with large chunk, shaped a bit like the South Island of New Zealand above and left of my binoculars. Can you find any more of these rafts in these or nearby outcrops? I've seen boulders of volcanics up to football-size.*

The track, now a tractor track, comes to the wall with its gate. Go through this – the footpath to Hafod Owen joins from the left (you saw the other end of this just after Locality 1 at Llyn Dinas) – and keep on right back to the Nanmor road. Notice how the area to your right is flat and rather featureless and marshy. The ineffectual attempts at drainage have had no effect but to expose the sub-soils to gullying. These gullies do show you what lies under the bog though. The top is a thin peat layer with a few tree roots preserved in it – mute testimony to former tree cover. Beneath this is a pale grey boulder-rich clay. This is a good example of a glacial till – the rubbish left behind by decaying ice masses. This featureless, boggy 'dead ground' typifies a landscape covered by till. Flat areas like this with clumps of soft rushes are almost always underlain by this non-draining stony clay (also called boulder clay). **Cross a ladder stile some 150 metres before the road.**

Just before the road, you'll see a trial level for slate to the right of the track with an oak tree growing out of it. This rock is quite different to anything you've seen today: a familiar grey slate with no trace of bedding but an almost vertical cleavage. These are part of the immensely thick former mud and silt deep seafloor deposits which preceded the megabreccias and the LRTF.

Turn left onto the road and walk on down the hill. In spring, this is enchanting. The pure white Welsh Mountain lambs skip about, observe you with innocent curiosity or suck from their dams, birdsong fills the woodlands and the little streams splash their way down towards the valley. Here too you see a remarkable variety of trees like redwoods, oaks, hazels, birches, hollies and the inevitable rhododendrons.

After ³/₄ kilometre, the road bends round to the left. Off to your right is a public footpath which you take. This crosses the Afon Llynedno after which you turn left (footpath sign) onto the track back to the carpark, passing through a white iron gate, and join the metalled road from Plas Gwynant. At first, approaching the bridge, you go through a tunnel of rhododendrons and holly though the woods include fine examples of deodar and blue Atlas cedars too. The bridge, a fine stone arch, seems partly collapsed and is covered in moss. The stream is clear with mossy boulders and a deep pool below the bridge. Plas Gwynant is built in some beautiful park land with gentle moraine hills and grand cedars, oaks and wellingtonias (*Sequoiadendron giganteum*). **Finally, you pass through the Plas Gwynant entrance gate to arrive back at the carpark.**

Rocky Ramble 8: The Crafnant Country

How to get to the start of the ramble

From Betws-y-coed, take the B5106 (to Llanrwst) which crosses the Afon Llugwy, turning immediately left just after the bridge by a little car park. This is the start of a small road that takes you through some attractive mixed woodlands not far above the river, but later climbs steeply past a small farm (Pencraig) to a T junction where you turn right. After half a kilometre, turn sharp left up through more forest and past several black mine dumps. The road drops down to a sharp right bend at Tan-y-llyn. Just 300 metres further on is an attractive picnic site and car park, right beside the south end of Llyn Geirionydd. The car park, operated by Forest Enterprise, cost (in 1995) £1 to park all day. This is the start of the ramble. Note that you can get here from Trefriw and Llanrhychwyn, but there are gates across the road which can be a bit tedious.

The nearest you can get to by bus is the Ugly House – Ty-hyll, Capel Curig – at the Afon Llugwy bridge [756 575].You then have a 4-kilometre road walk to the start but the road is tiny, quiet and pleasant through forests and past old mines. Services 19 and 95 can get you there. Check times with Alpine Bus/Crosville Cymru at 01492 596969 and KMP at 01286 878880. Selwyns buses, No. 19A, run on Sundays (01492 640814).

Needs, distances and times

You can do this ramble in half a day – if you're in a hurry. I'd recommend not hurrying and taking your time to look at the rocks and plants, lakes and valleys, as you walk. The walk is about 8 kilometres (5 miles) with about 120 metres (just under 500 feet) of climbing, and so it's easy. It's a walk that you might prefer to do on a day when the higher mountain rambles further to the west would be unpleasant because of the weather. The highest point on this ramble is only 330 metres, one third the height of Snowdon.

The Outdoor Leisure OS map is Sheet 17.

Llyn Geirionydd and a mine

Set off southwest along the road towards Tan-y-llyn. At the lake end, turn right onto a gravel forestry track and walk for around 100 metres whereupon the track swings left up the hill. To the right are a gate and stile. Hop over the stile to find the footpath that continues along the west side of the lake, starting below Ty-newydd (a cottage). Ahead now is an attractive area of mixed forestry plantation and you can see to perfection a perched block on the skyline, abandoned around 15,000 years ago by the glaciers.

Llyn Geirionydd is, like all the natural lakes in Snowdonia, the result of huge glaciers that once filled this valley, grinding and scooping out the rocky basin which the lake now fills. The lake actually exists because the glacier was able to scoop more deeply into the softer rocks below the valley floor. At the outlet is a natural rock dam. As the stream cuts down through the dam, it will lower the lake level so that the lake will diminish. At the same time, another process is gradually destroying the lake: it's slowly filling in with sands and muds from in-rushing flood waters. All lakes are ephemeral

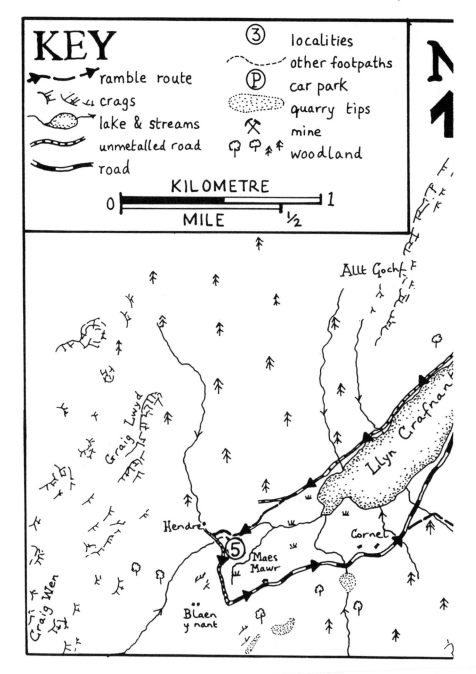

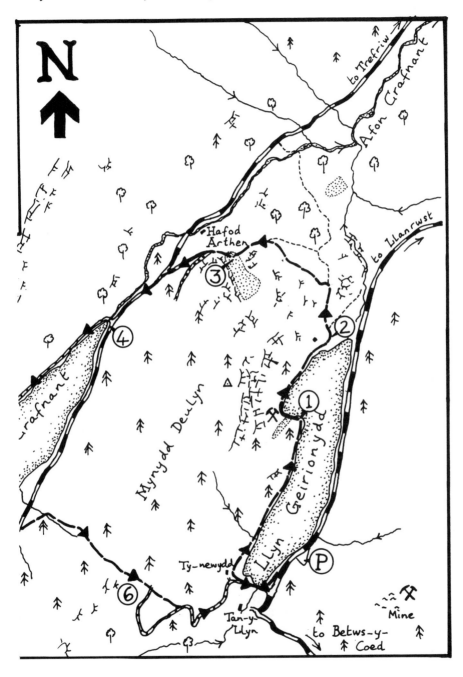

though the bigger they are, the longer they last. This is the same process that is gradually blocking up the capacity of Lake Nasser, impounded by the Aswan High Dam on the River Nile, and which will do the same to the gigantic new Yangtse River dams which the Chinese Government have begun to build.

The country around here has a striking 'grain' (like that in a plank of wood), with the streams, lakes and ridges all trending northeast-southwest. There's a good reason for this alignment: the rocks themselves.

After 100 metres or so, cross another small stile and enter the forest, at first a stand of young beech trees followed by beautiful larches. The path zigzags about, never far from the lake shore and, at one point, seems to run straight into the lake where the shoreline kinks sharply round to the west. This is the start of Locality 1.

Introducing the Crafnant rocks: Locality 1 [763 611]

Where the path seems to end, a great nose of rock plunges right into the lake (Fig. 8.1). If you examine this, you'll see that it is beautifully smoothed by the grinding and polishing action of the former ice sheets. Behind this nose of rock, you can see for the first time the imposing crags of Mynydd Deulyn with aprons of scree below. These crags, like the rock beneath your feet here, form the middle part of the Crafnant Volcanic Formation, the northeastern representative of the great Snowdon Volcanic Group which you've already seen. These thick units of ash flow tuff represented brief interludes of violence as these flows roiled and boiled across the deep seafloor on which mud would have been normally, quietly and slowly, settling out. It is the muds that formed the weaker rocks – the Cadnant Shales – gouged out by the Llyn Geirionydd glacier, but it is the orientation of the tough volcanic rocks which gives the country its northeast-southwest 'grain' which I mentioned earlier. Here, these sheets of tuffs are dipping at a moderate angle to the southeast, but as you'll see, this changes dramatically by Locality 3.

The path doesn't really disappear here, merely doubling back to give you a scramble up and over the rocky nose and then down to a little cove at the edge of the lake, protected by the nose of rock. Here you cross the remains of the lower workings of an old mine, now sturdily fenced. You can find numbers of large boulders lying about which are stuffed with white quartz veins. The miners were following some sort of fracture in the rocks – a fault. You can see this fracture exposed where the miners have driven levels into it, and stoped out the veins, which dip steeply southeast and are vertical in part, and in places reached a metre thick.

What were the miners after? It's hard to tell now for there's nothing much left apart from quartz and pyrite and you should spot some of the dark brown to black, zinc-bearing mineral, sphalerite. But this mine, like most in this district, was probably mostly for lead (galena).

Figure 8.1: *The Crafnant volcanics forming the crags and screes above Llyn Geirionydd.*

The host rock for the veins, as you can see, is not the Crafnant ash flows but a dark grey mudstone. Later, you'll see more of these muddy-silty rocks – the backdrop to the exciting but short-lived violence of the volcanic eruptions. These former muds and silts separate the ash flow tuffs everywhere in the Crafnant area.

The lowest entrance to the mine is just above the lake shore and to this day effectively drains the old workings.

Walk on to emerge from the forestry area, crossing a new ladder stile where a fence runs out into the lake. Above on your left is a neat white house, Glan Ceirionydd, with an interesting mix of trees planted in its garden. To your right is a monkey puzzle tree, native of the Andes in Chile (Araucaria araucana). These trees occur, like us, as separate sexes (many trees are hermaphrodites which certainly might offer some advantages to us too!). The female trees bear large round cones which contain up to 180 edible seeds. **Ahead is an obelisk, the next locality, though the path is now waymarked by posts sporting yellow arrows and walker symbols and takes you round to the right past a small building. You then turn left to the obelisk.**

Colofn Taliesin monument: Locality 2 [764 615]

As you can see from the plaque, Lord Willoughby D'eresby set up this monument to commemorate the reputed birthplace of Taliesin, Chief Bard in the 6th century. This monument was evidently destroyed in a storm in 1976, only to be re-erected in 1994. Just beside the monument are a couple of large stone blocks with a third block – the broken remains of the old column – resting on them to form a sort of bench for sitting on. If you're already sitting on it, stand up so you can see what I'm talking about! The blocks are silicified mudstone or fine-grained tuffs but what is interesting here is not the rocks themselves (for once), but the graffiti people have carved on them. Some are quite beautifully done with some at least 130 years old: Joseph Hughes of Liverpool.

> Today, although graffiti are as popular as ever, no one spends much time on them. A few crude scratches with a penknife are the rule or, even quicker, a spray paint can (as any New York subway traveller knows). The Lynas Law of Graffiti states that the quality of a graffitus is directly related to its antiquity. Is this a reflection upon the times in which we live?

From this column, you have a fine view back up the lake with an especially good view of the old mine workings at Locality 1: the black chasm, the stoped-out remains of the mine.

At this end of the lake, you can see several clear roches moutonées, small humps of rock separated by marshy or heathery hollows, clearly showing that the ice which fashioned them moved from south to north – down-valley as you'd expect.

Our ramble continues along the hollow to the west of the monument up an obvious grassy track heading slightly east of north. On one side is

bracken; on the other, gorse. This track was where the ore from the mine you've just visited was trammed out down to the old Klondyke Mine [765622] processing plant in the Afon Geirionydd valley. **To your left as you walk, you'll see variable-sized spruce trees whilst to the right is a stone wall and another roche moutonée quite high above you. A rather stunted holly tree grows on its top.** As you walk, a splendid view opens before you down the Crafnant valley. High on the opposite side is a farm with a pale green corrugated iron barn which is quite a landmark (well, sort of half way between a landmark and an eyesore really). If you come here in autumn, the colours are rather special because the valley is cloaked in a wonderful diversity of trees.

Just as the track starts to descend, you pass through the remains of a wall. Almost immediately on your left is a rather less obvious track, although it's quite well used. This is your route. The main track continues on down the hill. Your track drops down into a small boggy valley, passing under a power line as it does so. (Note that this path is not marked on the OS map. The one they show – green dashes – simply isn't there, the real path running parallel to the imaginary one, but about 100 metres north.) Just past the power lines in the little valley you should spot some beautiful little common polypody ferns growing amongst the bracken which are also members of the same Polypody Family.

Just after the little valley, you cross a dry stone wall by way of a sturdy wooden ladder stile. The path contours round the northeast side of Mynydd Deulyn passing groups of hawthorn, birch and ash trees – all small at present – **and a few rather fine hollies and, of course, the ubiquitous bracken. Shortly you meet another track coming in from the right, but you keep on round to the left, slightly uphill to a wall that you cross. Then descend steeply for about 20 metres,** following the volcanic rocks which also plunge down the slope quite steeply as smooth, ice-polished surfaces.

As the track climbs again slightly, away to your right you can see a level area on the valley side with orange-purple-grey screes of rocks, the dump from yet another mine. Below in the valley bottom (marked on the OS map as 'Works') is the site of the old Klondyke Mine mill). **Another prominent walking track angles into ours from the right, but you carry on round towards Llyn Crafnant.** High above, you can see the tips from an old quarry, right at the end of the ridge of Mynydd Deulyn. A little further along, you have a clear view of the quarry and the rocky outcrops above and around it. Here, the beds dip very clearly at around 40° to the northwest, contrasting with those around Locality 1 that dipped in the opposite direction. In fact, you're walking round the plunging nose of an anticline, a great fold in the rock sequence like the arch of a bridge, but tipping over sideways. You've seen one side of the arch. Now you'll see the other.

Continue on around towards the quarries. As you walk, you begin to have a view into the upper part of the Crafnant valley, across to Cae Crwn farm. High above the farm is an obvious dipping line of outcrops, marked by a dry stone wall that runs along the base of the screes generated from the rocks above (Allt Gôch on the OS map, immediately north of Llyn Crafnant).

This is the same unit of the Crafnant Volcanic Formation that you scrambled over at Locality 1 (just before the mine), but the rock unit, along with those both below and above it, has been squeezed by earth movements into a series of anticlines and synclines. Fortunately for the geologists who surveyed this complex area, the contrast between the volcanic units and the interleaved mudstones mean that they are quite easy to follow. The tough volcanics make craggy and vigorous features (like Allt Gôch) whilst the soft mudstones form hollows and you don't often see them as a result.

As you round the corner, you hear the distant roaring of the water flowing down a series of rapids and waterfalls from Llyn Crafnant and you're confronted by the massive inclined series of quarries that descend from the upper parts you saw at first. Now you begin to see that the canny quarrymen used the strong dipping slab of the overlying volcanic unit as a roof so that they could safely quarry away at the softer mudstones below (Fig. 8.2a). The mudstones have, as almost everywhere in Snowdonia, been converted into slates. **At the lowest quarry (Fig 8.2b) there's a flat grassy platform with ruined buildings and more tips below. Most of the quarrying was underground. The path makes its way down to the lower quarry across** the fairly steep dip slope of one of the several Crafnant ash flow tuffs.

Figure 8.2(a): *Upper quarry areas showing the Crafnant volcanics (C) forming the inclined roof of the slate quarries. M – mudstone (slate). See also Figure 8.2(b).*

Some **75 metres before the first quarry tips,** you cross quite a large bedding plane as you follow the path. This is perhaps 10 square metres is size, formed from pale ash flow tuffs, the top of the unit that lies buried beneath the slates the quarrymen were after. You see several more of these slabby bedding surfaces **as you walk towards the quarries of Locality 3, centred on the lowest of these quarry entrances.**

The underworld of Hafod Arthen quarries: Locality 3 [759 618]

Like so many of Snowdonia's slate mines, you can actually walk right into the underground chambers. With the usual provisos about no mine or quarry being safe – there have been roof falls since the quarry closed many years ago – walk past the almost totally ruined quarry buildings to find a track around the back that drops down into the main entrance of the lowest quarry opening: a huge cavern. If you decide to venture in, it's quite an impressive chamber with a musical backdrop of dripping water. The steeply dipping roof is one of the thick Upper Crafnant units that I mentioned earlier, overlying the cleaved mudstone (slate). The mudstone is the same unit as that you saw at the first locality, repeated by folding. This usage of hard rock

Figure 8.2(b): *A continuation of Figure 8.2(a), identifying the lower quarry area at the extreme end of the inclined roof (C).*

units for roofs you can see in very many quarries and mines in Snowdonia. Volcanic rocks – tuffs, lavas – or intrusive rocks like dolerite all make safe, strong roofs, though, as you see here, they have to be supported by rock pillars (hence the mining term 'pillar and stall') which is why there is a whole series of separate chambers up the steep hillside. Just how much you could take out without causing a major collapse must have been a rather doubtful 'triumph of empiricism', sucking it and seeing. When these – and other quarries like them – opened, there were no trained engineers with surveying instruments, rock bolts and strain gauges, and life was cheap. The falls that you see here are all quite small and the fact that these chambers remain many decades later shows just how stable they are.

> **Rembrandt, Titian and van Dyck at Ffestiniog?** Yes, paintings by these famous artists – and many others – were stored for 5 years in the underground Manod Quarry near Blaenau Ffestiniog during the Second World War, safe from German bombs. The collections of the Tate and National Gallery arrived at the quarry in 1940 in lorries supposedly carrying chocolate!

This quarry once produced slates for roofing and general construction (building stone, cornerstones, lintels, doorsteps – almost anything that could be fashioned out of slate). The quarrymen would have drilled and blasted the slate to manageable blocks and then loaded the blocks onto trucks and pushed them out along a small railway line, through a tunnel. The tunnel is now mostly closed off by rock falls though originally, at least in part, it was deliberately roofed over to prevent slips of rock waste from higher parts of the quarries from blocking the exit. Any faults in the blocks, plus the smaller useless chunks brought down by blasting, formed waste which was pushed over the end of the tips, hallmarks of every slate quarry that, unfortunately, do not readily succumb to recolonisation by Nature.

The underneath of the roof-forming unit is amazingly smooth. You can see no sign of any wave ripples or any other sedimentary structures. This is because the ash flow took place entirely in the deep sea. Yet elsewhere in Snowdonia, geologists have found bizarre structures associated with hot ash flows which flowed from land volcanoes into the sea. Sometimes, gigantic blobs of the still-hot flow had separated and sunk right down into the sloppy wet muds below, separating completely from the parent flow above (p. 118).

The cleavage which cuts pervasively through the dark grey mudstone is quite steeply inclined here, disrupting any bedding traces that there might be. This means that the slate only splits along the cleavage, making finding fossils very unlikely indeed. Any kind of fossil would lie along bedding surfaces (Fig. 8.3). You'll notice that many of the slate surfaces are covered in bright orange iron oxides, indicating that these rocks contain, as is quite usual, a good deal of pyrite, now oxidised from contact with the atmosphere.

As always in such places of low light, the only plants that can survive are lichens (on the roof), mosses and ferns. The ferns have their leaves carefully angled so as to pick up the greatest amount of light from the entrance.

Figure 8.3: *This is why you hardly ever find fossils in slates ... unless the cleavage and bedding are about coincident.*

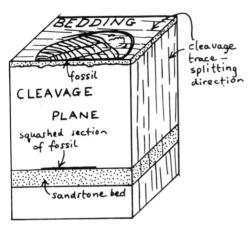

Back outside, look up to the upper workings and note the carefully built steep inclines, constructed to bring slate blocks down from the upper workings on an inclined tramway. The rail tracks were usually arranged so that two tracks ran parallel so that the weight of the loaded down-coming car was more than adequate to haul up the up-coming car (which might have carried mine supplies and even men, though this was usually strictly prohibited, p. 209). Looking at the inclines here, it's still not difficult to imagine them in operation .

Continue on now towards Llyn Crafnant. Just after the quarry tips, there's a stile. Around 10 paces before the stile, on the left of the track, you can see excellent outcrops of the Upper Crafnant volcanics and muds with some quite fresh surfaces worth looking at.

Finding fresh surfaces in which you can *see* what's going on is quite unusual. All rocks look grey (and, to be sure, these *are* grey) from a distance, usually because you can't actually see them. They're invariably covered in a thin crust of some sort of life, like lichens. Most lichens are composed of green algae and ascomycete fungi, for they are not one single organism, but two which depend utterly upon each other for survival. This explains why they're able to colonise lifeless rocks, sometimes in unbelievably hostile locations like the high Himalayas or remote nunatak peaks in Antarctica. Lichens are usually sensitive indicators of atmospheric pollution. Simply, they can't abide it (and neither should we).

Here you can see many bits and pieces of white volcanic rock (volcani-clasts), including welded tuffs, mostly thumbnail-sized or less, held together in a dark grey muddy-looking matrix full of feldspar crystals. But also, you should see some long thin squidgy-looking bits up to the length of your forearm. These are chunks of mudstone (not necessarily from here) which seem to have been ripped up and dragged into the ash flow base. Here, just above the track, you can see the actual contact between the underlying strongly cleaved and silicified mudstones and siltstones and the overlying ash flow.

Twenty paces back from the stile, also on the left, you can glimpse the mudstone itself, below the volcanic interference you've just seen. You can see distinct bands of tuffaceous sediments with small load casts and highly irregular lenticular beds, some the thickness of your palm, but which quickly thin down to nothing at all. So there's plenty of evidence of volcanic happenings before the great eruption that produced the Upper Crafnant ash flow, perhaps a few centuries or millennia later. (Remember, these fine grained sediments are deposited very slowly, so a few metres represent probably tens of thousands of years whereas one single ash flow tens of metres thick can arrive in about 10 minutes!)

Here you can pick out both cleavage and bedding quite clearly. The two structures intersect at an angle of about 30°. The bedding itself is quite noticeably disrupted in places. This might be due to compaction (differential loading) from the heavy tuff that once overlay this. Or it might be something to do with the smearing out of the delicate beds along the cleavage planes. Or both. Or something else. Any ideas?

Cross the stile and walk over the flat turn-around area at the angle of two forestry roads. Our route is the right hand one of these, down towards the river. Before you do walk on though, look to your left where recent road-making gives us some new exposures. The rocks, not particularly fresh here, seem to be largely mudstone with parts filled with chips of feldspar and volcaniclasts. This doesn't look much like the quarry ash flow that, on grounds of structure, you might expect to find here ... unless, of course, there's some kind of fault which has displaced the rock units up or down. This is wholly possible because this area is quite complicated with many irregular folds (you've already seen evidence of one of these as you approached Locality 3) and faults. On the other hand, the rock shows no sign of bedding, clear enough in the cleaved sediments as you've just seen before the stile. So what would you call this rock? Volcanic or sedimentary? In reality, such distinctions don't count for much in this sort of ancient environment, for mixed rocks (tuffites) are commonplace.

Before leaving the turn-around, take a look northeast to the hills on the other side of the Llanrwst valley. There, the scenery is quite different. The hills are lower with no crags, smooth slopes and rather boring flat-topped moorland. The scenery is different because the rocks forming it are. They are younger than these Ordovician rocks underfoot, being entirely of Silurian age: sandstones and finer-grained sediments, separated from the older volcanic-rich sequences of Snowdonia by a major series of faults that run along the Conwy-Llanrwst valley. No one knows how large these faults, which juxtapose Silurian against Ordovician, actually are ... but they're big for sure!

Now walk on down the lower (right hand) road to a gate. Below is the constant sound of the rushing Afon Crafnant whilst immediately to your right are many small birch trees and graceful hemlocks. You can always tell hemlocks (Tsuga) from afar because the tops of the trees flip over to hang downwards, almost as if the tree is tired from all the effort of just growing, quite unlike spruces, firs and pines which point straight upwards. The overall mix of trees around here, with oak woods behind, is really quite pleasing.

After going through the gate, the forest track joins the tarmac road opposite an attractive forest picnic site (Forest Enterprise). Join the road and walk for a short way up towards Llyn Crafnant and Locality 4. The Afon Crafnant has cut itself a little gorge that you see below you on the right as you walk. The river has cut this since the last glacier retreat since the powerful glaciers would have removed any earlier gorges. Now, the rapids and waterfalls provide us humans with a harmonious mix of water, sibilance and mossy boulders.

Quite abruptly, Llyn Crafnant appears before you with its backdrop of mountains and another obelisk, Locality 4.

Llyn Crafnant: Locality 4

Unlike the Taliesin monument, this one is made of polished granite (clearly not from the quarry you've just seen – the nearest worked granite intrusion being at Penmaen Mawr, Llanfairfechan), commemorating the gift of the lake together with 19 acres of land and a cottage, given by Richard James Esquire of Dyffryn, Llanrwst, AD 1896.

At the head of the valley on the left is Crimpiau, Castell y Gwynt and on the right, Craig Wen. The rugged skyline tells you immediately that these rocks are something to do with volcanoes. In fact, both Crimpiau and Craig Wen are formed of dolerite intrusions. These forced their way into the Lower Crafnant Volcanic Formation which forms most of the rough country at the head of the Crafnant valley (Fig. 8.4). The eastern and steep western slopes of the lake, including Allt Gôch (which I mentioned earlier), are all formed of the folded and faulted Middle and Upper Crafnant volcanics. In other words, this is really the heart of the Crafnant country.

Figure 8.4: *Llyn Crafnant.*

Like Llyn Geirionydd, this valley was gouged out, mostly from the softer interlayered mudstone units of these volcanic formations. In addition, a fault runs right along it, passing through the lowest part of the distant skyline between Castell y Gwynt and Craig Wen. The fault isn't very large but the shattering effect of the movement along it was quite enough to mark its site as a line of weakness for exploitative erosion for ever more. That's why today's valley is here.

The lake is here because of a rock bar that the glaciers couldn't shift, and through which the river is now slowly downcutting as you've just seen. The rock bar is, as you might expect, formed of the hard volcanic beds.

Leave the monument and cross the river by the bridge, after which you come to a galvanised kissing gate that takes you onto a broad forestry road running up the northwest lake side. Some way along the road as you approach the forested area, you come across a section cut right into the slope, showing you very clearly that the whole of the slope from Allt Gôch high above is formed by slaty scree although now completely covered in bracken or grasses. **Cross a small stream after which the forestry roads divide. Take the lower (left) fork that continues along the edge of the lake. Now you're back in forest with hemlocks, larches and beeches in addition to the more 'traditional' conifers. As you approach the lake head,** notice the usual wetland area with reeds, willows and bog plants telling you that this was once lake, but is now silted up. On the other side of the valley, you can see clearly the prominent tips of more slate quarries, exploiting mudstone units within the Crafnant Volcanics. One of these appears as a vast rectangular black hole in the rock. Look straight ahead now into the blind valley head.

Dead ahead now, partly obscuring the view behind, are four large spruce trees with a ruined building in front. About 100 metres before these, branch left off the forestry road down to a small stile. Cross this and walk past the ruin. This was, perhaps, a barn and is still quite impressive with its great slate lintel and huge rounded boulders forming the wall, pieced carefully together like a jigsaw in 3 dimensions, with smaller chocking pieces of slate and boulder and a minimal amount of mortar to help hold it all together. **Walk on with the four trees on your right, curving round to the left to cross a rather boggy area. The path gently descends towards the stream but doesn't cross it, running instead along the north bank (this is the public footpath marked on the OS map). The stream, straightened at some time, has been planted with alders along its banks. The path begins to climb slightly and you see in front a great mass of mossy boulders and oak trees. The stream now makes quite a noise as it cataracts down through this jumble. This is Locality 5.**

Rock bars and rubbish: Locality 5 [740 606]

Why this sudden change? you might wonder. This rocky barrier is, in fact, the terminal moraine of one of the last glacial advances in the area, almost certainly the Younger Dryas cold event that we now know took place not only in Britain and Europe, but throughout the world.

The path runs up to an iron gate and a couple of cottages. Go through the gate and cross a little wooden footbridge beside the cottage called Hendre Bach. Turn left onto the road from Hendre Bach to pass through another wooden gate almost immediately and so back down the ramp of the terminal moraine again, crossing another stream. Just after the stream, some 50 metres to your right in the oak wood, is a beautiful hump – a roche moutonée – showing that the moraine has rock just below. This moraine has draped itself over a rock bar – another ash flow tuff; so there are two reasons for this feature. The houses of Hendre, Hendre Bach and Blaen y nant are built on this because it is both better drained and well above any flood level. The juxtaposition of moraine and rock bar are not coincidence: the bar acted as something of a dam for the waning ice too, so it's not surprising the melting glacier dropped its terminal load of rocky garbage here.

Sex, stink and secretions: If you're here in autumn, you'll probably scent the distinctly unfragrant stink horn fungus (*Phallus impudicus*, **cingroen** in Welsh). This appropriately named fungus (Fig. 8.5) – both in its English and Latin names – is not a thing of beauty. Its revolting smell is intended to attract flies, which it does. The evil-smelling olive green slime is a real delicacy if you're a fly. It contains spores that the flies then distribute widely. It starts off as a white egg-like body filled with jelly. This egg bursts to liberate the distinctly penis-like white shaft and its conical 'glans'. This pungent erection can reach (no ribald laughter please) 8 inches long. Admiring it cannot give you AIDS but it might make you throw up!

Figure 8.5: *Stinkhorn.*

Walk on down towards the marshy area ahead, so distinctly different from the moraine, passing a white clapboard holiday cottage to the right. To the left, you can see how farmers have tried to drain the naturally boggy areas to provide more grazing for their animals. This doesn't seem to have had much effect because most of the drained area is still covered in soft rushes. You emerge from the woodland at Tan y Manod entering open pasture with odd trees dotted about. The quarry tips above Maes Mawr are now very clear, a little to the right above you, as you walk to where the road becomes asphalted. Here there's an iron gate at which you bear left. The other road climbs towards the head of the valley. Above you see more crags of the Crafnant ash flows cut by prominent white quartz veins, and you can see many boulders of quartz that have broken off and rolled down the scree slope.

Maes Mawr's garden wall is bedecked with quartz; you can't miss it. Behind its walls, the garden is attractive with a number of Fuchsia bushes and other plants which suggest that the climate here isn't always cold and wet (which is what jaundiced visitors can be forgiven for thinking on some summer days).

Just after Maes Mawr, you cross a little stream. Look up to the right to see the great opening of the slate quarry. As you walk back down the road towards Llyn Crafnant, you get plenty of pretty views of the lake and its forest-cloaked slopes. Cross another little stream and above on the right are dumps from the open slate quarry you saw earlier from the other side of the lake.

After passing the track from Cornel, which angles in from the left and crossing a tiny stream with a waterfall, just opposite a small building and telephone box, you find a clearly marked footpath to Llyn Geirionydd. Take this, crossing a wooden ladder stile. At first, you tramp over rather damp ground with a ruined wall on your left and larch forest on the right. Cross a stream and carry on (not taking fenced-off short cuts). The path is always clear and regularly waymarked with the forestry signs. Soon, you meet another track and bear right onto it continuing on up the hill, following the stream not far away to the right. If you like walking through young spruce forest with no views, then you'll get a lot out of this climb to the col. I'm afraid I have a thing about spruces: I don't like them. Nasty spiky things. Cross another broken-down wall and go over another stile. Now the trees are larches again. At the col, there's another wall and the path begins the descent. But before doing this, take a look at Locality 6.

The col, a view and dolerite: Locality 6 [7548 6034]

Walk about 25 metres to the right, just after the wall. Here is a little clear area in the forest where you can not only see some rocks but also a modest view away to the south and east across the forest, now mercifully concealing many of the old lead mines that used to exploit veins in the Crafnant volcanics and overlying Cadnant Shales. Here and there, you can see lakes and away in the distance, the Denbighshire moors.

The rock beneath your feet is hard to make much of, being covered in the usual lichens. It seems to be dipping to the northwest. Careful inspection shows it's a rather altered dolerite sill.

Return to the path and walk on down. After just a minute or so of walking, the path comes out onto a forestry road on which you continue down hill. Almost immediately, the track splits, a minor branch running straight ahead and the main branch to the right. The walkers' path goes straight on down hill between the forestry roads, passing through mature larches and cutting off a large loop of road. Presently, you come out onto the road again. The path continues directly on, but I recommend staying on the road now as parts of the path are very boggy (as I found out). The road does its last kink and you can see Llyn Geirionydd ahead. Beside the road, you'll find outcrops of dark grey slates. If you look more closely, you'll see that these are mixed rocks, like those you saw just after Locality 3. They're full of crystals and chips of volcanic rock, but the grains are rarely more than sand-sized. **Soon, you arrive back at Ty-newydd.**

Figure 8.6: *Grey heron.*

It's not uncommon to see, in these marshy valley heads with many streams, the majestic silhouette of a grey heron (Fig. 8.6). I've seen them here. If you happen to be a fish or a frog, you really wouldn't want to see a heron at all. This large bird has a vicious dagger of a beak, patience and acute stabbing accuracy and speed. Once caught, the heron swallows its prey whole. Their nests are large platforms of sticks that they usually build in trees or, more rarely, hidden amongst reeds.

This whole valley basin is much more subdued than that of Llyn Crafnant. There's hardly a rock outcrop to be seen in the headwater area. This is partly a response to the underlying soft rocks. A large downfold – a syncline – in the rocks brings a great area of Cadnant Shales as far south as Llyn Goddionduon [753 587]. This soft rock underlies all the ground south and east of the lake. The glaciers made mincemeat of it whilst they had to tussle with the volcanic rocks to make much impression on them.

On mines shall carparks be built ... Locality 7

Back at the car park, have a look around before you leave. Did you notice anything unusual about it? No? Well, take a look behind the public lavatories for a clue. Here's a stream in a gully and at the top end of this short gully is a mine entrance. This was the entrance of yet another mine – the New Pandora Mine – and the car park has been tastefully built from what were the dumps from the mine. You can still see what the miners were bringing out of this level on the lake shore, just on the other side of the road. A tramway used to run along the east shore of Llyn Geirionydd and then via an aerial ropeway to the Klondyke Mine mill. The host rock for the mineral veins is a dark mudstone with veins of calcite, rotten pyrite and sphalerite. This is the Cadnant Shale which followed on after the end of the Crafnant volcanic outbursts.

As you return to Betws-y-coed, you'll perhaps notice a little more of the old mine dumps – unattractive black decayed minerals and mudstone, but now you've seen a couple of these small mines for yourself and have some idea what it was the miners were after. The mines remind you that this area, the Llanrwst mining district, was once of some considerable importance for the extraction of lead and zinc, especially Parc mine (about 1½ kilometres east of here). About 20 mines operated here between 1848 and 1913, galena and sphalerite being the main ores.

Rocky Ramble 9: Cwm Croesor and Cnicht

How to get to the start of the ramble

When you arrive at Croesor village, you'll find a crossroads (Tan-y-bwlch off to the right). Turn left, and about 100 metres on the right is a new and free National Park carpark by the stream. The Beddgelert-Porthmadog buses, Services 97 and 98 (call Express Motors at 01286 674570 for information), will get you to Garreg. From there, you'll have a 3½-kilometre walk along the tiny road to Croesor village, but you do have beautiful woodlands and views to compensate.

The ramble: needs, distances and times

Like the Moelwyn and Moel Hebog rambles, this irritatingly falls on OS Outdoor Leisure sheets 17 and 18. Only a tiny bit (Croesor village) is on 18, so it's not too much of a problem. The distance is 12 kilometres (7½ miles) and involves about 640 metres (2000 feet) of climbing, including the ups and downs on the roundabout route to Cnicht summit. Give yourself a full day for this one. There are plenty of fine peaceful viewpoints or lunch spots where you may want to linger a while.

Cwm Croesor

Cwm Croesor was once the scene of much more bustle and industry than you see here today. The slate from the Rhosydd and Croesor quarries all passed through this sleepy village (and are the reason for its existence at all) along a narrow gauge railway which descended, via yet more quarries, to the great flat area of Traeth Mawr, and so down to Porthmadog, also the terminus of the Ffestiniog railway.

Croesor Quarry closed in about 1940, having been electrified for some years. Rhosydd closed in the 1930s, though its incline was still in use after World War II for hauling supplies up to repair a dam.

Set off from the car park back to the crossroads where you turn left up the tarmac road which continues on up the valley. (The noticeboard at the carpark entrance tells you some of the quarrying history. I've included this information at the appropriate places in the text.) The valley is little changed from the way it must have looked after the glaciers melted. On your left, you'll see a quite large roche moutonée just above a little bridge made out of flat slate slabs (what else?). This shows that the valley floor is here scraped almost clean of moraine. Higher up, much of the floor is filled by river gravels and sands, brought down by meltwaters and heavy rains.

Shortly, you pass a row of cottages on the left and the track divides. Take the right fork up the hill which runs up to Croesor Quarry. Pass a white house with imposing stone gate posts and then through a gate. Now you're on the open grassy mountainside with a few hawthorn trees dotted about. **Go through another gate.**

Ahead, you begin to see signs of former industry. Below in the valley is the main Cwm Croesor tramway, in places embanked or in cuttings as it runs through the alluvial deposits of the valley floor. At the head of the valley (Canolfan Blaencwm) is a building which looks like a chapel. It was the

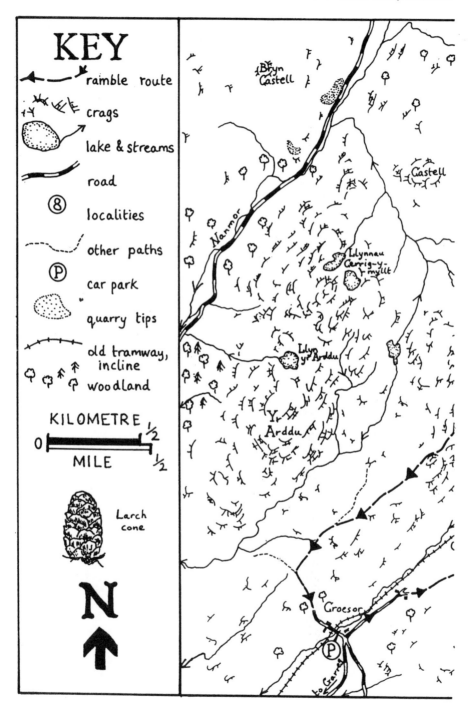

KEY

→ ramble route

crags

lake & streams

road

⑧ localities

other paths

Ⓟ car park

quarry tips

old tramway, incline

woodland

KILOMETRE
0 —————— ½
MILE   ½

Larch cone

N

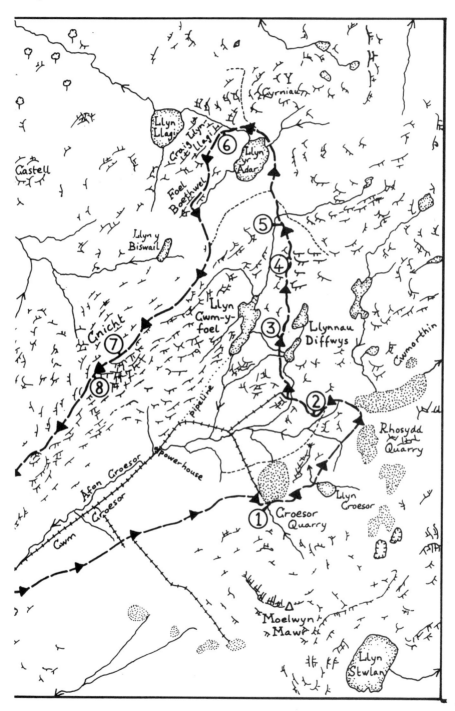

hydroelectric generating station for Croesor Quarry. Above it, you'll be able to make out rusty iron water pipes, now scattered about somewhat on the mountainside, the lower part running beside the first incline of the Cwm Croesor tramway. These come from the dammed Llyn Cwm-y-foel which you'll see from Locality 3. Ahead on the skyline is an incline which emerges from a tunnel higher up the mountainside. This comes from Fron-boeth Quarry on the southeast side of the ridge on your right.

At one place to the right of your track is a large excavation where slaty debris has been quarried from the hillside for track construction. This gives you an opportunity to see what underlies these grassy but steep hillsides: quite a thickness of small slate fragments – old scree. This tells us that the valley sides were once much steeper with many outcrops which now no longer exist. This is just what you'd expect if it has been glaciated. Now these screes are completely stabilised and so covered in protective grass. The opposite side of the valley is quite a contrast, for there are actively-forming screes with no vegetation at all. What's more, some of the screes are obviously not formed of slate, for they include large boulders. These, as you'll see later, come from several different dolerite sills which form much of the craggy southeast face of Cnicht. You can also pick up the general sense of the formations on Cnicht: sheet after sheet of rock inclined gently northwest, right to left (but these are apparent dips). Also in these screes, you may be able to make out vague zigzag trackways, former access to failed attempts at more slate quarrying or mining. On the right side of a prominent gully from Cnicht's summit ridge (west of the summit), you might just be able to make out yet another incline. At the top of this, right up under the higher Cnicht precipices and now almost inaccessible, is a tiny quarry in which to this day you can find neatly stacked piles of slates ready for transport. But the transport – the incline – was never completed. I have an immense respect for these hardy people who grubbed a living in the often-inhospitable mountains. Inaccessibility never seemed to be a consideration for them and their economical ingenuity.

Soon you cross the incline I mentioned which drops down to join the Cwm Croesor tramway. If you think this looks steep, wait till you see the Rhosydd incline (after Locality 2). You begin to have splendid views of the hanging valley of Afon Cwm-y-foel with its waterfalls and the old pipeline running to its left. Around to the right from that is the steepest incline ever built in Wales: the Rhosydd incline.

As you approach Croesor Quarry, at one point the track kinks in (to the right) to the mountainside. Here, you'll notice many jagged outcrops of hardened slate: hornfels. Since they are unusually tough, cleavage has not formed in these rocks. So what has caused this? As you already know, the sedimentary sequence in this area is stuffed with dolerite sills – I've just noted those over on Cnicht and you've seen some on the Moelwyn ramble (p. 78). One such sill intrudes the rocks near here and has cooked these mudstones.

Finally, you round a bend in the track and there in front are the large tips from Croesor Quarry. Behind the tips is another dolerite sill, dipping down from right to left. You'll cross this shortly. You can also see (to the left of the sill and upper tips) Bwlch Rhosydd and the tramway from Rhosydd Quarries along which you will walk. Below the lower part of the amazing Rhosydd incline are four rusting tramcars. To your right you now see the winding house for the incline which connected Croesor Quarry with the Cwm Croesor tramway system.

On your right is a mass of dolerite boulders, many criss-crossed by irregular veins (p. 76). This is all part of a great tongue of moraine which you'll see to perfection from Cnicht later today.

After passing a wall on the right which is almost completely covered in mosses and ferns, cross a ladder stile beside an iron gate: Locality 1.

Croesor Quarry, a desolate spot: Locality 1 [657 456]

On the right is a strange building with a circular steel structure built into the wall. To its right is the main, partly blocked entrance to this large and wholly underground quarry. I assume that the circular structure was once part of a large winding drum for hauling tramcars out of the mine. At the right hand side, you can see what looks to have been the wooden edge of a cable guide.

Moses Kellow (1862-1943) and Croesor. Moses Kellow was a great innovator as well as the last manager at this quarry and he introduced the electricity supply before the First World War. Hydroelectric power from Llyn Cwm-y-foel ran a 30 HP electric locomotive for haulage in the main tunnel of the quarry, the first in Wales. He also invented and installed reversible electric winches, slate planing machines, centrifugal pumps and the Kellow drill. This drill reduced the time for boring a 7½-foot hole from 10 hours to 1½ minutes! It was water-powered and so produced no dust. If his drill had been widely adopted in the other quarries, thousands of lives blighted by silicosis might have been saved. The underground workings were all lit by arc lamps and Kellow's pumps sucked out 400 gallons of water per minute from the deeper workings.

As I've mentioned, the quarry was the first to have electricity though even back in 1864, just 18 years after opening, it was producing over 1000 tons of finished slates every year. The power lines once brought a 3-phase AC supply for the quarry machines. Today, the place has been gutted. Even the armoured power cables have been burnt, perhaps to collect the lead shielding, and the buildings look to have been deliberately wrecked. **The path on to Bwlch Rhosydd runs through the back of a ruined building.** In the building are the remains of a large set of leather bellows built by Linley & Bingham, Sheffield, England. This must have been a forge, and at the back of the building, there's a pile of clinker and bits of coal to support this theory. **The path makes its way up the hill behind this, in places with steps.** It crosses dolerite outcrops at the highest point, for this is one of the several sills around here. **Ahead now is Llyn Croesor.**

The dam at Llyn Croesor – now ruined – is built of two stone supporting walls and the central core was packed with impermeable clay and mud to prevent serious leaks.

Quality and quantity; craftsmanship, safety and scale. The old quarrymen reckoned to be able to get 1 ton of saleable slates for every 9 to 10 tons they quarried. The rest was waste which had to be hauled to the tips and dumped. So it was in their interests to maximise the amount of usable slate. They were also economical with their rubbish: much of the waste was dumped inside the deeper underground workings so that some of the 'floors' represent worked out and backfilled caverns. Less work and less eyesore. Today's cheap and safer opencast quarrying techniques using mechanical diggers and trucks means between 80 and 100 tons of slate is quarried which yields just 1 ton of saleable slate products. So modern quarrying operations have the potential for making a much larger mess than the older ones — whose remains you see everywhere in Snowdonia.

Duchesses, Countesses, Queens, Ladies, Double and Singles ... No, this is not an account of an aristocratic game of tennis, though the names were instituted by the wife of one of the more unpleasant quarry owners, Lord Penrhyn. The names applied to standard sizes of slate. A Duchess was 24 inch x 12 inch, a Countess 19 inch x 10 inch, a Lady 16 inch x 8 inch and so on in a hierarchy rather like the British class system. All slates were actually split by hand using a mallet and wide chisel, a skilled job if you are to avoid breakages ... and quarrymen were paid by what they produced, not the time taken to produce it.

Cross the dam but don't continue around the lake – carry straight on. The path rounds the hilltop and then drops down an easy grassy (sometimes marshy) slope towards Rhosydd Quarries. To both sides, you can see more dolerites. The whaleback shape of all these outcrops tells you clearly that the glaciers moved over this col. **Shortly, you see the tramway running out of the ruins of Rhosydd. Join this and head west over Bwlch y Rhosydd.**

It's not difficult to imagine rail cars being hauled along here. Now and again, you can see wooden sleepers. The tramway runs through small cuttings in the rock, contouring neatly around the mountainside. The cuttings give you glimpses of gently-dipping bed surfaces contrasting with the near-vertical strong cleavage. **After about 200 metres, the track is raised on an embankment of stone. Just below to the right are the remains of a railcar which someone has pushed over the edge. At the point where the embankment ends is the start of Locality 2.**

In spring and summer, you may find violets and wild strawberries growing amongst the rocks in the cuttings.

Squishy sludgy stuff and weird wonders: Locality 2 [6602 4620]

This is a fabulous place to stop, munch a delicious apple, admire the beautiful view and be driven wild by these amazing rocks (and maybe think about purple prose and too many adjectives?!). For here you can see a wonderful section which was blasted through the rocks. It shows us details of structures that you might not see in natural outcrop, for the excavation gives quite fresh surfaces in which slight weathering picks out the structures and contacts between different beds.

At the start on the right is a fine sequence of bedded tuffites, with the usual strong penetrative fracture cleavage. In this you can spot ripples and small-scale current bedding, load casts, flame structures – all the sort of things you expect to find in sediments which were once saturated with water

(Fig. 9.1). In some places, you can see convoluted laminated bands. Have a really good look at this because you don't often see this sort of thing so clearly (except at Localities 4 & 5 on this ramble).

Figure 9.1: *I've enhanced the load casts (Val's finger points to one). The beds below are also highly irregular as you can see.*

As you walk on, similar beds continue for several metres with finer interbeds of darker material, but all with lots of siliceous laminae. Some of the beds are really screwed up and you have the strong impression that the cleavage was somehow involved in all this. You should be able to pick out discrete little balls of sediment, quite separate from one another. The separated balls seem to be arrayed along the planes of the cleavage. Maybe they were separated long before the cleavage even began to form, but have been dragged into the realignment forced upon the rock by this later structure. Elsewhere in Snowdonia at about the time these rocks formed, there's a good deal of evidence of instability. Older sediments, now rock, became exposed, broke up and slid down into the deeper sea, sledging on soft sludgy mud. This large scale slumping can sometimes give rise to colossal foundered masses of older rocks 'floating' in younger muddy sediments (p. 90). Exciting stuff.

Twenty paces from the end of the embankment is another good section where you can see cleaved mudstones in a striking contact with paler tuffites. What is of special interest here is that the contact is not in continuity: the bedding in the pale rocks is cut off on the left side. Within it, the beds dip from left to right, but at a much shallower angle than the contact itself (Fig. 9.2). What's going on here?

Figure 9.2: *M – mudstone; T – tuffite with bedding slightly enhanced so that you can see that the contact Val is pointing to is weird. The cleavage leans the other way, affecting all the outcrops in the same way.*

Well, here's an idea. The pale rock seems to be a completely separated body which, being heavier, has sunk down into the mudstones beneath giving this extraordinary cross-cutting relationship almost like an intrusion. Or it could be an older, already solid rock mass which has slid into this position due to increasing sub-sea slopes. Why the slopes should have increased, if this is what happened, is not a mystery. It happens all the time in areas where there is volcanic activity. As magma forces its way higher and higher through the Earth's crust, something has to shift. It does: the surrounding rocks themselves become tilted and pushed aside. Maybe this was what was happening here. There was always something volcanic brewing somewhere in this region most of the time between the Tremadoc Epoch and the climax during the Caradoc. The mere existence of tuffites shows that there was volcanic material being eroded somewhere not too far away.

Another 15 paces further on, you can see an identical setup with a large lump of this tuffite (about 2-3 metres up the cutting side) entirely surrounded by dark, faintly laminated mudstones.

Continuing on, you walk through hornfelsed sediments followed by a dolerite intrusion and then back into sediments again. You can see both top and base of this dolerite whose margin only is cleaved. This is because it is finer grained at the quickly-cooled margins, whereas at the centre, it is coarser and not affected by the cleavage. This tells us that the dolerite intrusions came in before the cleavage developed. This makes sense since the intrusive dolerites and rhyolites of Snowdonia were almost all connected with the surface volcanic activity. The sill here is at least 10 metres thick. Water drips constantly over it so it's covered in mosses and algae. Look back also to Croesor Quarry and the dolerite sills you crossed on the way to Rhosydd.

Before the incline at the end of the tramway, part of the track has collapsed onto the steep slopes below, but you can walk round this. The embankment here is quite impressive being perched half way up a precipice! **At the end of the tramway,** you can look down the incline. Steep, wouldn't you say? Above, the cable drum is well preserved (Fig. 9.3).

The Rhosydd Incline. This impressive incline was designed by Charles Spooner and linked Rhosydd Quarry (at 1,495 feet) with the end of the Croesor Tramway which carried the slate to Porthmadog. It opened in 1864 and is 1,250 feet long, rising 671 feet giving an average gradient of less than 1 in 2 though parts are less than 1 in 1 (i.e. more than 45°). It worked purely by gravity with the downward load pulling on the returning empties by a cable wound round a drum at the top. The drum was braked by a cable and lever operated from the incline head by one man. His slate shack remains as does the drum. 'Crewling' – incline operating – was a delicate business because the incline was not of constant gradient. The brakeman had to brake hard for the first part of the descent where the load was on the steepest gradient. Most of the downward traffic was roofing slate but sometimes included wool from the local sheep. Materials brought in included coal for steam engines, gunpowder, timber, building materials, fodder for animals and food. Men would ride up and down too though this was against the rules. A man would kneel on the back buffer and bend forward, going over headfirst!

From here, you can really appreciate the shallow U shape of Cwm Croesor. Remember (recalling the excavation you saw at the start of the walk) that the once-steeper valley sides have been masked by the major scree slopes. Remember too that the valley floor has been flattened by the river sediments of the Afon Croesor.

Now for the steepest bit of the ramble. You can either scramble up to the right of the cable drum (taking a look at it as you go) or return to the stream about 100 metres back to scramble up wherever you feel happiest (the west side is, I think, slightly easier). The idea is to head north to Llynnau Diffwys.

Figure 9.3: *View steeply down from above the cable drum. The steel brake band, operated by the man in the hut below, is on the right.*

When you reach the lake shore, skirt around it on the west side – there's a tiny path – and head for the highest point to the west of the first lake. There's a small pile of cleaved mudstones just below the skyline where someone has looked for a possible source of slate. Locality 3 is above this.

The two lakes (on which you may see wary mallard ducks) are unusual in that the southern one has three outlets. This is over the top. Most lakes are happy with just one.

Knocks, lochans and whalebacks: Locality 3 [6577 4674]

The rock underlying this area is all clearly bedded siltstone and fine sandstone, strongly cleaved. The beds dip gently to the northeast and the cleavage dips steeply northwest.

The two lakes and all the other humps and hollows to the north and east result from heavy erosion by the ice sheets (sometimes called 'areal scouring' or 'knock and lochan topography' after the scoured landscapes of northwestern Scotland). The humps show clearly that the glaciers moved from northeast to southwest, being smooth (as roches moutonées always are) on their up-side and plucked and pulled apart on their down – southwest – sides. You'll perhaps have noticed the numbers of perched blocks scattered about, especially to the northeast, all dropped when the ice sheets melted.

If you walk a few paces west, you have a bird's-eye view down to part of Llyn Cwm-y-foel. You can also see right down to Porthmadog. On the west side of the lake, you can see the most superbly ice-sculpted whaleback forms. It's easy to visualise the glaciers – moving uphill in certain parts – moving from right to left. The whalebacks (Fig. 9.4) are especially clear here because they mirror the grain of the country due to the strike and dip of the beds. The beds dip gently northwest (towards Cnicht) presenting us with rounded scarp faces. Higher up, slate screes mask much of the steeper slopes.

Figure 9.4: *Part of the spoiled Llyn Cwm-y-foel overlooked by whaleback glacial features. Cnicht is behind.*

From here, you can see the way ahead (Fig. 9.5). Locality 5 is clearly visible as a black tunnel entrance with a slate tip below. Locality 4 is partly hidden by a closer ridge of sediments (dark). Between the two, you can see a very prominent pale grey ridge which is the higher part of Locality 4. This view also shows you very well how simple the geology is around here. You have nothing more than the enormously thick Nant Ffrancon Group sediments, all dipping fairly gently and uniformly north, intruded by sometimes thick sills of dolerite. The well-bedded sediments and dolerites give the whole area a tremendous grain, like that of a well-weathered wooden plank, due to the glaciers picking out the softer layers as an easier option. Glaciers, like military commanders, always go for the weakest defences.

Figure 9.5: *View (taken from a little further north) north to the col over to Llyn yr Adar (FP – footpath). D – dolerite sills; Si – well-bedded siltstones and fine sandstones (Nant Ffrancon Group). The top dolerite sill peters out to the east of the col but the much thicker lower one continues west, across the Afon Cwm-y-foel valley, to underpin the whole Cnicht ridge. You'll see it later on the descent between Localities 7 & 8. I've marked Loc. 5 and (approximately as it's partly hidden) Loc. 4.*

Set off north, contouring around as needed, to Locality 4. As you walk, you're aware of how the grain of the country affects your progress. It really is scarp and dip slope all the way with a seasoning of dolerite perched blocks for good measure. The next locality begins when you start to climb the scarp of the thick dolerite (Fig. 9.5).

Crystal Mush makes beds hot and horny: Locality 4 [6586 4732]

And who is Crystal Mush? I'm sorry. I've been glancing at the tabloids again. I couldn't resist the alliteration of hot and horny, because these beds were hot and became horny ... well hornfels anyway. And a crystal mush caused it.

The lower third of the locality consists of beautifully bedded fine sandstones and interbedded siltstones (Fig. 9.6). These are striking because they have, in a sense, been protected by the dolerite (formerly crystal mush) which overlies them. The dolerite has baked them, preserving them from the damaging effects of cleavage.

Figure 9.6: *These heat-hardened sediments preserve some of the original structures rather well. The fine-grained sandstone beds pinch and swell and some (where Val's elegant finger points) are clearly the remains of current ripples which migrated from right to left across the ancient seafloor.*

Now for the crystal mush. This is, I think, a realistic description of the way the hot liquid dolerite was, for a time as certain crystals grew, forming a latticework in which the mush of the remaining melt also gradually crystallised. This gives us what geologists call ophitic texture and you can see this clearly on the weathered surfaces of this thick dolerite, particularly in the higher parts near the top of the ridge. The centre part of the dolerite magma took longer to cool (not being in contact with cold sediments) and so the crystals grew larger. You can see this with a hand lens: white lath-like crystals of feldspar (plagioclase) up to 5mm long form a mesh within which you can see black, shiny crystals (probably augite, a pyroxene) and a pale green irregular mineral which is probably olivine. The feldspar crystallised first and the other two minerals followed. This is why some of the feldspars look to have grown through the augite. In fact, the augite grew around the feldspar. Dolerite is chemically and mineralogically identical to basalt (which formed the lavas of the Bedded Pyroclastic Formation). The only difference is that the basalt flowed out onto the Earth's surface – often, as you have seen, under water. It cooled faster and so had much smaller crystals than dolerite. When this type of magma is intruded at great depth, it cools more slowly forming even bigger crystals; this is gabbro and as any Scottish climber knows, forms the Cuillin Hills of Skye. Gabbro is the basic equivalent of basalt just as granite is of rhyolite.

This is classic dolerite, not to be bettered anywhere in Snowdonia. Here it forms massive solid-looking, jointed outcrops, typical of this rock. As you saw on the Moelwyn ramble, it is criss-crossed by thin quartz veins which in places slightly mimic bedding. But they have nothing to do with bedding.

From the top of the dolerite ridge, you can readily see Locality 5, the slate mine. Head for this across the next hollow. This is underlain by the very end of a rhyolite sill which thickens to the east of here. You may find a few outcrops.

Echoes, bizarre sausages, Dr Jekyll and Mr Hyde: Locality 5 [6578 4754]

This was another enterprise which failed. The slates on the tip look good but obviously something wasn't right. Inside the adit entrance is a wonderful display of plants that can survive in low light: ferns, water plants and liverworts. The echoing tunnel continues out of sight into the darkness.

The rocks around the tunnel, as you'll have seen, are all well-bedded siltstones and sandstones again, but worth inspecting in the outcrops and fallen boulders to the east of the tunnel. Here are some very weird looking things indeed (Fig. 9.7).

The real nut to crack here is the meaning of these oval bodies, often with holes in the middle. Can we explain these in terms of what was happening on that ancient seafloor? I think the answer is both yes and no. Yes, these formed on the seafloor. That's obvious because everything else here is quite unexceptional although very beautifully presented for you to see in these exposures. We begin to get some clues when we examine these shapes more carefully. In parts of the outcrop, you can see some of the ovals as if they were half formed. The ones in Fig. 9.7 are complete. Overall, they seem to have been actual sand ripples resting on a finer-grained seafloor of silt. The sands were not in any abundance so they didn't always form complete beds. Currents winnowed them and they commonly were separated from their neighbours. That I think explains these beds which look like short strings of sausages. But where are the cross beds you'd expect to see in them? Well look ... many of them *do* contain these internal cross beds. It's as if these are ghosts of their former selves. They seem to have become overprinted.

Figure 9.7: *What are these things? Bizarre, eh? Some of the beds are perfectly normal, parallel bedded or cross bedded; but what about these oval objects with rings? (See text for ideas.)*

This then is my best offer of an explanation. The bizarre oval structures – sausage strings – you see in Fig. 9.7 were separate sand ripples. They changed, Jekyll and Hyde-like, from one persona to another. They are the result of diagenesis – of secondary modification after the rocks were laid down. Each ripple has become the nucleus for the precipitation of silica forming what are, in fact, secondary nodules (a little like those back at Locality 2). This silicification process must have been controlled by the grain size of the sand. Only the relatively coarse ripples need have applied. The silts simply weren't going for it. They were too dense (not permeable) to allow themselves to be changed into something new. The rings of coarser and finer material, so clear in Fig. 9.7, must represent retexturing stages as pulses of silca moved through the rocks. I'd bet that this had something to do with the nearby rhyolite or dolerite sills. What do you think?

Continue on towards the col, up and round to the west of the tunnel, crossing the Afon Cwm-y-foel (which does a right angle turn as it splashes down from the tiny lake which is its source to the east). Underfoot you find faintly laminated mudstones and siltstones. **After crossing the stream, you join the footpath with another dolerite sill above, forming the ridge here.**

At the col, you have a surprise view north and northwest with the Snowdon range dominating the scene. Llyn yr Adar lies in front of you with a tiny island. You are now 600 metres high but here still is all the usual evidence of glacial scouring: knock and lochan country, whalebacks and many perched blocks. So the glaciers vigorously scraped at the whole of this area, in fact burying Cnicht completely as you will see later. To the northeast is wild country of dolerites and sediments, with the hollows filled by peat.

If you wish, you can skip the next locality and turn left onto a fairly clear path which runs up the ridge to the summit of Cnicht. Otherwise, make your way around the east and north of Llyn yr Adar, crossing a few small streams and boggy peaty bits. The peat here is still forming. At the north end of the lake are some fine roches moutonées.

Peat and mummies: Peat forms mostly from Sphagnum moss which grows in bogs, ponds, and lakes. Glaciers leave an ideal landscape for peat to form because of the bare rocky hollows with no drainage. The moss builds a mesh of large, inflated, thin-walled dead cells forming a spongy, waterlogged mass. Indeed, you can use a piece of wet Sphagnum as a sponge. Initial decay releases humic acids which prevent further decay, mummifying both the moss and anything else — plant or animal — which falls into it. If you fall into an actively-forming peat bog, your corpse may be found thousands of years later, as happened to Lindow Man. This poor fellow was thrown into a bog near Manchester about 2,200 years ago having been executed in a bizarre fashion: he was bashed on the head, garotted and had his throat slit. Less exciting though equally important is the function of peat in preserving pollen (p. 168) and the remains of former forests which tell us in no uncertain terms that the landscape looked very different a few thousand years ago.

Follow the outlet stream towards Craig Llyn-llagi and bear left to a suitable viewpoint before it plunges down to Llyn Llagi: Locality 6.

Sill with a view: Locality 6 [6536 4819]

You'll have recognised this ice-smoothed rock for sure: dolerite again. This is another sill whose upper surface dips fairly steeply northwest to form the crags which overlook Cwm Llagi. The stream plunges down a straight, steep gully to Llyn Llagi. This formed along a small northwesterly fault which has moved down the dolerite on its north side.

The dolerite has a pitted surface as though it is dissolving slowly. This is partly true because some of its component minerals (the iron-magnesium silicates like pyroxene and olivine) are more easily attacked by weathering processes and even living organisms like lichens.

To the west and southwest, you can see the same sort of sequence with the dolerite at the base followed by a sequence of units dipping from left to right (northwest). Llynnau Cerrig-y-myllt which you can just see is enclosed within the Yr Arddu Syncline (p. 175), also the base of the LRTF. As before, this whole tract of country has a striking grain and you can see that it continues to the north too.

Where did all these dolerites come from? We know now that they were closely linked, both in space and time, with the Caradoc age volcanicity which gave us the Snowdon and Llewelyn Volcanic Groups. The closer you get to the Snowdon caldera margin, the more dolerite sills you see. Some reach 600 metres thick and you can follow them for up to 6 kilometres: real whoppers. Many are intimately associated with the basalt eruptions of the Bedded Pyroclastic Formation, behaving like the rhyolite intrusions which were likewise linked to the LRTF and other ignimbrite-type eruptions. The volcano and intrusion plumbing systems had the same sources, but the intrusive rocks – a colossal amount of magma – never made it to the surface. Today, the rhyolite and dolerite intrusions are responsible for much of the rugged Snowdonian terrain.

Further afield is Moel Hebog where you can make out your traverse of the Pitt's Head Tuff up to the LRTF. To the right, you can see the Bedded Pyroclastic Formation which builds Moel yr Ogof. Snowdon, the final ramble, is also built largely of these two volcanic formations together with rhyolite intrusions. The great ridges of Glyder Fawr and Glyder Fach, further round to the right, are much the same (Ramble 5).

Cwm Llagi was, probably during the Younger Dryas cold event, filled with a corrie glacier which excavated and steepened up the backwall below. It's a fine example of a glacial corrie or cirque.

To the northwest of the lake is a 'settlement' which you can see clearly with binoculars: walls and piles of stones built upon the crest of the rather degraded terminal moraine which dams Llyn Llagi. Millennia later came the quarrymen, searching for quality slate as you can see by the trials to the northeast of the lake.

Walk on south-southwest keeping close to the ridge edge and heading for Foel Boethwell. Staying on the ridge is, as always, much more interesting both because of the rocks underfoot and the views to the west out to Llŷn. You have to cross a hollow with ice-sculpted outcrops of slate to get to Foel Boethwell, worth the short scramble up for another fine view.

At the south end of Foel Boethwell, itself decorated with perched blocks, you can see another glacially excavated lake: Llyn y Biswail. The lake basin is scooped out of slates with the northwest shore formed by the same dolerite sill as that you are standing on.

Head south to join the path up the main Cnicht ridge and walk on up towards the summit. The rocks underfoot are all laminated slates.

Cnicht has two summits. The western one being slightly higher is the one everyone heads for. For some reason, the path misses the eastern summit [648 469], skirting it on the southeast side. As a result, hardly anyone visits it so it's quite a peaceful spot, not eroded by the tramp of many boots. There is absolutely no reason why you shouldn't pay it a visit. There are no difficult bits at all and personally, I prefer it. Even so, the next locality is at the west summit.

Cnicht: Locality 7 [6452 4661]

This point is 689 metres high ... and the glaciers (as I said earlier) have been right over here too. How do I know? Because 2 metres below the summit is a good sized dolerite block, perched on the laminated slates which form this summit ridge.

Now you have a good view down to the Yr Arddu Syncline. The trace of the downfold runs roughly from Yr Arddu passing through Llyn Yr Arddu, Llynnau Cerrig-y-myllt and Castell (to the northeast). On the near side, the grain of the country is the same as you've seen all day, with the bedded units and dolerite sills which cut them all dipping northwest (Fig. 9.8). The LRTF is more or less defined for you by heather growth instead of grass. The beds on the other side of this axis of folding dip towards you. Yet if you imagine yourself back at Locality 5 on the Llyn Dinas ramble, the LRTF there dips once again to the northwest, so between here and Moel Dyniewyd, you cross first a downfold and then an upfold. The upfold – anticline – is broken by the large faults which run along the Nanmor valley (p. 175).

Figure 9.8: *Yr Arddu Syncline from Cnicht. MD – Moel y Dyniewyd (Loc. 5, Llyn Dinas ramble), LR – LRTF, D – dolerite sills. I've marked the syncline's approximate axis trace with dashes and Xs.*

Looking around, you can trace the whole of this ramble's route, including the return path down the west ridge. To your southeast is Moelwyn Mawr which (Fig. 9.9) looks almost like a miniature Mount St. Helens after the famous eruption there in 1980. During this mammoth (by human standards) release of energy, the east face of the mountain, part of the Cascade Range in the western USA, collapsed triggering a titanic blast. Moelwyn Mawr had no such origin. Instead, you can see that its northwest face has a glacial 'bite' out of it with a great tongue of moraine running right the way down to the right of the Croesor Quarry. I mentioned this briefly just before Locality 1 (and also p. 81).

Cnicht itself, in the famous view from Traeth Mawr, is a classic product of valley glaciers. In the later stages of the glaciation when the glaciers' levels had dwindled somewhat, ice must have streamed past on both sides, carving the beautiful whaleback features over towards Yr Arddu and ripping into the side of this mountain to give it its knife-edge form: an arête.

You also have a wonderful view to Traeth Mawr which was occupied for a time by the sea after the last glaciers melted (p. 84).

Figure 9.9: *Moraine tongue from the northwest cwm of Moelwyn Mawr. You can see clear lateral moraine ridges to its right and left. Croesor Quarry tips to the left.*

Drop down one of the well worn paths to the southwest and watch your step as you do. Parts are a little slippery and quite steep. Shortly, you're back in dolerite again, for it is the underlying dolerite sill (which you saw at Locality 4) which gives this slate mountain its 'backbone'. **You have to descend through a notch which cuts through the dolerite, but there are plenty of handholds. Then you emerge onto a flat grassy area at the top of the prominent gully (caused by a fault) which slashes its way right down the mountainside to the southeast. Just to the right of the grassy area and a pile of stones is the final locality.**

One last contact ... of what?: Locality 8 [6434 4650]

Here you can almost put your finger on the contact between the top of a thin rhyolite sill and the overlying hornfelsed laminated sediments. The thick dolerite you just came through stops at the gully fault.

The sediments here are not as well behaved as they appear because in some outcrops close by the contact, they have formed slumps (Fig. 9.10). Or are they sediments at all? Does some of this remind you of the flow-folded rhyolites at Clogwyn Du'r Arddu (Locality 10, p. 58)? What do you think?

Figure 9.10: *These exposures are just a couple of metres west of the contact. What do you make of these flat folds to the left of my tape recorder?*

The descent from here is a delight. It's almost all smooth, gentle and grassy, yet with wonderful views all the time. Simply follow the fairly obvious path. Below to the right after a while, you'll see several small slate trial quarries including one collapsed underground working. Once again, the backbone of this ridge is an intrusive sill – this time not dolerite but rhyolite. (You can actually follow these sills right down to just above sea-level at Garregelldrem [614 431], north of Garreg. The A4085 runs right underneath it.) **After a long descent, you see this rock forming a prominent knoll. Two walls runs up to this from the right. The path skirts the knoll on its right side, over a patch of scree, crossing the first wall at a gap. A stile then crosses a wrecked wire fence and the path continues down the ridge.**

Yr Arddu is about the same height to your right and is, as you see, very rugged country even if quite low. Underfoot, well laminated siltstones continue, dipping quite steeply northwest and commonly devoid of much cleavage. This may be due to the hardening effect of the once-hot sill not far below.

After a while, you cross a ladder stile over a wall and, following footpath

signs, bend round to the right to join a track from Nanmor, continuing down towards Croesor. Yr Arddu is now quite close and you can see where the LRTF outcrops cease at the south end of the syncline, the contact being roughly defined by a wall. **The track is partly made up with slate from some of the old trial levels close at hand. Soon you come to another wall and a gate and stile.** Below here, bluebells are common in the late spring. **The track joins another from the northwest and turns to the left to pass through a wooded gap in the lower ridge crest.**

As you go through this gap, you're probably scarcely aware that the mossy outcrops above you are the same siltstones you've been walking over all day. By now, you probably don't want to ever see another siltstone anyway! It all feels so different, back in this oak, rowan, blackthorn, hawthorn and birch woodland, filled with bluebells, birdsong and the calls of cuckoos in spring.

Just before another ladder stile to the road, on the left you'll see two huge slate slabs covering a water tank showing how useful these slates could be for other purposes than just roofing. **Continue straight on down the tarmac road into Croesor village and the carpark.** The verges are full of stitchwort, tormentils and foxgloves and the whole feeling here is of soft, gentle countryside contrasting with the exposed mountain slopes above. Just before the bridge over the Afon Croesor, the old slate tramway crossed the road (though you wouldn't know it now) to continue on down to Pont Garreg-Hylldrem and then join the later – and short-lived – Welsh Highland Railway which ran from Porthmadog to Beddgelert.

By the bridge on the left is a tiny garden made by the local schoolchildren. Large slate slabs commemorate the history in pictures of local events or people and there's some neatly carved Welsh poetry. A kind gentleman from a nearby cottage did explain to me how Welsh poetry works but it was beyond my minimal comprehension of linguistics. Perhaps he will do better with you?

Today I've tried to show some of that marvellous poetry written by Time and Nature. I hope you appreciated it as much as I do.

Rocky Ramble 10: Cwm Llan and Snowdon

How to get to the start of the ramble

At Nant Gwynant [628 507], you'll find a large free carpark (with toilets), marked on the OS Outdoor Leisure Map 17 with a 'P'. The Snowdon Sherpa bus (Service 95; Llandudno/Porthmadog – Llanberis) passes the start of this walk. Call KMP at 01286 878880 for times which vary considerably.

The ramble: needs, distances and times

The distance, including the spur up to Y Lliwedd, is about 14½ kilometres (9 miles) involving an arduous, though never difficult, 1170 metres (3840 feet) of climbing. Without Y Lliwedd, it is 1010 metres (3315 feet). This is obviously a very full day of walking if you are to have time to notice things as you go along. Equally obvious is that this is the ramble to do on a good day. The summit, Yr Wyddfa, is quite simply the highest point south of Scotland and the views on a clear day are the best. You'll need OS Outdoor Leisure Map 17.

Introduction

This ramble takes you from Nantgwynant up into Snowdon's great east-facing cwm – Cwm Llan – up the southern ridge of Wales' highest peak to the summit, Yr Wyddfa, returning via Y Lliwedd. The rocks you'll see are mostly part of the mighty Snowdon Volcanic Group. If you're lucky, you may find some purple saxifrages – rare alpine plants that survive quite well on the lime-rich Bedded Pyroclastic Formation (BPF).

The oldest rocks you'll walk over are the slates in Cwm Llan. You'll cross the striking Pitt's Head Tuff once you're on the Allt Maenderyn ridge. After that eruption, local earth movements along fault lines uplifted the seabed and much of the Pitt's Head Tuff and underlying muds (part of the Cwm Eigiau Formation) before the beginning of the massive and violent Snowdon volcanics which form the whole of that mountain as well as Crib Goch and Y Lliwedd of the famous Snowdon horseshoe.

Set off from the carpark up the track towards Hafod-y-llan, marked with a public footpath sign. This is the start of the Watkin Path up Snowdon. Just before the first cottage, Y Bwthyn, branch left up a cobbled track skirting the oak woods to the left. Right away you have views up to Y Lliwedd and Gallt y Wenallt. The oak wood becomes rather more mixed with rhododendron bushes, spreading vigorously as they unfortunately do, and a few tall conifers: larches, spruces and a very large cypress. As you'll hear, the woods are full of bird life: mostly wrens, robins and chaffinches.

The track itself exists for two reasons only: the slate quarries of Cwm Llan and the copper mines below Y Lliwedd. The quarrymen built a whole series of inclines and tramways to bring the slates down to the valley. The lowest of the inclines ended at a building below you on your right. From there, it was carted to Beddgelert and so to Porthmadog. **You can see the old incline clearly below a viewpoint with iron railings, just before an iron gate that you go through. Twenty five metres further on, the incline crosses the track**

though the bridge has gone. Here, the incline oozes water and supports a wonderful community of damp-loving ferns, mosses and liverworts. Almost vertically above is a rounded roche moutonée looking like one of the granite domes at Yosemite National Park in the US. This will be Locality 1. **The track curves left a little to head up the valley and you walk up through a small cutting in ice-polished outcrops.** The rock is a rather drab lava or intrusion. In the track bed, you may be able to make out some flow banding in this rock, sure evidence that it was once liquid. **As you continue the gentle climb, you begin to both hear and see the waterfalls – of which there are many – in the Afon Cwm Llan.** Ahead, the slopes are partly covered by pines and larches in natural-looking clumps, amongst which are scatterings of deciduous trees. Suddenly, you see the first of the main waterfalls, the top of another incline and, far up the valley, the craggy buttress of Craig Ddu. Even further away is the rocky knife-edge ridge that you'll later walk up between Bwlch Main and Snowdon. Already you can see evidence of apparently flat-lying beds forming this part of Snowdon.

The track swings round the small tributary valley (Afon Gorsen) before running close by the waterfalls higher up Cwm Llan. On your left, you can see the top of the dome-shaped roche moutonée and many others like it. This tells you what is pretty obvious: there was once a heavy and powerful mass of ice grinding its way down this valley. The waterfalls too formed because of this ice which somewhere around here must have merged with another large glacier coming down from Snowdon's most famous cwm, source of the Afon Glaslyn. The latter glacier, being particularly large and powerful, spread sideways, so scraping away and steepening up the lower part of Cwm Llan. This over-steepening left the beginnings of a hanging valley here and provides us today with the lovely series of waterfalls. You can see that the river hasn't cut much into the bedrock in the 15 millennia since the main ice sheets melted, but this is tough volcanic rock.

Shortly, coming in from the left, is the tramway to the lowest incline. Turn off onto this and follow it to the incline top at Castell.

Castell: Locality 1 [6256 5130]

The summit of Castell is a short scramble up from the incline top where the winding drum once used to be. The pillars that supported the winding drum axle are full of a small Polypody fern: common spleenwort. You'll also find foxgloves and penny-wort.

From the top, you have a wonderful view of the valleys. Beyond is Moel Siabod. To the southeast, the skyline is like the teeth of a saw (from which the Spanish word for mountain range comes; 'sierra' is a saw), each peak being formed by dolerite intrusions or the LRTF, both of which are similarly hard

Figure 10.1: *Common spleenwort (Asplenium trichomanes).*

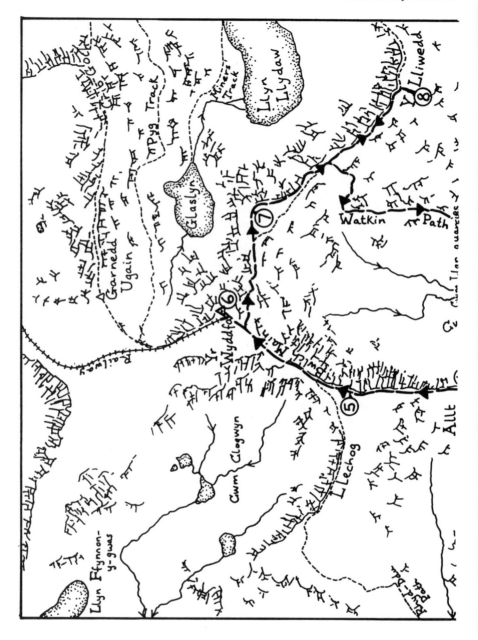

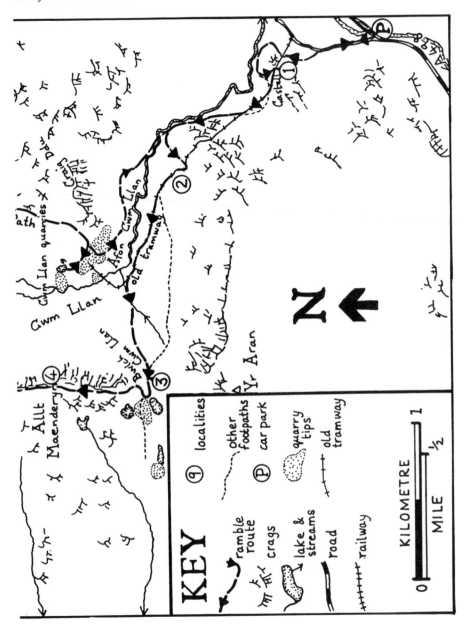

and resistant to ice erosion. The lower areas are mostly slates of the Nant Ffrancon Group. Nearly south of you is Cnicht looking rather uninteresting from here. You can see (if the weather is fair) the summit of Snowdon itself from here.

Up on Y Lliwedd are many prominent quartz veins. Some of these carried base metals like copper, lead and zinc, and were once mined. You'll soon see traces of this. The continuation of the incline system is clear where it descends steeply from Clogwyn Brith just half a kilometre northwest.

Figure 10.2: View of Cwm Llan from Castell. Snowdon summit just peeps out above Craig Ddu. The ice-scraped outcrops in the foreground are clear where the river cascades down them. Note the incline dropping down from Clogwyn Brith on the upper left.

The rock that forms Castell is a flow-banded rhyolite, part of the same mass you saw in the cutting a few minutes ago.

Join the track again or, if you wish, simply follow the tramway to join the track at the base of the incline. Now and again, you'll spot the odd wooden sleeper for the steel rails. The aggressive rhododendrons have started growing here too around a small ruin before the incline starts. **Pass through an iron kissing gate.** Just before this, a path branches off to the right to cross the river. This was the main access to the old mines high up on the east side of Y Lliwedd. Shortly, on your left by the track, you find outcrops of dark grey strongly cleaved mudstones, much stained with reddish iron oxides, carved into beautifully smooth whalebacks by the ice. The slates are overlain by tuffs which have fragments up to plum-size scattered about in them. They them. They too are strongly cleaved and the rock is criss-crossed by thin veins of quartz. The river on your right is beautiful with its series of little falls and deep clear pools. Look out for dippers as this is a favourite haunt of these remarkable little diving birds with their characteristic dipping flight and neat white bibs.

Ahead on the opposite bank, you see several ruined buildings with ochreous dumps telling us that these were the processing plants for the base metal ores. The veins were mined higher up, as you'll soon see, but the ores were processed here, probably using water power.

At the top of the waterfalls where the track more or less flattens out, watch for a left turn. This is your route, via the old tramway, to Bwlch Cwm Llan. Within a few paces of the left turn, the rocks are cut by red hematite veins and you'll see red soils along a gully. But look again ... this isn't a natural gully but a collapsed mine entrance where the miners were following this set of veins. They must have dragged their ore from this level across the stream to the processing plant, the ruins of which you just saw. A ford is still marked on the map here. If you look across to the small valley to the northeast on the other side of the Afon Cwm Llan, about 500 metres away, you can see more remains of mine entrances and open stopes, marked by brownish-red scree dumps below. The OS map shows these as 'Levels (disused)'.

As you continue on up to the southwest, you're walking up another older incline that shortly joins the main Cwm Llan quarries tramway. Turn right onto the tramway over a well-built raised section which crosses a small stream. At the next bend just after the cutting is Locality 2, on the right hand side of the tramway.

Locality 2 [6187 5194]

Here you can see two things: one is the rocks underfoot and the other is the view. The rocks around you, best seen in the rounded outcrops to the right of the cutting, are massive tuffs with a few larger fragments up to pea-size and many broken feldspar crystals. It's much easier to see this on weathered surfaces; where the quarrymen have cut through, all you can really see is the cleavage. These rocks are part of the LRTF.

From here, you can see right up into Cwm Llan. In the lower middle distance is the first of the Cwm Llan quarry slate tips (Fig. 10.3). You can also see a strange structure below Allt Maenderyn (which you will shortly visit at Locality 4). The upper part of the ridge here is made of a pale-coloured rock which, if you trace it to the right, suddenly stops and appears to continue below to the right (annotated on Fig. 10.3). A gently curving line running from the west end of Allt Maenderyn summit down towards the centre of the figure separates the two rock masses. This is a beautiful example of a normal fault where the rocks have broken apart, the right hand side of the fault having slid down, due to gravity, for some considerable distance. Snowdonia is full of such faults though they are rarely as clear as this one. Normally, geologists have to infer their presence when rock formations simply don't match up. Because faults represent actual fractures in the rock, they usually form lines of weakness. Erosion picks these lines of damaged – often smashed up – rock out like vultures pick the flesh off a carcass.

Figure 10.3: *Cwm Llan, Allt Maenderyn with the clear normal fault (F) (see text), Clogwyn Du and Snowdon.*

Walk on along the tramway through more cuttings and outcrops of the LRTF. Some are very clearly pyroclastic with broken lumps up to grapefruit-size indicating powerful explosive events nearby.

As the tramway continues, now and again, you can see the remains of sleepers. **Dead ahead is Bwlch Cwm Llan with a clear path ascending to it. After a long straight section of tramway, you pass through another cutting and see the stark ruins of Cwm Llan quarries. Close at hand on the right is a mysterious 'field' with numbers of slates sticking out of it like a drunkards' graveyard.** Behind the quarries but below the crags of Snowdon you can make out a pale rampart-like ridge. This is probably the terminal moraine of the last gasp of the Younger Dryas glacier that existed for a time in the upper cwm, finally melting 11,500 years ago.

The tramway curves round into the quarries and runs into a system of inclines down which the quarrymen moved the slate blocks to the dressing sheds below, which you can briefly visit if you wish. The quarry opened in 1840 and was worked by a London company. By 1880, it had closed.

Now head up to the west towards Bwlch Cwm Llan, an easy walk over rolling moraine hillocks to join the obvious track which runs up to the col.

(The actual footpath marked on the OS map branches off the tramway some distance back, but I find it more interesting to walk along the old tramway and then make my own route up to the col.) Close to the col, you reach a broken-down slate wall that you cross and follow, below a failed attempt at a quarry, towards the lowest part of the col. Just before the final steep scramble where the wall is almost totally ruined, cross it again so that you're back on the south side of it. Follow the small track round towards the col, a mere 30 metres, marked by a pile of stones and another ruined wall. Ten metres from where you crossed the wall, just before you reach the col, is a rocky knoll. This is Locality 3, a fine viewpoint.

Knoll with a View where things ain't what they seem: Locality 3 [6055 5213]

Take a seat and have your binoculars ready. You can see some odd things from here but what do they mean?

First the uncontroversial bit ... Why is the pass here? Easy. Being underlain by soft slates, it represents the weakest link in the ridge between Yr Aran and Snowdon. Most of this ridge is built of hard volcanic rocks or a thick sequence of sandstones that formed on a shallow seafloor before the volcanic activity began.

Figure 10.4: *Rocky wraiths sending out siren signals to the unwary? What are we seeing here? Are these really folds?*

Now for the harder stuff. Looking back down Cwm Llan, you can make out the beds with the mines that you saw before Locality 2. Now look at the craggy mass of Craig Ddu (Fig. 10.4). On its east side, the beds seem to be dipping steeply southeast (A) whereas on its west side, they seem to be dipping at around 70° northwest (B) whilst at the grassy top, they seem to be flat (C). Okay, you reasonably say, that looks like an upfold, an anticlinal fold in the rocks. And where you have an upfold, you should have a downfold, a syncline, next door. And so it seems to be for even more striking to the left of Craig Ddu is a great 'U'-shaped fold-like structure (D). To the left of that, you can see clear bed surfaces (E) just below the Watkin Path, above the quarries. Further still to the left, vertically above the end tips of the quarry, is what seems to be another upfold: two folded beds flexed over just above the tips (F) and another (G) half way up towards Y Lliwedd west ridge. And you can continue to see more of these up- and down-fold structures even further to the left. Finally at Bwlch Ciliau, the rocks are clearly dipping southeast.

No problem really, you might think. The beds have been buckled into folds by earth movements. It makes a good story. There's just one problem: the story is wrong! Not wholly wrong, because there really are some folds here but they aren't the ones you can see. Yet so far as we are concerned, what we can see here is a good line of evidence for folds. If we had time, you could check these things out for yourself. If you did, you'd find that the Craig Ddu 'anticline' is nothing of the sort; it's actually a huge patch of the LRTF which was sufficiently hot for it to weld. The whole craggy face of Craig Ddu is welded tuff. Detailed mapping of these tuffs has shown us that the welding within them occurs as irregular 'pods' confined to the lower and middle parts of this thick ash flow. The upper part would have vented its heat to the overlying shallow sea.

Finally, look up towards the moraine rampart at the head of the cwm. Is this really a terminal moraine? It looks like a continuation of the scree slope higher up with the middle part missing. This may have been formed by a persistent snow patch which remained at this fairly high location (450 metres above sealevel) down which falling debris from high above bounced and skipped to form the rampart at the base: a protalus ramparts.

At the pass, a small path continues on west to Rhyd-Ddu through the slate quarries which are now in front of you. Some 50 metres west of the col (before you start up the ridge towards Snowdon) you can walk into the nearest of these quarries, a narrow chasm excavated in the slate. *Enter with care for there have been recent rock falls here.* Within, a level curves away into the darkness. The cleavage is strong in these rather monotonous dark grey slates in which you can see faint laminations. Higher in the quarry, the laminations are much clearer and thin beds of fine sandstone occur. At the top of the quarry, thin beds of tuffite appear indicating some not-too-distant volcanic activity. Both cleavage and bedding dip steeply northwest so if there were fossils to be found, this is where you might find them (graptolites).

All the rocks hereabouts are distinctly ice-smoothed so glaciers have flowed right over this pass (glacial diffluence), excavating the hollows now occupied by the small lakes (whose levels were artificially raised for a quarry water supply) just to the south of this path.

Valley of Ten Thousand Smokes: This was the largest ignimbrite eruption to have happened in modern times. It started on June 6, 1912 centred on a volcano called Mount Katmai in the Aleutian islands of Alaska. Three days later, the eruption was over having produced ash falls over half a metre thick in Kodiak, 170 kilometres away. No one witnessed the eruption and it wasn't until 1916 that an expedition went to find out what had happened. The top of the volcano had gone, replaced by a 2-km crater 600 metres deep. Nearby, a new vent had opened up – called Novarupta – and a previous river valley had disappeared, filled by the eruption and gushing steam vents everywhere. Geologists deduced that this eruption had been of red-hot glowing ash which in just a few hours had filled the valley up to 250 metres deep and over 4 kilometres broad. The steam vents were caused by the still-hot mass slowly releasing the vaporised river and groundwater the ignimbrite flow had buried. Later calculations showed that the flow filled the valley in less than 20 hours. The total volume of 15 cubic kilometres of magma had been erupted. How many tonnes is that? Well work it out! One cubic metre of volcanic rock would weigh 3-4 tonnes (1 cubic metre of water weighs 1 tonne). One cubic kilometre contains 1,000x1,000x1,000 cubic metres. Multiply that answer by 4 (the volcanic rock is about four times more dense than water) and then by 15 (the eruption total) and that gives ... What? Forgot your calculator? Okay, I've done it for you: 60,000,000,000 (60 billion) tonnes. Quite a lot you'd think, but this eruption was small compared to the LRTF or the Pitt's Head Tuff eruptions that laid the foundations for so much of the mountain scenery you see today before you.

And so you begin the long ridge ascent to Snowdon. You have just over 500 metres of climbing from here having already come almost 450 metres from the carpark. At first the ascent is steep and the path not well defined until it crosses the wall to join the clear main track from Cwm Llan. The rocks are all strongly cleaved mudstones with thin fine sandstone beds.

The path is a sad example of what the tramp of many feet does to the soils and plant life here. Parts have been washed out into deep gullies, stripped of the protective mat of plants. At the top of the first steep sector is a pile of stones and several thick white quartz veins. From here you have a bird's eye view of the fanned-out tips of the various small quarries below.

Now the ridge becomes broad and grassy with ever-improving views and many slate outcrops. Snowdon's summit is like a beacon right ahead. Here and there, you'll spot the odd glacial erratic boulder showing that the ice sheets once flowed over this ridge too, some 600 metres high. You can also tell this from the ice-moulded outcrops all around.

There is no law that states 'thou shalt stick to the path at all times', and here it runs along the west side of the ridge so you don't see down into Cwm Llan. So if you prefer it, drift over to the eastern edge of the ridge to look at the ever-changing vista of the great cwm and Y Lliwedd.

> **To Be or Not To Be? Footpaths and Erosion ...** You can't fail to notice the damage done to the mountains by the tramp of many feet. There are two points-of-view here: some feel that people shouldn't be allowed into the mountains because of the damage they do. Others – myself included – feel that this is a price worth paying so we can all marvel at the beautiful and wondrous landscape and its inhabitants that Nature has made. It is only when people come to know wild country and understand something of how it all formed and the plants and animals that live there that they become seriously interested in conserving it. You can also argue that slavishly following paths is not always the best thing for the local environment. If a mountain is broad and grassy, what sense is there in following a path up it? If everyone picks their own route, avoiding damaged areas, then, unless usage is absurdly high (like on the Llanberis Path or the now-cobbled track to Llyn Idwal where hundreds of thousands of people walk every year), erosion could be less of a problem. This boils down to your own estimation of the way things are on a particular mountainside and of how good you are at route-finding. It's not an answer to the problem for there is no viable answer. One final thing ... if the weather's warm and the route grassy, you could always try bare feet! It feels great and, unlike Vibram-soled boots, does no harm to the ground. In 1995, I climbed Scafell barefoot all the way ... but I had my boots with me for the descent!

The protalus rampart or moraine is particularly fine from here. All quarrying and mining operations need water and the Cwm Llan quarries were no exception. You can see the remains of a dismantled dam higher up the cwm. This once impounded a small lake, now just a marshy area as it was before; Nature reclaims her own. By now, you can see the more distant mountains to the east and south: Moel y Penamnen, Arenig Fach and Arenig Fawr, Manod, Moel Llyfnant, Moel yr Hydd, Moelwyn Mawr, Cnicht. In the opposite direction is the top of the red-coloured Crib Goch ('goch' = red) peeping out over Bwlch Ciliau.

Underfoot, the slaty sediments continue, often with distinct bands of fine sandstones which show that the beds dip steeply northwest like the strong cleavage that affects them.

The slope shallows right off as you approach the top of Allt Maenderyn. You'll see a large outcrop a few paces to the left of the track that is obviously different. This summit area is the next locality, after which the path descends slightly to a col before starting to ascend steeply again.

Allt Maenderyn: beginnings of the volcanic maelstrom [6053 5279]

This is where it all starts to happen. But first, take a look at the rocks here. The outcrop forming the prominent feature to the left of the track is pale coloured and obviously streaky. Like the slaty sediments over which it lies, it dips steeply northwest. Perhaps you recognise it, for it's an old friend: the Pitt's Head Tuff. But this is about as far east as you find it because both it and the sediments onto which it flowed were progressively removed by erosion before the LRTF eruption. So this area must have been uplifted above sealevel for a time.

Although most of the streaky foliation in the Pitt's Head Tuff here is planar (Fig. 10.5), parts of the hot flow moved a little after settling, causing small folds within the fused mass of flattened pumice lumps.

Figure 10.5: *Smeared-out streaks of flattened pumice – eutaxitic foliation – make the Pitt's Head (and other) ignimbrites highly distinctive. This outcrop is close to the path and the edge of my tape recorder tells you the size.*

On the east (right) side of the path, you'll find a quite different rock: it's dark green with reddish to bright red iron staining and is mostly broken up into lumps: a breccia. In one place, this seems to cut straight through the Pitt's Head Tuff and you can follow the junction between these two very different rocks for some tens of metres towards Cwm Llan. What's going on? The green rock is a basalt lava flow which broke up as it flowed and cooled. We know this because you can follow it along just like any other bed in a normal sequence of rocks. It actually overlies the Pitt's Head, being the first event in the main Snowdon eruptions that later produced the LRTF and the BPF, both of which you'll shortly see higher up the mountain. The contact you've examined between the two rock types must therefore be a fault, one of several which cut the ridge in this area. Like the one you saw back at Locality 2 (Fig. 10.3), this fault is normal; the younger basalt has slipped down to end up cheek by jowl with the Pitt's Head Tuff. Very confusing unless you actually map the area in detail. A few metres north, you can see clearly that the basalt does indeed overlie the Pitt's Head.

Geologists from the British Geological Survey have mapped Snowdonia in detail. Indeed some of my old friends – and I too – worked on this lengthy project some years ago. One result was a series of detailed, coloured 1:25,000-scale geological maps that show you exactly what is going on. These do require some geological training to make much sense of (which is why I don't include geological sketch maps with these rambles) but they are real works-of-art as well. For more information, see Appendix.

Looking down into Cwm Llan, you can see below the remains of a water leat that once conducted water from the dam to a pipeline, (the remains of which you can see also), which carried the water to the dressing sheds you saw back at the 'drunken graveyard'. You have a real bird's eye view of the quarry working too: a network of cuttings, tunnel entrances and the quarry holes themselves. This was never a large quarry by Welsh standards though it has left its mark in the long history of this cwm.

Clubmosses are particularly common around here. There are two common species of the genus *Lycopodium*: stagshorn and alpine (Fig. 10.6 A and B).

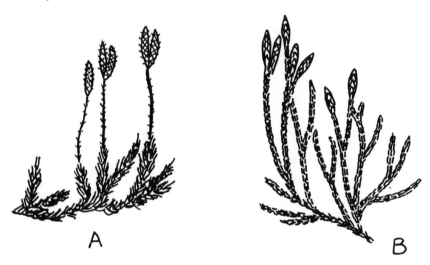

Figure 10.6: *Stagshorn (A) and alpine (B) clubmoss..*

Continuing over the col, largely underlain by the Pitt's Head Tuff, you come to a fence and ladder stile and begin to climb again. It is about here that the big fault you saw from Locality 2 cuts through the ridge. Almost immediately after the stile to the right of the path, you see jagged outcrops of white-looking rocks which are rhyolite tuffs, the beginning of the LRTF.

The path splits into several options here. The ones to the right involve more scrambling but you do see more rock.. The tuffs are clearly welded and in parts show good columnar joints. Other parts of the tuff have a platy foliation.

Nearby on the precipices, quite a few juniper bushes and some heather – all inaccessible to nibbling sheep – grow on some of this jointed tuff. **The white rhyolites continue for some way as you scramble ever upward until you come to a kink in the ridge above Clogwyn Du. The track drops very slightly before continuing to ascend.** Here, the rocks change dramatically. Quite abruptly, you find yourself on dark-coloured, red-weathering basaltic tuffs full of feldspar crystals, ash and larger lava chips. A great gully descends here and much of this rock has slipped and toppled into it, having broken up along cleavage planes, so everything's fairly chaotic around here.

As you continue to climb towards the junction with Llechog, you become aware that the slope to your left is littered with pale grey boulders of well-bedded tuffs full of fragments. Why are they there? You might think that they're all glacial erratics but they aren't. In fact, they've all come from a source higher up the slope and have moved down because of freezing and thawing – periglacial movement during the last stage of the Ice Age. **A little more climbing and you arrive at the source of these rocks and the next locality.**

BPF begins in earnest: Locality 5 [6048 5353]

The jumbled pile of boulders and outcrops, source of the slipped boulders I just mentioned, are the start of the third major formation that builds the Snowdon Volcanic Group: the BPF. The volcano dynamics changed abruptly at this time. Suddenly, the eruptions changed in both style and chemistry. The magma that produced the LRTF was rich in silica which made the eruption style violent and explosive. Now, the silica-rich magma was exhausted (p. 107) and a new phase of basaltic eruptions began. Some of these were direct extrusions of lava whilst others, such as those which formed the rocks around you here, blasted out showers of scoria that fell back into the shallow sea to build this thick mass – which included the summit of Snowdon. How do we know most of the eruptions were under the sea? When you reach Snowdon's summit, the next locality, I'll reveal all.

In some outcrops, you can see clear current bedding (foresets) with steeper dips of laminae within individual beds as tiny deltas advanced, in this case from left to right, telling us that the source of the scoria showers was somewhere to the left. Some beds seem to have load casted bases though the later cleavage has confused this because of its shearing action.

Just by the track is a fine example of these bedded tuffs in which you can see a whole series of load casts (Fig. 10.7), accentuated and separated by the cleavage. You can also see some examples of foreset beds and small unconformities (actually due to channels that eroded and cut into the loose and rapidly-laid-down scoria underneath) in this and other rocks around here. All in all, these are a beautiful set of bedded pyroclastics, living up to their official name.

Figure 10.7: *Beautiful bedded pyroclastic boulder showing cleavage 'smearing out' the load casted bed bases. I've marked a small unconformity (U) at the top in which some of the tilted underlying beds have been cut out by strong current scouring.*

Walk on up towards Bwlch Main. The rock changes back to less obviously bedded tuffs which actually should underlie the BPF. But you've unknowingly crossed a fault that has dropped down the outcrops you saw at Locality 5. The rocks here, the top of the LRTF, are all tilted and unstable and in the process of sliding down into Cwm Tregalan (the head of Cwm Llan). The process continues today as the heavy rains and the freeze-thaw action of winter frosts weave their endless dance of destruction on the mountains whose destiny, rather like that of you and me, is to be converted back to the ashes from which they were created in fiery violence hundreds of millions of years ago.

The ridge of Llechog with its own track joins from the left. Now below you can see five glacial lakes in Cwm Clogwyn, each with its moraine ridge, the best of which forms a crescent around the southwest side of Llyn Coch.

It's not difficult to imagine the glaciers in various stages of advance and retreat in Cwm Clogwyn. The ridge you're on is now a real arête, sliced into by glaciers from both sides. The rocks ahead are, once again, BPF with the bedding completely flat-lying. As you walk out along Bwlch Main, keep your eyes peeled for the rare and beautiful purple saxifrages (Fig. 10.8) which grow in clefts and gullies near the track. These little plants enjoy the relatively lime-rich basalts of the BPF.

Figure 10.8: *Purple saxifrage (Saxifraga oppositifolia)*

From now on, you climb through BPF with clear bedding and strong cleavage. More and more, the rocks forming the whole ridge are smashed up and heaved around by periglacial action, with screes on both sides. **Fortunately, this ridge is quite easy and safe to walk up.**

A view I'd happily do without ... The restaurant below Snowdon's summit is a blot on this mountain beauty that you see rather too well. It has no elegant architectural pretensions being – in my opinion – the worst of vernacular British brick bunker-style architecture ... and painted pale green. Yuk! Aaugh! Shame!

After a grassy broad sector at almost 1000 metres' altitude with a fine view of the aforementioned restaurant, you reach a sort of sentinel rock set up to mark where the path down towards Y Lliwedd branches off. This is the path you'll be following after Snowdon's summit **(Locality 6)**. This rock is worth examining for it's a beauty; a tuff full of white knobbly pyroclasts which form distinct showers – each representing perhaps a single explosion from a nearby vent.

A camper's eyrie, philosophy and perspectives. When I was researching this ramble, I camped just a few metres away from this stone, beside a snow patch (it was April) which gave me water. I was lucky: it was a perfect calm evening with a full moon. After the huddled masses had left the summit deserted, I watched the sun set and the moon rise. It is a very special experience to be able to stand alone on this lovely mountain with the surrounding silent ridges and mysterious deep valleys and lakes far below bathed in silvery moonlight. I had no torch and didn't need one. I was back at the summit again for the sunrise – still alone. If you like mountains, there's no better way to feel at one with them than to spend a solitary night like this. I've done it a number of times and the experience is always special. And you may think me stupid, but I always thank the mountain for the privilege of being able to be with it. This is as close as I get to any kind of religious worship: a worship of the harsh (mountains kill people) and impassive beauty of these high fastnesses, indifferent to humankind and all their trivial pursuits. Being far away from motorways and cities, you do wonder what it's all for. I conclude it's all meaningless. Ours is a pointless – but endlessly fascinating – universe.

Now for the final 40 metres of climbing to the summit and Locality 6. The final climb passes through more well bedded pyroclastics, the source for the sentinel stone. **You'll find an easy path to the left, avoiding most of**

the outcrops, and a more scrambly one to the right running up the ridge spine. I'd take the latter because you're here to see the rocks, aren't you? The outcrops are strongly cleaved with a distinctly rubbly appearance, full of blocks and bombs and lapilli. This tells you you're now fairly close to the original vent which erupted these. It must have been quite a sight to see, with huge steam and ash eruptions blasting up into the sky from submarine vents or small temporary volcanic islands. These eruptions would have been like those well-documented ones at Surtsey off the Iceland coast that began in November 1963 (Fig. 10.9).

BRY LYNAS 5/96

Figure 10.9: *Surtsey in violent mood, shooting out bombs and ash a month after the eruption started (my sketch from a photo in 'The Surtsey Eruption', Heimskringla, Rejkjavìk, 1966).*

Snowdon summit; Yr Wyddfa: Proof positive it was formed under the sea. Locality 6.

Yes, I can prove it for you – right here in this unlikely spot, the highest point in England and Wales. The rocks forming the summit were certainly laid down in the ancient Ordovician sea. More of that in a minute.

So first to the view. On a clear day, you can see a very long way indeed but pollution usually makes this impossible. It's helpful to have a smaller scale map to identify the more distant summits. If you want to confirm an identification, use a compass bearing and 'lay it off' on your map. Closer at hand are Crib y Ddysgl and Garnedd Ugain, only 20 metres lower than Yr

Wyddfa where you are now. The top of this ridge is formed by the Upper Rhyolitic Tuff Formation as are the rocks under your feet here. Further to the right is Crib Goch, mostly formed of the BPF and intrusive rhyolites. You can see the fairly flat-lying bedding outcropping all the way down the south face above Glaslyn.

> The Great Triangulation Triangulation is the method used to give the relative angular position of key marker points to each other on the Earth's surface. This was the basis of all map-making, which is why you find trig points on mountain summits. The measurement used to be done by theodolite. Now, the satellite-borne global positioning system can do this in a trice. But back in the early days of the Ordnance Survey, a network of surveyed-in trig points all over the country became the basis of all the new 1-inch maps. The further away a point is – the longer the baseline – the more useful the linking in is. The greatest of all was between Snowdon, Scafell (in the Lake District) and a summit in the Irish Wicklow mountains. The sightings took months to obtain because of weather conditions and had to be done at night with a beacon fire on each summit. I have once seen Snowdonia from Coniston Old Man in Lakeland, but it is rare to have such clarity. You usually need a nice clean westerly gale.

Above the blockhouse and just below the summit platform, you can find pale coloured, well-bedded tuffs, dipping gently northwest. These are the lowest beds of the Upper Rhyolitic Tuff, actually preserved here in the core of a shallow downfold. The axis of this fold you have unknowingly walked along from Locality 5. But it is in these beds here just below the trig point that you can find proof that they were laid down under the sea. What is this proof? Fossil shells which are of species which only exist in shallow seas. You'll find these (Fig. 10.10) in the outcrops (and in loose blocks) of light grey unbedded tuff just below the rocky platform that supports the trig point. They are casts of shells of the orthid family, mostly with quite thick ribs, though you may find some finer-ribbed ones too.

Figure 10.10: *Coarse-ribbed orthids from Snowdon's summit. These animals only lived in shallow seas, so here's proof that the rocks you're standing on formed as part of an ancient seafloor. Eruptions of ash nearby buried the animals from time to time, preserving them for you to look at hundreds of millions of years later.*

The rocks that form the actual trig platform are bedded tuffs that are, at first, quite coarse and full of crystals and small lava fragments. Higher, they become finer.

Amazingly, despite the constant pounding of feet and the climatic extremes of the summit area, you can still find mosses and a few blades of wiry grass in cracks in the rocks.

Now for some time travel. Find yourself a comfortable perch a little away from the crowds but with a view east. Tweak the imaginary levers of your mind Time Machine and set the dial for 18,000 years ago. Vrrooom! Now here you are at the peak – maximum ice extent – of the last Ice Age (the Weichselian). The wind is bitterly cold for it's about −25°C and the chill factor takes that down another 15°C as far as your warm flesh and blood is concerned. Half a kilometre to the north, you can see the Garnedd Ugain nunatak. A bit further away to the southeast, Y Lliwedd nunatak pokes defiantly out of the apparently featureless white glacial 'sea' all around. Almost every other landmark is buried under enormously thick icefield and snow. Further away, you can make out more nunataks where the other high mountains still keep their heads and ridge shoulders just clear of the all-encompassing ice sea. Crib Goch is visible too, but here the glacier below is stained red from a recent rock and ice avalanche.

Now look more carefully at the ice itself. It is not monotonous – instead, it is a slowly-heaving mass of ice falls, huge crevasses and moraine-strewn glaciers, all moving relentlessly downwards driven by gravity. What you can't see is the immense erosive damage the base and sides of the thick heavy ice streams are doing to the rocky valley floors. Unseen boulders are prised and torn from their rocky moorings and dragged into the ice. Others fall as avalanches into the frigid depths of the bergschrunds which gape at the junctions between the rock walls of the mountains and the ice itself. The rocks become embedded in the body of the ice and, where they happen to be at the base, they rip and gouge deeply into the bedrock, like nature's own extra-coarse sandpaper. Beneath the ice, roches moutonées are being moulded and grooves – striae – are being scratched by this erosive combination of heavy, moving and enclosing ice and hard rocky chisels. This is a lifeless landscape – or seems to be: just rock and ice. Yet if you were to look on some of the south-facing rocks of the nunataks, I'll bet you'd find some life ... probably lichens which today can be found on nunataks in Antarctica.

Set your machine for about 14,000 years now. The difference is profound. Below are the puny remains of the once-great glaciers, melting rapidly in the warm sun. You can hear the roar of meltwaters surging out of subglacial tunnels at the glacier snouts. The water, look, is filthy: milky with ground-up rock. And it's filling many new lakes in the cwms below. Waterfalls cascade down from melting ice patches stranded high up the valley sides. Ugly piles of moraines, little more than piles of clay from milled rock and boulders, litter the cwm floor and sides. Some of the vigorous streams are washing these away and sorting their material into deltas where they flow into the newly-formed – and mostly quickly filled – lakes. And so as you slowly return to the present, you watch the glaciers disappear and screes begin to form on the valley sides. The first blades of green plants quickly appear on the moraines. At about 12,500 years, suddenly the climate cools again. Snow falls heavily and small glaciers build once more where you now see Glaslyn and Llyn Llydaw. One thousand years later and it's all over. The ice has gone. Just over 11,000 years later, you can see the first traces of man: the beginnings of mining below in the great eastern cwm. Later, more noise interrupts the serenity: a railway is built up to the summit. Steam engines clank and puff. Then suddenly, nearly 11,500 years after the final ice melt, roads appear, car parks and thousands of human beings twinkle over the landscape, etching ugly paths on the once-pristine mountainsides. Aeroplanes and helicopters roar overhead, the atmosphere is laden with ozone and acid gases and ... well, you know the rest. And your Time Machine brings you back to the present with an unpleasant bump.

Time to continue ... To descend to Bwlch y Saethau – the col between Snowdon and Y Lliwedd – you'll probably have noticed a plexus of rough tracks, some of which run from the summit area. I don't recommend these. Better to return to the sentinel stone and turn left onto the Watkin Path. The descent is steep and slippery in places but otherwise no problem.

As you drop down towards the col, you pass some good exposures of the BPF again with clear bedding and showers of lapilli, all dipping gently northwest – for this is the southeast side of the Snowdon Syncline. In the damper crevices and gullies, you'll probably find tiny clusters of starry saxifrage. I even found another fossil shell the size of my thumb nail lying in this track, almost certainly slipped down from the locality you've just seen.

Quite abruptly, the path flattens out to become broad and terrace-like with green mossy slopes above and below. Ahead of you is a magnificent perched block (see Locality 7 for its significance). As soon as you get to the col (Bwlch y Saethau) in front of the perched block, you'll find a small path off to your left. The idea is to follow the edge of the ridge here with its attendant views down to Glaslyn and Llyn Llydaw, rather than follow the rather drab Watkin Path from which you see nothing much.

Just after you've passed the perched block, you see a large bed surface dipping northwest and coated with a thick veneer of quartz. If you look carefully at this, you'll see it's covered in parallel grooves called slickensides, now moulded by the white quartz, due to the upper and lower bed surfaces grinding against each other during later earth movements. **Just past this, take a small track off to the left for about 25 metres which stops suddenly at the precipice.** This gives you a marvellous view down to Glaslyn and its cwm.

Return to the ridge path and follow the top of the broad ridge until you come to a little lake (marked on the OS map). The next locality is just to the north of this.

A welcome break and a bit of everything: Locality 7 [6163 5417]

This is a fine place for resting, contemplating, eating a snack and even camping, being sheltered, flat, grassy and with water. For here you can see a bit of everything: the rocks underfoot, the majestic east face of Snowdon, Cwm Glaslyn and down to the great rocky basin of Llyn Llydaw not to mention the great bulk of Y Lliwedd (the next locality). Glaslyn is a little spoiled by the ochreous mine dumps from the defunct Britannia copper mine, but you can also see more or less exactly where the original veins were from the old open stopes and adit mouths. Most of the veins were in the BPF.

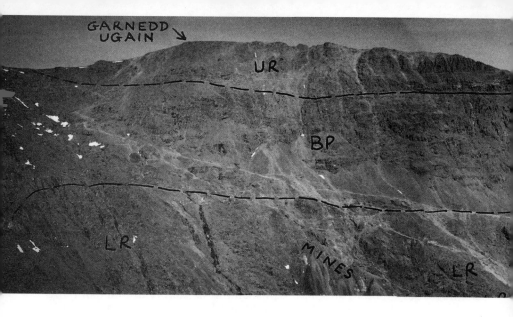

Figure 10.11: *Composite view of the Garnedd Ugain and Crib Goch ridges opposite showing roughly where the various rock formations crop out. BP – Bedded Pyroclastic Formation, UR – Upper Rhyolitic Tuff Formation, LR – LRTF, R – intrusions of rhyolite.*

You can see clearly from here the reddish BPF that forms much of the mountainside below Garnedd Ugain, sandwiched between the summit Upper Rhyolitic Tuffs and the LRTF which form the more irregular ground below the Pyg Track. You can also see very clearly the massive grey unbedded bulk of the rhyolite intrusion I mentioned earlier. This forms most of the mountainside from the north end of Glaslyn almost up to the ridge connecting Garnedd Ugain to Crib Goch. Crib Goch itself is largely intrusive rhyolite (Fig. 10.11). The northeast face of Snowdon – Clogwyn y Garnedd – is entirely made out of BPF and you can – with binoculars – easily see that the tuff beds all dip gently northwest.

> The miners were economical. They had to be because everything they did was by hand. So they took all the best and richest ores – which included lead and zinc – and avoided removing any more rock or worthless mineral than they had to. These were high grade vein deposits, quite different from most of today's copper mines that generally exploit low grade but big deposits – sometime called copper porphyry – on a vast scale ... making an equally vast mess of the landscape.

You'll find several items of interest around this locality, that happens to be in the very lowest parts of the BPF, with the LRTF cropping out all around slightly lower down as well as forming the whole looming mass of Y Lliwedd. **Walk south from the lake. You come to a drop down to a deep hollow which once held a lake.** On the left side of the hollow, you can see two bedding planes that you might want to look at. The surface seems to be covered in what may be ripple marks, entirely likely if these beds were formed under the sea. But the ripples may be fakes ... an artefact of the intersection of this

CRIB GOCH

bed surface with the inevitable cleavage, giving this slight riffling effect. What do you think?

The grey rubbly screes just above the lower former lake have broken off a lava flow. If you examine this greenish-grey basalt lava at its outcrop, you should find that it is often peppered with gas cavities – vesicles – which are sometimes so common that the rock becomes almost like scoria. (The lava is the lowest event in the BPF and the rippled bed surfaces below are the top of the LRTF). At the top of this lava flow, which forms the rim of the lower marshy basin, you'll notice a pedestal-like outcrop (Fig. 10.12). This is the broken-up – brecciated – top of the lava overlain by a cap rock of coarse lapilli tuff. Back towards the lake, these become well-bedded coarse tuffs with white-weathering lapilli.

Littered all over the ridge you've just come down, you can see obvious perched blocks and the other unmistakable sign of former burial and erosion by ice – ice-smoothed and rounded outcrops. So there's no doubt that ice buried this col in a fairly substantial way, telling us just how thick the glaciers were in this area. Parts of the col are over 820 metres above sealevel so the actual surface of the ice may have been at 900 metres. That doesn't leave much of the Snowdon range unburied and is why I described the 18,000-year-old vista as showing little but a few nunataks (Locality 6, your Time Machine trip). For here, you can see the strong evidence that this col was buried and eroded by a diffluent tongue of ice. Have you any idea which way it went?

Continue on the ridge towards Y Lliwedd. The path shortly descends into a hollow, connecting through to the possibly rippled bed surfaces you've just seen. Stop in the bottom of the hollow and turn to your right to look behind you at the rocks you've just crossed. These rocks just scream at you. They are full of white-weathering (rhyolitic) beds showing weird structures defying explanation: balls, rolls and bits of beds 'floating' in other different beds, slumps, folds ... truly remarkable-looking rocks. What do you make of them? (Fig. 10.13).

Figure 10.12: *Brecciated lava (B) full of gas cavities overlain by capstone of lapilli tuff (T).*

On the other (east) side of the hollow, near the top and some 15 paces to the right of the path, you can see another sequence of bedded tuffs. Some beds, you'll note if you try to follow them along the strike, simply pinch out to nothing in just a few paces. Some of the lapilli are walnut-sized and shaped. This is a fine area to spend a little time looking about at these fascinating beds and their structures and trying to tell the story of what went on here for yourself. You might prefer this to the steep ascent to Y Lliwedd, the next locality.

You also have good views to Llyn Llydaw and the moraine humps which fringe most of it. Notice how the Afon Glaslyn has built out a delta of gravel and cobbles, probably enhanced by the debris created by the miners. The ice from Snowdon's east side actually carved four separate cwms: the highest is occupied by Glaslyn, the next by Llyn Llydaw, the third is Cwm Dyli and the fourth, the head of Nant Gwynant.

You now have some choices. If you want to continue on the Y Lliwedd spur of the ramble, the ridge path drops down, with a little scrambling, to cross Bwlch Ciliau. You may prefer to skip this and drop down to rejoin the Watkin Path as it descends clearly and easily into Cwm Tregalan. The Watkin Path is less than 100 metres away, just below the ridge to your south.

Figure 10.13: *These beds, as you may have guessed, are all the result of movement of the water-saturated material just after it was laid down. This may have been due to slumping down a submarine slope or to the weight of the lava and later rock units which loaded down on this – or both. Here they look like a pile of entrails though you can just detect ghostly bits on bed amongst the intestinal chaos. Most of the beds have simply been ripped apart into tattered blobs.*

Either way, you're back on the thick LRTF, with some coarse tuffs and other finer ones. All are strongly cleaved and the bedding is rarely obvious; a conspicuous difference to the later BPF. You have no reason to know it, but you've crossed an anticlinal fold whose axis runs roughly from Llyn Llydaw through Cwm Llan.

As you make your way up Y Lliwedd's steep track, you'll see that the monotony of these rocks is relieved by showers of lapilli and blocks. The precipice of Y Lliwedd is host to a number of species including dwarf juniper. Another common though transient species is Homo sapiens, sub-species rock climbers. I always find this version of humanity fascinating to watch but I regret to say I'd be too scared to do that kind of thing. The rock precipice is slashed by thick white quartz veins.

Just before the top, the rock becomes much paler, almost white-weathering in parts and much finer grained. It forms the west summit. The east summit is the final locality.

Y Lliwedd: Locality 8 [6242 5322]

This is the last of the great views of the Snowdon cwms – the classic Snowdon horseshoe. Opposite is Crib Goch, slightly higher than Y Lliwedd and entirely composed of rhyolite intrusive. Above the scree slope you can see a great mass of quartz veins that cut the rhyolite (Fig. 10.24). Since the last locality – and indeed right the way down into Cwm Tregalan as you will soon see – you cross nothing but rhyolitic tuffs. This formation is really thick and massive, being almost devoid of bedding or any suggestion of a sedimentary interlude between eruptions. It is built mainly of a series of almost unvarying pyroclastic flow deposits – ignimbrite – and certainly we know that parts of it are welded (as I mentioned at Locality 3). The whole LRTF 'event' probably took place over a matter of months – and here it's about 600 metres thick. In all, about 50 cubic kilometres of ignimbrite belched forth in this astonishingly short time, more than half of this volume remaining inside the Snowdon caldera. The remainder burst out as submarine flows (p. 125) heading northeast into deeper waters. You can find outcrops of the LRTF almost as far away as Conwy.

Did the LRTF hide its candle under a bushel? We know the LRTF eruption was entirely beneath the sea. There are many reasons for supposing this, such as the total absence of any evidence for this event in most rocks of this age elsewhere in Wales. Had such a colossal eruption occurred from a land volcano – consider the relatively small Mt Pinatubo eruption which affected the entire world's climate for several years – then you'd be able to find layers of ash from it tens or hundreds of kilometres away. You don't. The reworking by waves and currents of the LRTF is very local and only to be seen in the Cwm Idwal and Moel Siabod areas. The outflow tuff which reached almost to Conwy (25 kilometres) was an actual ash flow, stopping only when it ran out of energy. The absence of ash falls anywhere else tells us that the eruption cloud you'd normally expect must have been almost wholly quenched by the sea which overlay the area. Also, you've seen for yourself earlier today (and pages 108 and 134) that the BPF, which followed the LRTF directly, was at least partly submarine. And just imagine what would have happened to a big volcanic island built of ash in the sub-tropics (as this area then was). It would quickly be torn down by rainstorms and vast amounts of ash material washed out as mudflows and debris-laden streams into the surrounding seas, contaminating the normal quiet rain of mud and silt. But there is, as I've said, no evidence of this whatsoever.

Although Y Lliwedd is formed of LRTF, an odd quirk occurs to the east. If you walk down, southeast, for a mere 300 metres, you drop down onto younger rocks: the BPF again. How can this be? Normally, you get onto older rocks as you go down. If you could see the dips here, you'd see that they are all now steeply to the southeast, much steeper than the hill slope. So if you walk that way, although you're going downhill, you're walking up the beds. In fact the entire southeast flank of Y Lliwedd containing the mineral veins you saw at the start of the ramble is BPF. There are even a few outlying remnants of the Upper Rhyolitic Tuffs like those you saw on Snowdon's summit. This is because there's a broad synclinal fold which runs roughly along the Nant Gwynant valley. Like lesser fleas on the back of bigger fleas, this southeast dipping fold flank is itself folded into a series of irregular and impersistent anticlines and synclines.

Return now to the Watkin Path and drop down through the LRTF into Cwm Tregalan. As soon as you rejoin the Watkin Path, you pass through numerous outcrops of strongly cleaved tuffs stuffed with rhyolitic bombs, blocks and lapilli. **After some distance, when the old quarry dam to your right is perpendicular with the line of the track, a stream crosses. About 100 metres after this, you suddenly find that you're walking on slates again.** The contact is by the track and is interesting because it's quite irregular with masses of the same basalt flow you saw at Locality 4 loading down into the siltstone to form ball-like masses; the flow actually has sagged into the underlying sediments.

A little before the quarry, you'll see below the track to the right the large 'bedding planes' dipping southeast that we discussed back at Locality 3. If you were to examine these surfaces, you'd find that they are bogus! They aren't bedding planes at all. They are actually huge joints formed during a later episode of cleavage formation (called kink bands), masquerading as bed surfaces. These are indeed a lesson for the unwary. The bedding is not easy to see, but it actually dips steeply northwest.

If you have any energy left, you might like to have a brief look at the Cwm Llan quarries. If not, simply follow the Watkin Path down. The bedding in the quarry is usually hard to spot, for these were very uniform muds and silts with not many 'events' going on. In some of the open quarries the beds quite clearly dip northwest at a moderate angle. The cleavage dips in a similar direction at about 80°. And the strange kink band joints I mentioned look, to the casual glance, like beds, dipping gently southeast, almost at right angles to the main cleavage.

Kink bands form in a rather complex way, affecting rocks that already have a strong and penetrating foliation. They tell us of later earth movements and of the stress directions which operated during those movements. When clusters of kink bands form, you get a second cleavage known as 'strain slip', 'chevron' or 'crenulation' cleavage. This may become so strong as to obliterate earlier structures. In Snowdonia, the earlier 'main' or 'slaty' cleavage, mostly steep-dipping and trending northeast-southwest, is always the strongest.

The quarries are now the domain of pale-coloured wrens, boggy patches with soft rushes, small pools and frog spawn (in spring) ... and silence. Some of the holes are now completely inaccessible. Rhododendrons have even begun to appear here.

Rejoin the Watkin Path and continue on under the crags of Craig Ddu. This, we now know, is a welded 'pod' of the LRTF, pretending to be an anticline (Locality 3). As you see, there's not a shred of evidence for this now you're right underneath it, so that's that hypothesis booted out. Nice idea. Still, that's science at work. If your pet theory doesn't hold water, it sinks like the 'Titanic'.

To the right of the track below Craig Ddu, the rocks have been heavily ground down by the ice into roches moutonées. **Soon you come to Gladstone**

Rock with a large granite slab set into it commemorating Gladstone's speech made here in 1892 when he was 83. Perhaps you feel that someone should insert another plaque here commemorating the successful completion of your long and arduous ramble over Wales' highest mountain.

All that remains now is for you to follow the easy track back down past the ruin of Plas Cwm Llan and the old mine you saw at the start of the day, to Nant Gwynant and the carpark. If it's a warm day, you might try dipping your aching feet in the cold, clear pools of the Afon Cwm Llan.

> If it seems to you that the west wall of Plascwmllan is pock-marked with bullet holes, you're right. It was used for target practice by commandos during World War II.

Final note: a plea

If you've enjoyed this, and all the previous rambles, you've probably learned a great deal about Snowdonia's history and landscape. This puts you in a strong position to take an active role in its conservation – and other perhaps less exciting parts of Britain too. This great natural heritage is constantly under threat from commercial pressures. You've seen how long it took Nature to form this beautiful mountain area and you've also seen the ugly scars left by mining and quarrying. It will take Nature many thousands of years to repair all that damage. It will, of course. But by simply being here, you and I are part of the more insidious process of damaging our environment. You'll have come here by some form of transport which, unless you cycled or walked from where you live, will have added more pollutants to the already-poisoned air we breathe. Remember that all the animals, plants and even the rocks here are constantly bathed in that same, often corrosive, air. It does none of us any good.

If you care about these things, don't feel you can't do anything about it. You can ... in all kinds of ways. Like walking up hills in bare feet to avoid hurting their fragile plant cover, we have to learn to tread lightly on our planet. If I have helped you to a better understanding of how Earth – Gaia – functions, I hope that you will remember whenever you drive, turn up the central heating or buy more useless products that by these acts, you are indirectly stomping on Nature with hobnailed boots!

Happy rambling!

P.S. If you're interested in 'living gently on our planet', connect to **http://www.oneworld.org/penguin/** – if you have a computer with a World Wide Web link. If not, write to Penguin (People's Ethical News and Globally Useful Information Network) at Environmental Unit, 67 Fore Street, Totnes, TQ9 5NJ.

Glossary

Note that you'll find all formal time and rock period names (Arenig, Caradoc, Ordovician, Snowdon Volcanic Group. LRTF, Pitt's Head Tuff etc.) on the Timescale in the Appendix.

aa	blocky lava (q.v.) which breaks up into clinkery masses as it flows. Hawaiian name. q.v. pahoehoe.
acid *(of igneous rocks)*	igneous rock which is high in silica (q.v.); q.v. basic.
acritarchs	microscopic plankton which floated around in the ancient seas and oceans of the world. Their skeletons were very tough so that they can often be found in old marine sedimentary rocks where no other larger fossils survived.
alluvial cone or fan	a mass of silts, sands and gravels deposited by a river at a point where its gradient decreases
anticline	a fold in a rock sequence which is concave-downwards (q.v. syncline).
apparent dip	the inclination of rock beds which you see in a rock face not at right angles to the strike (q.v.). It is always less than the true dip (q.v.).
arête	sharply chiselled, knife-edge ridge formed by glaciers grinding away on both sides of the ridge e.g. Crib Goch.
ash	pulverised rock blasted out of a volcano, with a maximum particle size of less than 4 millimetres.
ash flow tuff	tuff (q.v.) deposited from a turbulent mix of hot gas and ash from certain violent types of eruption. q.v. ignimbrite, pyroclastic flow.
augite	dark heavy silicate mineral; a pyroxene. Important constituent of some basalts (q.v.).
autobreccia	lava-like rock which breaks itself to pieces as it flows whilst solidifying. q.v. aa.
basalt	a fine grained, dark, heavy lava low in silica (q.v.), consisting of feldspars (q.v.) and iron/magnesium silicate minerals such as olivine and pyroxene (q.v. augite). Gabbro is the plutonic (q.v.) intrusive equivalent of basalt. Basalt eruptions are normally the least destructive of all, usually being non-explosive.
basic *(of igneous rocks)*	igneous rock low in silica (q.v.); q.v. acid.
Beddgelert *Fracture Zone*	a belt of important faults which runs northeast from the Beddgelert area. It includes, loosely, the Beddgelert, Nantmor and Yr Arddu fault zones and controlled the southeastern part of the Snowdon graben (q.v.), some of the eruptions, the caldera (q.v.) margin, megabreccias (q.v.) and the later mineral veins (as at Sygun Mine, p. 170).

bedding,
bedded, beds
the layering or layers, sometimes called 'strata' and usually flat (planar), in which sedimentary (q.v.) rocks are laid down. q.v. laminated.

bedding plane
the dividing planes (flat surfaces) which separate beds or layers of strata. q.v. bedding.

beds
see Bedding.

bergschrund
deep crevasse which separates the head of a corrie glacier from the steep mountain wall against which it rests.

BFZ
Beddgelert Fracture Zone (q.v.)

block
angular lump of volcanic rock larger than 32 millimetres. q.v. block tuff.

blockfield
area of shattered rocks characteristic of periglacial (q.v.) weathering in which rock outcrops are broken up into 'fields' of blocks

bomb
lump of lava larger than 32 millimetres, blasted out of a volcano. q.v. pyroclastic, block, ash, lapilli.

boulder clay
old name for till (q.v.).

brachiopods
sea-dwelling invertebrates (='no backbones'), commonly called lamp shells. They have two unequal-sized valves (a valve is one half of the shell) and are rather uncommon today. From 'brachio' = arm; 'pod' = foot.

breccia
a rock made up of large, angular fragments of other rocks.

calcite
white or colourless crystalline mineral composed of calcium carbonate. It occurs in mineral veins and also forms limestones (q.v.).

caldera
a volcanic crater over 1 kilometre wide, usually resulting from the collapse of the upper part of a volcano into the underlying, partly empty magma chamber (q.v.).

Caledonian
orogeny
usually refers to earth movements (folding, faulting and resultant cleavage) associated with the collision of the two great plates of America/Greenland (Laurentia) and South Britain/Applachia (Avalonia, part of the ancient Gondwana supercontinent). See p. 6.

chalcopyrite
a lustrous yellow ore of copper (copper iron sulphide), usually found in mineral veins.

chlorite
a green secondary mineral similar to mica (q.v.) which grows in a rock as a result of the alteration of original, primary, minerals.

cirque
French name for 'cwm' or 'corrie'.

clast
an individual particle of a rock, which may vary from hardly visible to the size of a boulder. q.v. volcaniclasts.

cleavage
a series of normally parallel, densely spaced planes within a rock, produced by the high temperatures and pressures of large earth movements. If the rock is strongly cleaved, it usually splits easily along these planes and is often quarried for roofing slates and other building materials. q.v. fracture cleavage. p. 25.

columnar jointing	column-like joint structures which often form in rocks which were liquid, as they cool.
cordierite	metamorphic (q.v.) mineral which grows inside rock subjected to later heating because of a nearby intrusion (q.v.).
cross bedding	sedimentary (q.v.) rock unit in which individual beds – foresets (q.v.) – are laid down at an angle to the normal horizontal beds. This happens because of traction currents of water or wind at the front of an advancing delta or sand dune.
current bedding	see Cross bedding
debris flow	another rather more descriptive term for mass flow (q.v.). Also known as gravity sediment flow since it is gravity which gives the flow its energy.
devitrified	process by which igneous (q.v.) glassy rocks gradually become crystalline.
dewatering	removal of water from wet sediments, usually because of compaction from the weight of overlying material. This can result in characteristic structures such as the injection – upwards squirting – of water-saturated sludgy sediment. q.v. flame structures, load casts. Usually, the water migrates slowly as diagenesis (q.v.) proceeds, causing no disruption.
diagenesis	process which occurs within sediments after their deposition in which they eventually become hardened into rocks. q.v. dewatering.
dip	see Strike.
dip slope	land surface slope parallel to the true dip of the bedded rocks below. q.v. dip, strike.
diffluence, glacial	what happens when a valley glacier becomes so large that it spills over into an adjacent valley, breaching the watershed and cutting a connecting trough between two separate valleys e.g. between Llanberis Pass glacier and Cwm Idwal/Nant Ffrancon.
dolerite	medium grained igneous (q.v.) rock, the intrusive (q.v.) equivalent of basalt (q.v.).
dyke	a thin sheet of igneous (q.v.) rock injected along a line of weakness such as a fault (q.v.) and usually steeply dipping or vertical, generally associated with volcanic activity. q.v. intrusion.
erratic (glacial)	out-of-place boulder dropped by a melting glacier.
eutaxitic foliation	streaky texture characteristic of welded tuffs (q.v.) due largely to drawn out, extremely flattened pumice (q.v.) lumps. The Pitt's Head Tuff shows perfect eutaxitic texture.
extrusion	igneous (q.v.) rock which is erupted at the surface of the Earth.
fault	a fracture in the Earth's surface along which the rocks on one side have moved relative to those on the other. Faults may have horizontal, oblique or vertical displacements which range from millimetres to hundreds of kilometres.

feldspar   an important rock-forming mineral (silicate), often white or
                       pink in colour. Two important types exist: orthoclase feldspar
                       (potassium aluminium silicate) and plagioclase feldspar (so-
                       dium – calcium aluminium silicate) of which there are six
                       distinct mineral types.

fiamme   from Italian for 'flame' used to describe flattened lumps of
                       pumice (q.v.) looking like candle flames which are a charac-
                       teristic of welded tuffs (q.v.). The flattening which compresses
                       lumps to squeezed-out pancakes, is caused by the intense heat
                       of the welded tuff flow and by the weight of the upper layers
                       of the flow. q.v. ignimbrite.

flame structures   the result of squeezing of soft, wet sediment when a lower bed
                       irregularly 'squirts' up into the overlying bed, giving structures
                       which look like small flames. q.v. load casts, fluidisation,
                       dewatering.

flow breccia   the breaking up of a body of lava by its own movement as it
                       cools and solidifies, into angular fragments. q.v. autobreccia,
                       aa.

flow folds   the folding which can develop in thick, sticky lava (q.v.) as it
                       flows.

fluidise, fluidisation a change of state of loosely consolidated, water-laden sedi-
                       ments which makes them behave like fluids rather than solids.
                       This means that, once fluidised, they flow or squirt through
                       other beds. Usually caused by earthquake shocks. Fluidisation
                       also occurs in ignimbrite (q.v.) flows where violently expand-
                       ing hot gases keep the solid volcaniclasts (q.v.) separated so that
                       the entire mass behaves like an extremely mobile liquid. This
                       may even occur in rare types of landslide.

foliation   planar structures within a rock which may be due to a variety
                       of causes such as cleavage (q.v.) and flow (in lavas).

foreset   the inclined leading bed in cross bedding (q.v.).
(current bedding)

formation   the name for a set of strata which is internally consistent and
                       which forms an easily-recognised unit. The Pitt's Head Tuff is
                       a distinctive example. In geology, 'beds' and 'members' make
                       up a formation (they are really miniature formations) and
                       several formations make a 'group', such as the Snowdon Vol-
                       canic Group (See Appendix, Timescale).

fracture cleavage   widely spaced cleavage joints which occurs in hard brittle
                       rocks like dolerites. q.v. slates, cleavage.

fumarole   small vent which emits steam and other gases after volcanic
                       eruption has ceased. They often become coated with sulphur
                       crystals.

galena   the principal ore of lead, lead sulphide. It occurs as silvery
                       cubic crystals associated with quartz (q.v.) and other sulphide
                       minerals in veins.

geochemistry   the study of the Earth by means of chemical analysis of its
                       rocks.

geophysics	the study of the Earth by remote means such as magnetism and gravity.
glacial erratics	see Erratic, glacial
glacial striae, striations	scratches and shallow grooves cut in the polished rock surfaces over which glaciers ground their downward course. The striations are made not by the ice, but by lumps of rock stuck in the base of the ice sheet, rather like sandpaper on a giant scale. They show us the direction of the former ice flow.
graben	a deep fault (q.v.)-bounded trough or basin.
granite	a coarse grained igneous (q.v.) rock made up chiefly of quartz (q.v.) and feldspar (q.v.). The intrusive equivalent of rhyolite (q.v.).
graptolites	an extinct group of small, free-floating planktonic animals which existed only as colonies. Some are used for dating the rocks in which they are found since they changed (evolved) rapidly over time and so are characteristic of particular time periods (e.g. gracilis Biozone, p. 70).
greywacke	'dirty' coarse sandstones which have a good deal of mud matrix, usually the product of turbidity currents (q.v.).
grit	old but still-useful word for coarse sandstone (c.f. Millstone Grit of the Pennines which was indeed used for millstones)
hanging valley	gross overdeepening of a principal valley by a powerful glacier can leave its tributary valleys 'hanging' high up on the sides, usually with fine waterfalls (as in Fiordland, New Zealand). q.v. truncated spurs.
Harlech Dome	large domed area of Cambrian rocks roughly centred on Rhinog Fawr. This dome seems to have been in existence from at least the early Ordovician, forming an island or positive area.
hematite	iron ore; red iron oxide.
hornfels	tough rock created by 'cooking' due to nearby intrusion (q.v.).
horst	uplifted block bounded by faults (q.v.) forming a positive area; the opposite of a graben (q.v.).
hyaloclastite	from 'hyalo' = glass, 'clast' (q.v.) = fragment and '-ite' = rock. Glassy lavas (such as obsidian) form when the molten lava is so quickly cooled that crystal structures have no time to form. Water-quenching of such lavas may cause them to disintegrate just as a hot glass bowl would if you poured cold water into it. This results in a highly distinctive rock. q.v. devitrification.
hydrothermal	from 'hydro' – water 'thermal' – hot. Hot watery fluids circulating in the crust can profoundly alter the rocks they pass through and can deposit new minerals, including ore minerals like chalcopyrite (q.v.).
igneous	from 'ignis' – fire. Rocks which have solidified from a molten state.
ignimbrite	literally 'fire cloud rock'. A hard rock formed from a hot, rapid, fluidised (q.v.) gassy flow of volcanic debris from a particularly

violent form of nuée ardente (q.v.) eruption. In certain cases after the flow stopped (often tens of kilometres from the volcanic source), the internal heat was so great that the component particles welded together to give a very characteristic-looking rock: welded tuff. q.v. pyroclastic flow, ash flow, welded tuff, fiamme, shard.

intracaldera tuffs tuffs which were erupted but confined to the caldera.

intrusion, intruded, intrusive a mass of igneous rock which is injected into and cools within existing rocks. q.v. dyke, sill.

isocline rocks folded so tightly that the limbs parallel each other.

isotopic age the age of a rock (in years) determined from study of natural radioactive elements occurring within a (usually igneous) rock. *See* Appendix. q.v. radiometric age.

joints a fracture in a rock along which no movement has occurred. q.v. fault.

knock and lochan topography Scottish term for heavily glaciated landscape with rounded crags and many small lakes.

laminae very thin layers of sediment which collectively form beds.

lapilli volcaniclasts (q.v.) from the Italian 'little stones' between 4 millimetres and 32 millimetres in size. q.v. ash, bombs, blocks, pyroclastic.

lateral moraine moraine which develops at the edge of a glacier, found on the valley side after melting. q.v. terminal moraine.

lava igneous (q.v.) rock in liquid state which flows out from volcanoes or fissures in the Earth's surface. q.v. magma.

limestone sedimentary rock made up mostly of calcite (q.v.) (calcium carbonate).

load casts when blobs or sections of denser sediment beds founder or sink into water-saturated underlying beds due to differential compaction, they form load casts. This is characteristic of waterlain sediments. q.v. flame structures, fluidisation, dewatering.

LRTF shorthand for Lower Rhyolitic Tuff Formation (see Timescale).

magma molten rock within the Earth's crust. When this reaches the surface, volcanic eruptions occur. q.v. lava.

magma chamber cavity in the Earth's crust filled with magma.

malachite green ore of copper (hydrous copper carbonate) which occurs in the oxidised part of a mineral vein.

mantle the thick, hot and plastic interior of the planet above which the crust forms a thin skin. It is from the mantle that most magma (q.v.) originates, rising slowly into the crust either due to subduction (q.v.) processes or due to 'hot spots' in the mantle itself.

mass flow a jumbled mobile mass of sediment, rock and water or gas

	whose downslope motion is a response to gravity. q.v. pyroclastic flow, fluidisation, turbidite, gravity flow, debris flow.
massive	rock bed which has no internal structures like bedding (q.v.) or flow foliation (q.v).
megabreccia	breccia (q.v.) with very large lumps, sometimes many tens of metres in size. These formed by collapse as the Beddgelert Fracture Zone (q.v.) faults moved.
melange	jumbled up mix of chunks of older rock formations which have slipped down a steep offshore slope and foundered in deeper water.
metamorphic, metamorphosed	third class of rocks which are altered versions of igneous (q.v.) or sedimentary (q.v.) rocks. They are altered by heat and pressure, usually during orogeny (q.v.).
metasediments	sediments which have been metamorphosed (q.v.).
microgranite	finely crystalline granite (q.v.).
moraine	debris produced by the erosive action of glaciers, often forming mounds as in Cwm Idwal. q.v. till.
mudstone	sedimentary (q.v.) rock made up of mud particles and clays.
MVF	shorthand for Moelwyn Volcanic Formation (see Timescale)
nuée ardente	'glowing cloud' (French); violent type of eruption which produces pyroclastic flows (q.v.). q.v. ignimbrite. First observed in Martinique.
normal fault	fault (q.v.) in which movement is vertical.
nunatak	isolated ice-bound peak. e.g. Transantarctic Mountains.
olivine	heavy green mineral, important in basalt magmas which come from the mantle (q.v.).
orogeny	mountain-building period during which rock sequences are buckled, faulted and metamorphosed (q.v.).
pahoehoe lava	Hawaiian name for lava which has the appearance of coiled ropes; ropy lava. q.v. aa.
palaeontology	the study of fossils which helps with rock dating (see Appendix).
palynology	the study of pollen preserved in sediments. This branch of palaeontology (q.v.) is vital for dating peats and many rock sequences too.
penetrative cleavage	cleavage (q.v.) which totally pervades a rock, usually destroying its original textures.
perched block	erratic (q.v.) block left by glaciers prominently perched on the top of a roche moutonée (q.v.).
periglacial	extremely cold conditions characteristic of the Arctic, usually associated with glaciers but affecting areas not covered by ice. Periglacial processes form blockfields (q.v.), tors and cause

	slow downslope movement of broken-up debris (q.v. mass flow), often called solifluction (q.v.).
pillow lavas	the form taken by lava when erupted underwater, with piles of concentric-banded 'pillows' which sag into earlier ones giving an easily identified rock.
plagioclase	type of feldspar (q.v.).
plate tectonics	study of the Earth's crustal structure in which the rigid 'plates' of the crust (lithosphere) slowly move about relative to each other, floating on and driven by slow convection currents in the hot plastic mantle below (q.v.). See Introduction, p. 4.
protalus rampart	a ramp built of lumps of scree which have bounced down a former snowpatch, now vanished, so leaving a rampart at the base of the later scree slope.
pseudomorphs	secondary minerals which replace original ones, but retain original mineral's shape. q.v. metamorphism.
pumice	very light volcanic rock which floats on water due to its expanded polystyrene-like texture. The magma (q.v.) from which it forms is typically highly charged with dissolved gases. It is the sudden release of pressure in the violent types of eruption such as nuées ardentes (q.v.) which inflates the pumice, formed mostly of gas trapped by thin, glassy bubbles. q.v. shards. The sharp, glassy bubble walls give pumice its abrasive quality. Maybe you have a piece in your bathroom.
pyrite	Fool's Gold, a common brassy yellow iron sulphide mineral found especially in mineral veins.
pyroclastic	material produced by explosive volcanic eruption.
pyroclastic flow	catch-all term for a mass flow triggered and partly driven by volcanic eruption; from 'pyro' meaning 'fire' plus clast (q.v). These includes nuées ardentes, ignimbrites, ash flows and other phenomena, some of which are the most violent eruptive processes known.
quartz	a glassy mineral, silica (q.v.) (SiO_2), sometimes called 'rock crystal' when forming large crystals. Very important constituent of most rocks.
quartzite	a tough sedimentary rock made of quartz grains sutured together by mild metamorhpism (q.v.).
radiometric age	*See* Isotopic age.
rhyolite	a fine grained, quartz (q.v.)-rich volcanic rock; the extrusive(q.v.) equivalent of granite (q.v.).
ripple marks	small ridges due to waves or currents which form on shallow sandy seafloors, often preserved in sandstones (q.v.).
roche moutonée	from the French, literally 'sheep rock'; referring to the characteristic shape of rock outcrops in valley floors and sides, once moulded and ground by the passage of heavy glaciers q.v. glacial striae.

sandstone	a sedimentary rock composed of sand-sized grains.
scoria	loose rubbly lumps of volcanic debris blasted out of a volcano and often forming a characteristic cone.
scree	a fan or cone of shattered rock fragments which have been prised off the crags above by frost action (q.v. periglacial). Water expands as it freezes, so any water that freezes in fractures in the rock gradually opens up the fracture. When the ice melts, the prised-apart piece falls away to the cone of rock debris below. All the screes you see today must have formed after the last glaciers melted for earlier screes would have been removed by the flowing ice.
sedimentary	a rock deposited from either water, air, or ice e.g. (q.v.) sandstone.
sedimentary structures	structures which form within a sedimentary rock which tell us something of their mode of formation. q.v. load casts, flame structures, cross bedding.
sedimentology	study of sedimentary structures so that they tell us the story of their origin.
shards	fragments of glassy lava bubble walls blasted apart when the degassing during an eruption is extreme. The intermediate stage is pumice (q.v.). If expansion continues, the bubbles rupture leaving tiny fragments of glass. q.v. ignimbrite.
shear	sliding (simple shear) or compressive (pure shear) stress between two rock masses. When movement occurs, the rocks are said to suffer strain. cf. cleavage, orogeny.
silica	silicon dioxide (SiO_2), a fundamental consituent of most rocks, commonly occurring as the mineral quartz (q.v.). q.v. silicification.
silicified, silicification	a form of diagnenesis (q.v.) in which a rock becomes enriched with silica (q.v.) due to circulating fluids (q.v. hydrothermal). This effect hardens the rock and commonly obscures primary structures like bedding (q.v.) or glass shards (q.v.).
silicosis	disease of the lungs due to rock dust which killed many quarrymen after the introduction of compressed air drills.
sill	intrusion (q.v.) of igneous (q.v.) rock which forces its way into a bedded sequence parallel to the beds. This occurs simply because the bed surfaces, like any fracture, represent a plane of weakness which is exploited by the molten magma (q.v.). q.v. dyke.
siltstones	sedimentary rock made up of silt particles.
slates	usually mudstones (q.v.) or siltstones (q.v.) with strong cleavage. I often use 'slates' as shorthand for this.
slickensides	grooves on a fault surface due to the sliding movement between the two sides.
solifluction	slow downslope movement of debris or soil, partially due to freezing and thawing. q.v. periglacial, mass flow.
sphalerite	an ore of the metal zinc (ZnS), also called 'zincblende,' 'blende' or 'blackjack'.

stadial   short cold period during a generally warmer climatic phase. e.g.
                       Younger Dryas Stadial; see Timescale.

stope, stoping   technique used by miners for removing a steeply dipping,
                       ore-bearing mineral vein involving as little waste rock material
                       as possible.

strain   permanent deformation of a rock due to shear (q.v.) stress.

stratigraphy   the study of sequences of rock formations.

stress   forces acting on a body of rock. q.v. shear, strain.

striae   see glacial striations.

strike   the compass bearing, measured in degrees, of an imaginary
                       horizontal line drawn on a bedding plane (q.v.). This, together
                       with the dip (q.v.) of the plane (measured in degrees from the
                       horizontal and perpendicular to the strike), uniquely defines
                       that plane in space and allows the geologist to represent the
                       three dimensional geometry of inclined or folded structures on
                       a two dimensional map. The steeper the dip of a bedding plane,
                       the easier it is to measure the strike. For vertical (upstanding)
                       beds, the strike is easy to measure because the dip is vertical
                       (90 degrees) but for flat-lying (horizontal) bedding, the planes
                       have no strike. Are you confused? If so, try this experiment with
                       this book: Hold it so that it is horizontal. Now you can see that
                       if the book were a bed of strata, you couldn't measure any
                       direction of dip – or strike. Now hold it so that it is vertical. The
                       strike is the compass direction (bearing) of the book's spine and
                       the dip is, obviously, vertical. Finally, hold it so that it is
                       inclined about half way between horizontal and vertical (about
                       45 degrees). Move it (if necessary) so that its spine is horizontal.
                       The spine now gives you the strike direction. The dip direction
                       is always perpendicular to the strike (the book's spine), meas-
                       ured in the plane of the book's cover. So the actual angle of dip
                       is the greatest angle you can measure between the tilted plane
                       of the book's cover and the horizontal.

strike-slip   refers to horizontal movement along a fault (q.v.). Strike-slip
                       faults may be left-lateral (left-handed or 'sinistral') or right-lat-
                       eral (right-handed or 'dextral') (q.v.). Strike-slip faults are also
                       known as 'wrench' or 'tear' faults.

structure   describes the relationships of beds in terms of faults, cleavage
                       and folds.

subduction   process whereby two of the Earth's rigid crustal plates collide
                       so that one is forced down as the other overrides it. This
                       produces a zone of subduction and is characterised by volca-
                       noes and earthquake activity (e.g. Andes, Indonesia). q.v. man-
                       tle, plate tectonics.

subglacial stream   meltwater stream which runs beneath a glacier.

syncline   a fold in a rock sequence which is concave-upwards. q.v.
                       anticline.

tectonics   study of major structural features of the Earth's surface.

terminal moraine   ridge of moraine debris dumped at the snout of a glacier and

	indicating its maximum advance. These may actually form a dam so that a lake develops after the ice has melted. e.g. Llyn Idwal.
till	general term for the blanket of rubbish – ranging from boulders to clay – left by melted glaciers. q.v. moraine.
tourmaline	borosilicate mineral often associated with granites (q.v.). Well crystallised varieties are gemstones.
transfluence, glacial	diffluence (q.v.) on a larger scale.
truncated spurs	result of powerful main valley glacier which tears away the tributary valley bottoms, leaving abrupt spurs and hanging valleys (q.v.). e.g. Nant Ffrancon.
tuff	volcanic ash (q.v.) hardened to form a rock.
tuffaceous	rock containing some tuff (q.v.).
tuffite	sedimentary rock containing at least 25% pyroclastic debris.
turbidite	rock formed from a turbidity current (q.v.).
turbidity current	turbid and dense current which forms, often triggered by earthquake shock, at the bottom of a water body (lake or sea). It flows into deeper water, carrying sand, silt and mud in suspension. The sand etc. falls out as the flow loses its energy; q.v. mass flow.
unconformity	a break in deposition during which erosion of rocks may occur. This can happen at any scale from small to very large, representing millions of years-worth of missing rocks. e.g. sub-*gracilis* time break (p. 70).
vesicles	gas cavities in a lava (q.v.). Sometimes called 'amygdules'. Commonly the cavities become filled with secondary minerals such as silica (q.v.), calcite (q.v.) or zeolites.
volcaniclasts	rock fragments derived directly from volcanic eruptions. q.v. pyroclastic, pyroclastic flow.
way-up criteria	small sedimentary structures (q.v.), such as flame structures (q.v.) and load casts (q.v.) in sedimentary rocks, which always develop in such a way that they indicate whether the outcrop in which they occur is upside down (inverted) or right-way-up. Cross bedding is a clear example (p. 120).
welded tuff	a tuff (q.v.) which has been hardened – welded – by its retained heat. Individual fragments such as glass fragments – shards (q.v.) – and lumps of pumice (q.v. fiamme) become plastic and flatten together in a strikingly characteristic rock. e.g. Pitt's Head Tuff.

Appendix 1: The geological sketch map

Figure A.1 is an enormously simplified map of the Welsh rocks and the faults that affect them. The key explains what the rocks are.

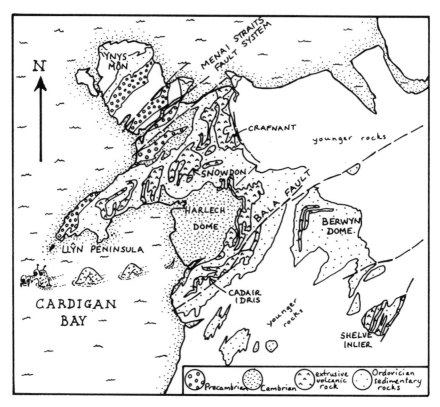

Figure A.1

A ramble through Time ... The Timescale: what it is and how to use it

In order to unravel the fantastically complex rock formations which form our Earth's crust, we have to give them names so we know which is which. Geologists have three ways of doing this. Firstly, they name distinctive rock units like 'sandstone' or 'basalt' or 'Pitt's Head Tuff' (lithostratigraphy; litho = rock); secondly, they name the periods of time represented by 'bundles' of rock units (chronostratigraphy; chrono = time); and thirdly they name divisions according to the fossils the rocks contain (biostratigraphy; bio = life forms).

Eras

This is at the left side of the Timescale and summarises the entire time history of the planet from its formation 4,600 million years ago to the present day. Geologists have divided up this unbelievably long period of time into a ranked family – a hierarchy – of ever smaller time chunks, each of which has some consistent feature which makes it different from the others. Top of the bill with the longest chunk of time is the Eon. The last 4,000 million years is broken up into three Eons: the Archean ('ancient,' the oldest), the Proterozoic ('earlier life') and the Phanerozoic ('abundant life'). Rocks which formed before the Phanerozoic are usually lumped as 'Precambrian' ('before the Cambrian'). The Phanerozoic Eon started about 545 million years ago with the 'Cambrian explosion' of new life forms. Suddenly, complex animals with shells appeared and quickly proliferated where before there had only been soft-bodied animals, simple plants like algae, and bacteria.

The Phanerozoic is itself split into three great Eras: the Palaeozoic ('old life'), the Mesozoic ('middle life') and the Cainozoic ('recent life'). But as you see from the actual scale of the column, these three eras together only amount to about 1/9th of the time which has elapsed since the planet formed; almost 3,500 million years had already passed since the first life evolved at the start of the Archean.

These time scales are hard to appreciate, aren't they? To help put them even more into perspective, note that the first appearance of modern man (about 100,000 years ago) would be only 1/250th of a millimetre from the top of the Era column. And the Roman conquest was only 1/12,000th of a millimetre from the top. Our industrial capability, which in only 200 years or so has caused so much damage, began 1/125,000th of a millimetre from the top ... that's only a few tens of atoms thickness!

> One way of looking at the various time divisions – the hierarchies – is to think of them in terms of familiar units like months (= Eons), weeks (= Eras), days (= Periods), hours (= Epochs), minutes (= Stages) and seconds (= Zones). (The 'minutes' and 'seconds' don't concern us here, being rather specialised details.) But don't take this analogy too far because, of course, real clock time involves units which are always the same length: there are always 60 minutes in a hour; 24 hours in a day and so on. This isn't the case in the Timescale where, for example, the 'hours' (= Epochs) can range between 10,000 and many millions of years. And there's no set number of Epoch 'hours' in a Period 'day. And so on.

Periods

This column represents all the Phanerozoic, now much expanded so that just over 545 million years occupies the same space as 4,600 million years in the Eras column. I've drawn tie-lines connecting the Palaeozoic, Mesozoic and Cainozoic Eras to the Periods into which these Eras are split (from 'weeks' to 'days'). You'll see that I've added small details about important new appearances (a tick) or extinctions (an X) of animals and plants during the Phanerozoic. 'E' denotes mass extinctions of many different life forms.

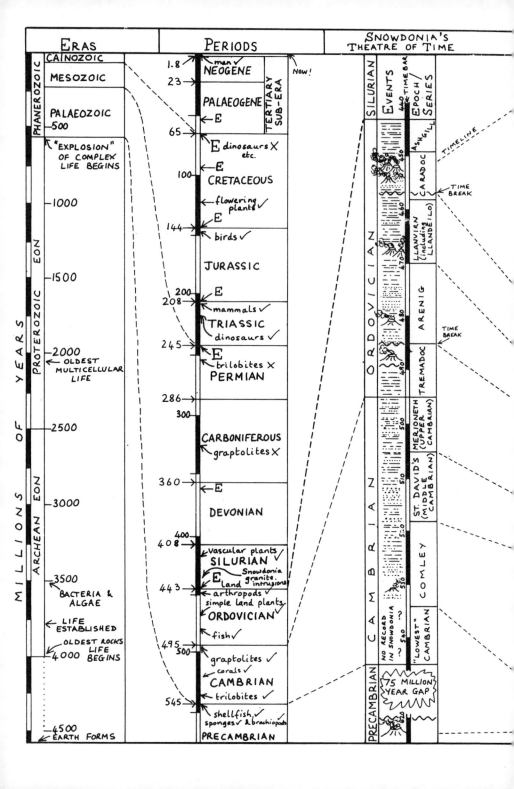

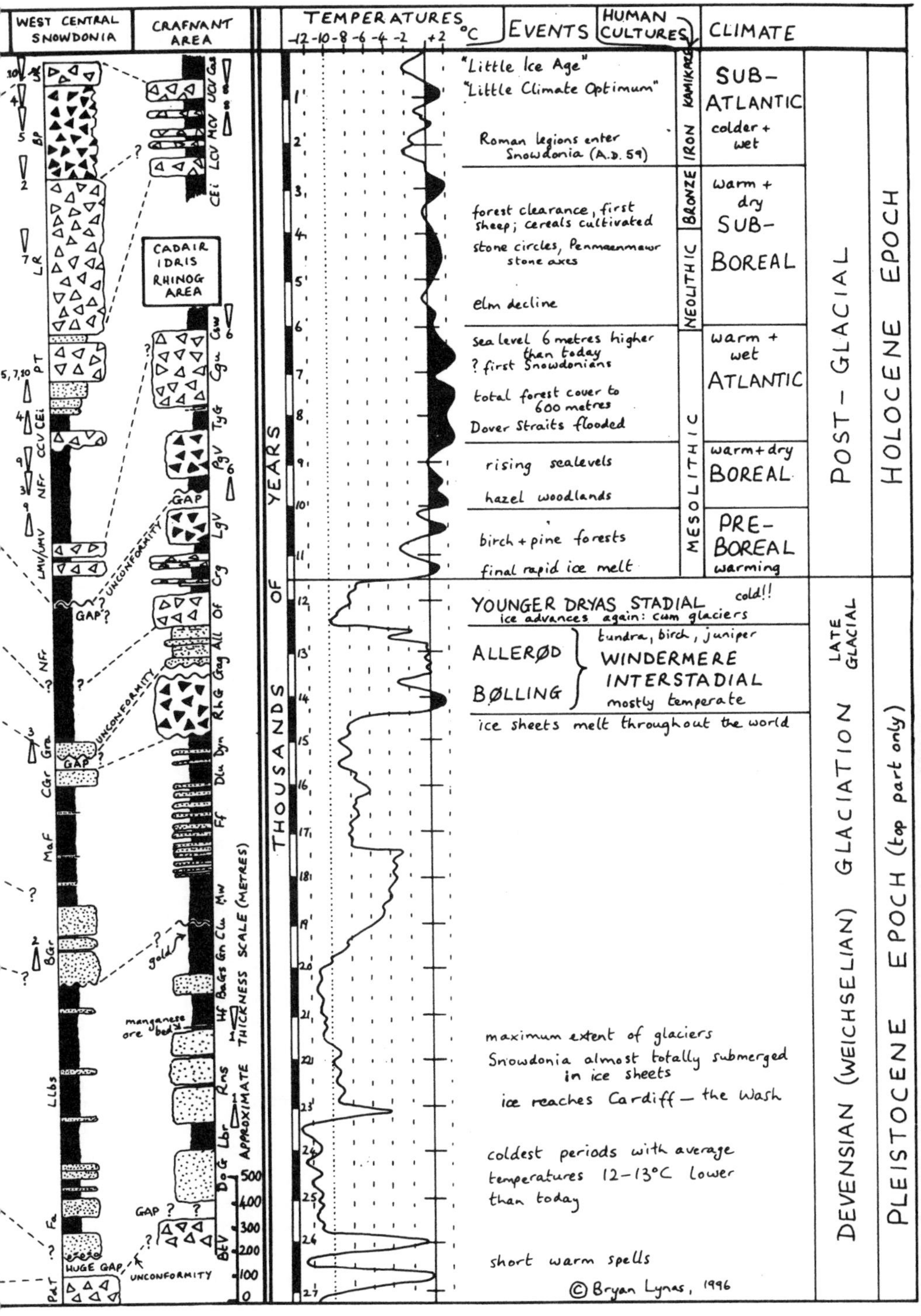

WEST CENTRAL SNOWDONIA	CRAFNANT AREA	TEMPERATURES °C -12 -10 -8 -6 -4 -2 +2	EVENTS	HUMAN CULTURES	CLIMATE		

			"Little Ice Age" "Little Climate Optimum"	KAMIKAZE	SUB- ATLANTIC colder + wet		
			Roman legions enter Snowdonia (A.D. 59)	IRON			
				BRONZE	warm + dry SUB- BOREAL		
CADAIR IDRIS RHINOG AREA			forest clearance, first sheep; cereals cultivated	NEOLITHIC		POST-GLACIAL	HOLOCENE EPOCH
			stone circles, Penmaenmawr stone axes				
			elm decline				
			sea level 6 metres higher than today ? first Snowdonians		warm + wet ATLANTIC		
			total forest cover to 600 metres Dover Straits flooded	MESOLITHIC			
			rising sealevels		warm + dry BOREAL		
			hazel woodlands				
			birch + pine forests		PRE- BOREAL		
			final rapid ice melt		warming		
			YOUNGER DRYAS STADIAL cold!! ice advances again: cwm glaciers			LATE GLACIAL	
			ALLERØD } WINDERMERE BØLLING } INTERSTADIAL mostly temperate tundra, birch, juniper				
GAP?			ice sheets melt throughout the world				PLEISTOCENE EPOCH (top part only)
GAP						DEVENSIAN (WEICHSELIAN) GLACIATION	
			maximum extent of glaciers Snowdonia almost totally submerged in ice sheets				
			ice reaches Cardiff — the Wash				
			coldest periods with average temperatures 12–13°C lower than today				
			short warm spells				

THOUSANDS OF YEARS

APPROXIMATE THICKNESS SCALE (METRES) — 500 400 300 200 100 0

© Bryan Lynas, 1996

These extinctions mostly coincide with Period boundaries. They are the main reason why geologists have divided the Phanerozoic into these 11 Periods for they represent important changes in the fossil record. The mass extinction everyone knows about is that at the end of the Cretaceous (65 million years ago) when the dinosaurs finally bit the dust, probably aided by an asteroid hitting the planet in what is now Yucatán in Mexico. But the granddaddy of all mass extinctions took place at the end of the Permian. This was far more important in terms of the number of species which died out, though the cause is a mystery.

Snowdonia's Theatre of Time

This is an expanded part of the Period scale showing you the time names between the end of the Precambrian and the start of the Silurian Period. Again, dotted tie-lines connect to show how much expansion there is. I've split the right hand side of this column into Epochs, also called Series. These are the 'hours' in my analogy. The Caradoc Epoch or Series was an over-whelmingly important time in Snowdonia for it was then that the biggest of all the volcanic eruptions happened. By way of summarising what went on during the Cambrian and Ordovician Periods in what would become Snow-donia, I've used the left side of the colum to show – in a crude way – 'events'. Volcano symbols tell you that major eruptions happened at that time. Dots mean coarse sediments (sands, tuffites and so on) were forming and dashes/lines mean that the sediment being laid down was silt or mud. This last was the backdrop of our Time Theatre ... always there but often not noticed because of boisterous players like the volcanoes and active fault systems. Wiggly lines represents time breaks – unconformities – of major importance throughout the area.

Rock columns: West central Snowdonia, Crafnant, Cadair Idris and Rhinog areas

These columns summarise an immense amount of information. The idea is simple: each column is a reconstruction of what you might see if the whole Snowdonian rock sequence was exposed for you to examine in a sea cliff, unaffected by folding or faulting. The harder units (like volcanic rocks) stick out as ribs and the softer ones (like mudstones) are 'eroded' in, leaving hollows. I've drawn three columns (the Crafnant one is very small) because the rock types laid down at the same time are quite different in different parts of Snowdonia. As you'd expect, these columns are enormously simpli-fied but they do represent quite well the way things are. You can actually measure off the greatest thicknesses any unit reaches from the scale (0 to 500 metres) at the bottom right of the Cadair column.

I've linked the rock units to the 'Theatre of Time' column so you can see roughly how old a particular unit is. The time breaks – unconformities – show up clearly: the most important of these lie between the Precambrian and Cambrian, at the base of the Arenig Epoch and low in the Caradoc (the 'pre-*gracilis*' erosion, p. 70). Each of these represents long periods of time in which major uplift above sealevel occurred, exposing the former seafloor sediments to erosion. From my liberal sprinkling of questionmarks, you can see that there are still many uncertainties!

The slender vertical open triangles, each with a number, which lie beside the columns show you the rock sequence you walk through on each rocky ramble. As you can see, there's scope for many more rambles because I've tended to concentrate on the most exciting 'events' in our Snowdonian Theatre.

Finally, there's no space to write in the full names of all the rock formations, many of which I've referred to in this book so I've used abbreviations (like 'PT' for 'Pitt's Head Tuff', 'Cgu' for 'Craig Cau Formation' etc.) and tabulated them below alphabetically. These abbreviations correspond with those used by the British Geological Survey on all their maps. Rock units in brackets are ones you won't see on these rambles and I've missed out many more.

ROCK UNIT	ABBREVIATION	AGE
(Allt Lwyd Formation)	All	Arenig
(Barmouth Formation)	BaGs	St David's
Bedded Pyroclastic Formation	BP	Caradoc
Bronllwyd Grit Formation	BGr	?St David's
(Bryn-teg Volcanic Formation)	BtV	?Precambrian
Cadnant Shales	CaS	Caradoc
Capel Curig Volcanic Formation	CCV	Caradoc
Carnedd-y-Filiast Grit	CGr	Merioneth
(Clogau Formation)	Clu	St David's
Ceiswyn Formation	Csw	Caradoc
Craig Cau Formation	Cgu	Caradoc
(Cregennen Formation)	Crg	Llanvirn
Cwm Eigiau Formation	CEi	Caradoc
(Dol-cyn-afon Member)	Dyn	Tremadoc
(Dolgellau Member)	Dlu	Merioneth
(Dolwen Formation)	DoG	Comley
(Fachwen Formation)	Fa	Comley
(Ffestiniog Flags Formation)	Ff	Merioneth
(Gamlan Formation)	Gn	St David's
(Garth Grit)	GaG	Arenig
(Graianog Sandstone)	Gra	Arenig
(Hafotty Formation)	Hf	St David's
(Llanbedr Formation)	Lbr	Comley
Llanberis Slates Formation	LlbS	Comley
(Llyn y Gafr Volcanic Formation)	LgV	?Llanvirn
(Lower Crafnant Volcanic Formation)	LCV	Caradoc
Lower Moelwyn Volcanic Formation	LMV	Caradoc
Lower Rhyolitic Tuff Formation	LR	Caradoc
(Maentwrog Formation)	Mw	Merioneth
Marchlyn Formation	MaF	Merioneth
Middle Crafnant Volcanic Formation	MCV	Caradoc
Nant Ffrancon Group	NFr	Arenig to Caradoc
(Offrwm Volcanic Formation)	Of	Arenig
(Padarn Tuff Formation)	PdT	Precambrian

(Pen y gadair Volcanic Formation)	PgV	Caradoc
Pitt's Head Tuff Formation	PT	Caradoc
Rhinog Formation	RnS	Comley
(Rhobell Volcanic Group)	RhG	Tremadoc
Ty'r Gawen Mudstone Formation	Tyg	Caradoc
Upper Crafnant Volcanic Formation	UCV	Caradoc
Upper Moelwyn Volcanic Formation	UMV	Caradoc
Upper Rhyolitic Tuff Formation	UR	Caradoc

N.B. The Snowdon Volcanic Group includes the PT, LR, BP and UR. The CCV is part of the earlier Llewelyn Volcanic Group which occurs mostly in the Carneddau range.

Understanding rock unit names: Big fleas have little fleas ... Let's make a similar analogy to the time units (Periods = 'days' etc.) which I mentioned earlier. This analogy comes from the world of business: The biggest type of business is the Multinational, the equivalent of a rock 'Group'. Multinationals are often made up of a number of Companies (= rock Formations) and Companies are made up of, say, Divisions (= rock Members, which don't concern us here) with the basic commodity, People (= Beds). Without people, companies are nothing. Without 'brick and mortar' beds of rock (including volcanic rocks as well as sediments), none of the higher units can exist. Like the time clock divisions, this analogy has its limitations, but gives you the gist of the scheme for rock-naming.

So rock 'Groups' (= Multinationals) like the Snowdon Volcanic Group are made up of 'Formations' (= Companies) such as the Bedded Pyroclastic Formation.. Ultimately, everything is built up of Beds (= People), though the Beds usually don't have formal names and are just spoken of anonymously as 'beds' (rather like the people in many companies so the metaphor holds rather well here).

The timescale dates are subject to constant revision as dating methods improve. (I explain how. rocks are dated below.) They are probably all about right, but other timescales may give slightly different dates to mine which are the most recent I could find (1995).

The last 27,000 years:
Temperatures, Events, Human Cultures, Climate

The final part of the Timescale occupies the righthand third of the drawing separated from the rock columns by two heavy vertical lines. This shows you details of the very end of the ice age (Pleistocene Epoch) right up to today (Holocene Epoch). Note the enormous expansion of the scale which is now in thousands of years and not millions!

The world started to cool about 5 million years ago. The first major ice sheets began to form in the northern hemisphere between 1.8 and 2 million years ago. But it wasn't all cold. The glacial freezes were punctuated by regular warmer spells ('interglacials' or 'interstadials') when the temperatures rose – sometimes remaining warm for tens of thousands of years, equalling or even exceeding those of today, and most of the ice sheets disappeared. I've summarised what we know about temperature changes in vertical graphic form. As you see, they range from as much as 12-13 degrees Celsius colder than today to about 3 degrees warmer. The data on temperatures comes from a wealth of new climate and dating information from the Greenland ice sheet drilling programmes, GRIP and GISP. These ice cores show that temperatures were never constant. Even in the depths of the freezes, they were shooting up and down, sometimes very rapidly. By about 22,000 years ago, the ice sheets reached their maximum extent for the last glaciation in the northern hemisphere. In Britain, they reached as far south as Cardiff, though with a very irregular front.

Earlier glaciations were even more severe once reaching further south than London. Only the southern strip of Britain — Cornwall to Kent — was never glaciated.

I've also given the names of the major climate change events. The last glacial is widely known as the Weichselian (in northwest Europe), but is usually called 'Devensian' in Britain. Same thing; different name. Confusing but inevitable.

Around 14,500 years ago, the world warmed dramatically and most of the continental ice sheets melted almost completely, liberating oceans of water and causing sealevels around the world to shoot up at least 100 metres (no, that's not an error: around 330 feet!). This mild spell (known as the Bølling and Allerød or Windermere Interstadial) only lasted for about 1,800 years. Then the temperatures plummeted once more into the Younger Dryas cold event (also known in Britain as 'the Loch Lomond Stadial' or 'Loch Lomond Readvance') which lasted from 12,700 years BP (Before Present) to 11,550 years BP. It was this which caused the reappearance of glaciers in the higher Snowdonian cwms.

BP (Before Present) dates are almost always used by geologists. This is internationally taken to mean 'before 1950 AD' since we have to have a fixed time datum to measure back from — which is why most modern dates are given as Anno Domini, AD, rather than BP. Just to complicate the issue, always easy to do, many of the BP dates you see are 'radiocarbon dates'. 'Radiocarbon years' are not exactly the same as calendar years and have to be calibrated using a special curve to give the true number of years BP. Get it? If not, see below for more details.

The Younger Dryas lasted about 1,200 years. Temperatures dropped right back to the way they had been during the earlier glaciation. Snowdonia became a freezing wilderness with sparse tundra vegetation and intense periglacial activity such as scree and blockfield formation. At about 11,550 years BP, the temperature shot up... within about 50 years. Suddenly, the frozen mountains were warm once again; the glaciers melted like snowballs in mild weather, dumping their boulders and moraine mounds, and releasing floods of sediment-laden meltwaters.

Why did the temperatures climb so fast? Almost certainly due to major changes in deep 'conveyor belt' currents in the North Atlantic and a dramatic break-up of sea ice cover. The ultimate causes of these remarkable warmings and coolings remain elusive, though we now have some very good ideas. But we don't yet know how to predict another glacial deep freeze, the true test of how well we understand climate processes.

What we like to call 'the end' of the glacial freezes occurred about 11,500 years ago with a change to warm conditions again. This is taken as the boundary between the Pleistocene and the Holocene (also known as 'Recent' or 'Flandrian') Epochs. Actually, we're probably still in an interglacial and we have no means of knowing (yet) whether the world will plunge back into another glacial phase. Maybe our 'greenhouse effect' atmospheric tampering will prevent this happening ... or maybe it will trigger something worse. No one knows.

For the following 7,000 years, the climate stayed warm and mostly wet. The temperatures I have plotted on the Holocene sector of the graph are from a variety of sources including studies of pollen and beetles from the sediments laid down at these times (p. 168). The graph represents average July temperatures at latitude 55-60 degrees north. The early Holocene warming throughout the world meant that the sealevel continued to rise, reaching a maximum of nearly 6 metres higher than today around the Snowdonian coast (p. 152).

The first humans probably appeared in the Snowdonia around 7,000 years ago. Over 4000 years ago, people were making axes and other tools from the Penmaenmawr granite and were beginning to cultivate cereals.

Documented history begins with the arrival of the Roman legions sometime after AD59 (just under 2,000 years ago). By this time, the climate had cooled again, bringing the familiar rainy weather we all know and love. After another warm period ('Little Climate Optimum'), a prolonged cooling called 'the Little Ice Age' began. During this time, the Thames would freeze over to such an extent that winter fairs were held upon it by Londoners. Since then, the climate has been warming slowly, possibly helped by industrialisation and fossil fuel burning ... and the rest is history.

How old is a rock? Age determination ...

Whole books have been written about this and it's a complex subject involving the union of several different approaches. The most important are palaeontology (the study of fossils and their relationship to the strata you find them in) and isotopic age determination.

The role of fossils...

One approach to rock dating is to record fossil species which occur in sedimentary rocks. From extensive collecting for well over 150 years by palaeontologists all around the world (including Charles Darwin on his long 'Beagle' voyage), we know very well the relative ages of fossils in relation to one another. How should that be? Simply we know that if a rock contains a trilobite, then it must be Palaeozoic because these animals became extinct in the Permian (see Timescale). No trilobites have ever been found anywhere in rocks younger than the Permian Period or older than the Cambrian. We also know that certain types of trilobite existed only for brief periods during the Palaeozoic. Each new species evolved, flourished for a while and then became extinct. Let us assume a trilobite species – we'll call it Fred – is common in the Bedded Pyroclastic Formation but no one has ever found it in younger rocks that overlie it. If we find lots of Freds in some other rocks we are looking at in the Lake District, say, we can be sure that those rocks are the same age as the BPF. This is the basis of 'stratigraphic palaeontology'. It tells us accurately about relative ages ... which rock is the same age, or older, or younger than another.

But how many years old is this rock?
Absolute ages and atomic clocks.

How can we put actual dates in years on the Timescale? These figures are the result of complex analyses and calculations based on well-known physical laws which govern the atomic disintegration of certain elements. Elements (92 occur naturally) exist in several chemically identical forms called isotopes which have a different number of neutrons in their atomic nuclei. This makes some isotopes unstable; they break up – decay – into lighter elements and in doing so, spit out tiny bursts of radioactivity. We know accurately how long it takes for most of these isotopes to decay. This is measured as 'half-life.'

Half-life. If you have a lump of uranium-235 (meaning that each atom of this isotope of uranium, the one we use in nuclear power stations, has 92 protons and 143 neutrons) weighing one gram, you'd have to wait 713 million years for it to lose half its mass by atomic disintegration: its half-life is 713 million years. So the uranium-235 acts as a very slow but absolutely constant ticking clock.

But how can you apply this idea of 'half-life' to rocks because you can't tell how much isotope there was in the first place without going back to measure it, can you? Well yes, you can. The uranium that disintegrates doesn't vanish; it becomes something that wasn't there before ... another lighter metal: lead-207. The 'daughter' lead-207 stays right there with its 'parent' uranium. So for every gram of 'parent' uranium that disintegrates, slightly less than a gram of 'daughter' lead-207 appears. The weight difference is because the atomic disintegrations emit radiation – radioactivity – such as an alpha particle (two neutrons and two protons) which accounts for the loss of mass. So if we can precisely measure the amount of parent uranium remaining and the amount of daughter lead which has built up, we have a ratio which can tell us how much uranium was there in the first place. So from that, we can calculate the time interval which has passed because we can measure in a laboratory the rate at which uranium-235 disintegrates: its half-life. Thus our natural ticking clock is calibrated and it tells us the time very accurately.

I've simplified this example of what is called the uranium-lead series to illustrate the general principle. Fortunately, we have many isotopic clocks which run at very different speeds. Potassium-40 decays to argon-40 with a half-life of 11,850 million years. But carbon-14 has a half-life of only 5,730 years, decaying to nitrogen-14. Other clocks include uranium-238 to lead-206; rubidium-87 to strontium-87 and other rarer elements.

Setting the clock.

How is the radiometric (= time measurement using isotopes which naturally occur in rocks) clock set in the first place? Take the example of potassium/argon (abbreviated to K/Ar) dating, one of the most useful since potassium minerals are widespread in igneous rocks. The technique works only for rocks which start as liquids (like lavas) and that then solidify. It is the act of solidification that sets the radiometric clock ticking. Whilst the lava is liquid, any argon (a gas) liberated by the potassium isotope will bubble off and be lost. But from the moment the potassium is locked up inside a newly-formed feldspar crystal (for example), its 'daughter' product, argon gas, is trapped with it. And there it stays (we hope, because in some cases our radiometric clock can be reset by later geological events which may release some of the 'daughter' argon) until a geologist analyses it to measure the relative amounts of argon and potassium. She can then calculate the 'absolute' or 'isotopic' or 'radiometric' (same thing; different names) age of the lava.

Fossils + isotopic ages = accurate dates

It follows from what I've said that if you isotopically date a lava within the Bedded Pyroclastic Formation as 454 million years old, then the Cwm Eigiau Formation (and its accompanying trilobites and other fossils) must be older than 454 million years. This is where the two different approaches to rock dating link so effectively. So if you find a trilobite called Jane in the Cwm Eigiau Formation, you know that Jane lived over 454 million years ago. If a colleague finds a trilobite identical to Jane in rocks in the Antarctic, then you can be pretty certain that those rocks are also older than 454 million years. But then assume that the Antarctic geologist later finds that the Jane-bearing rocks also include some lava flows. Samples from these flows give K/Ar dates of 458 million (±3 million, for example, which gives the expected limits of any error and which geologists always quote with their isotopic dates) which means that not only are the Janes in the Cwm Eigiau Formation older than 454 million years, they are very likely to be about 458 million years old.

It is this constant fine-tuning by comparison of strata and their fossils – stratigraphic correlation – with rocks which have yielded isotopic ages that enable geologists to build up an accurate overall timescale. Simple, isn't it!

Radiocarbon and the end of the last ice ages.

I mentioned carbon-14 as being a useful isotope for measuring ages, but because its half-life is quite short (5,730 years), it is only useful for measurements over the last few tens of thousands of years. Because it occurs in almost all traces of plants and animal life – shellfish shells, bones, peat, wood and even lumps of charcoal from ancient cooking fires – it is enormously useful to us for dating relatively recent events. But nothing is ever simple. Radiocarbon ages are subject to variable amounts of error – sometimes considerable error – and they are continually being refined by checking with other dating methods.

One such check is counting tree rings (dendrochronology) which obviously give calendar (real) years, linking radiocarbon dates of the same tree to the true dates. Another new technique is to count the years in ice cores from Greenland. This can be done in several ways, rather like tree-rings. From the same core, we can establish when warm and cold periods occurred, using a sophisticated technique involving isotopes of oxygen. (Tiny bubbles of this gas are trapped in the snow as it turns into ice due to the weight of later snowfalls). So important climate 'events' like the Younger Dryas (Timescale) can be spotted in the ice core and dated accurately. The Younger Dryas seems to have affected the whole world and has been repeatedly dated using radiocarbon methods. These methods give ages of around 10,000 years BP (before present) for the sudden warming which marked the end of the Younger Dryas. But the ice cores show that this warming took place around 11,550 years ago. This means that the radiocarbon ages are about 1,500 years too young: a 15% error!

But help is at hand in the form of calibration curves. These are simply graphs on which an error curve is plotted. If you take a radiocarbon date of, say, 5,600 years, you simply look at the point of the curve representing that date and see instantly that you have to add 800 years to it to make it true, calendar years. So a radiocarbon (written ^{14}C) date of 5,600 years is actually 6,400 calendar years BP. I've adjusted all the Timescale dates in this way though you may find many similar scales which are plotted in 'radiocarbon years', a convention adopted by many scientists to 'avoid confusion'. Then, at least, you know you're dealing with incorrect dates which you can correct if you want.

> How is radiocarbon, carbon-14 (^{14}C) formed? Cosmic rays from the Sun bombard the nitrogen gas that makes up most of our atmosphere and change it into ^{14}C.

How does the radiocarbon get into shells and plants? The newly-formed carbon immediately combines with oxygen to form carbon dioxide (CO_2). And CO_2 is taken up by plants and shellfish (to make their shells) and some of the plants are eaten by animals. So the ticking isotope clock is set, waiting for someone to measure how much of the ^{14}C remains, centuries or millennia later.

Appendix 2: Bibliography

In this list, books marked with ** are recommended reading.
Material for more detailed follow-up is denoted with *.
Items with no asterisks are background reference.

***Mountain Weather: a guide for skiers and hillwalkers* by William Burroughs, Crowood Press, 1995, 112 pages. Learn how to predict the weather.

** *Lakeland Rocky Rambles: geology beneath your feet* by Bryan Lynas, Sigma Press, 1994, 282 action-packed pages. If you enjoyed Snowdonia Rocky Rambles, this book is a must! Well worth the money. (Well I would say that, wouldn't I?)

***Gwynedd* by Ian Skidmore, Robert Hale, 1986, 219 pages. If you want to know more of the fables and human history of this land, this is a fine book.

***A History of the North Wales Slate Industry* by Jean Lindsay, 1974, David & Charles, 376 pages. If you're interested in the history of this once-great industry, this is a good start. You can find many similar books in bookshops or climbers' shops throughout the area.

**The Holocene: An environmental history* by Neil Roberts, Basil Blackwell, 1989. A useful account of the last 11,000 years.

**Glacial Environments 1994*, Michael Hambrey, UCL Press: an excellent and well-illustrated book with everything you wanted to know about glaciers.

**The Periglaciation of Great Britain* by Colin K. Ballantyne & Charles Harris, CUP, 1994, 330 pages. A detailed account of how periglacial processes moulded the British landscape. These processes still operate in Snowdonia.

**Snowdonia* by M F Howells, B.E. Leveridge and A.J. Reedman, 1981, Unwin Paperbacks, 119 pages. This is a little field guide produced by my old colleagues some years back. It includes 14 field trips aimed at amateur or professional geologists. If you want to find out more, this guide will help you do it.

**Ordovician (Caradoc) Marginal Basin Volcanism in Snowdonia (North-west Wales)*, British Geological Survey, HMSO, London, 1991, 191 pages. This magnificent and well-illustrated work is the last word on this topic; the culmination of a century and a half of deliberations. It is not, however, for those without some geological training.

**Geology of the country around Cadair Idris*, British Geological Survey, HMSO, London, 1995, 111 pages. This, like the above, is not really for beginners. It is intended to go with the Cadair Idris geological sheet 149, published at about the same time.

**Volcanoes: A Planetary Perspective* Peter Francis, 1993, 443 pages. Beautifully written and well illustrated.

Industrial Archaeology of Wales, by D. Morgan Rees, David & Charles, 1975, 302 pages.

Atlas of Palaeogeography and Lithofacies edited by J.C.W. Cope and others, 1992, published by the Geological Society of London, Memoir 13, price around £290! But you can find it in large libraries – or request it – and it's well worth looking at to see the way Britain's geography has changed over the last 600 million years or so.

There are several excellent geological maps available from the British Geological Survey (BGS), some of which I was involved with years ago:

Bangor (106), Snowdon (119), Harlech (135) and Cadair Idris (149). All these are at 1:50,000 scale (2 centimetres to 1 kilometre), somewhat small but giving a good synoptic picture for those who know how to interpret such colourful and complex maps.

Snowdon, Capel Curig and Betws-y-Coed, Passes of Nant Ffrancon and Llanberis and Llyn Padarn (also BGS) are special maps at 1:25,000 scale, the same as the OS Outdoor Leisure maps. Being at a larger scale, these are more easy to make sense of – but you do need some understanding of geological map interpretation. This is beyond the scope of this book but is basically the ability to visualise in three dimensions the mass of information given in two dimensions (the map sheet). All these maps show cross sections and summarise the names and thickness variations of the rock units as well as their relative ages.

Other titles of interest from:

HILL WALKS IN MID WALES
The Cambrian Mountains

Dave Ing

This is one of the very few books to explore the pleasures of walking in Mid Wales - far from from the big mountains of Snowdonia and away from the crowds, yet so accessible for a day in the hills.

(£7.95)

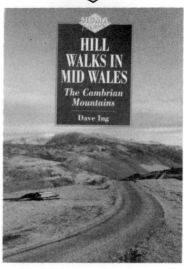

WALKS IN MYSTERIOUS WALES

Laurence Main

Follow the spirit paths of Wales - visit the most sacred and secret sites and discover ancient traditions of this historic country in the company of a leading expert. And, while you're discovering Welsh heritage, enjoy some excellent walks across the length and breadth of the country.

(£7.95)

For further details or to obtain our complete catalogue, please contact:
Sigma Leisure, 1 South Oak Lane, Wilmslow, Cheshire SK9 6AR
Phone: 01625-531035; Fax: 01625-536800; E-mail: sigma.press@zetnet.co.uk

ACCESS and VISA orders welcome – 24 hour Answerphone service! Most orders are despatched on the day we receive your order – you could be enjoying our books in just a couple of days. Please add £2 p&p to all orders.